US Marine Corps M16A2

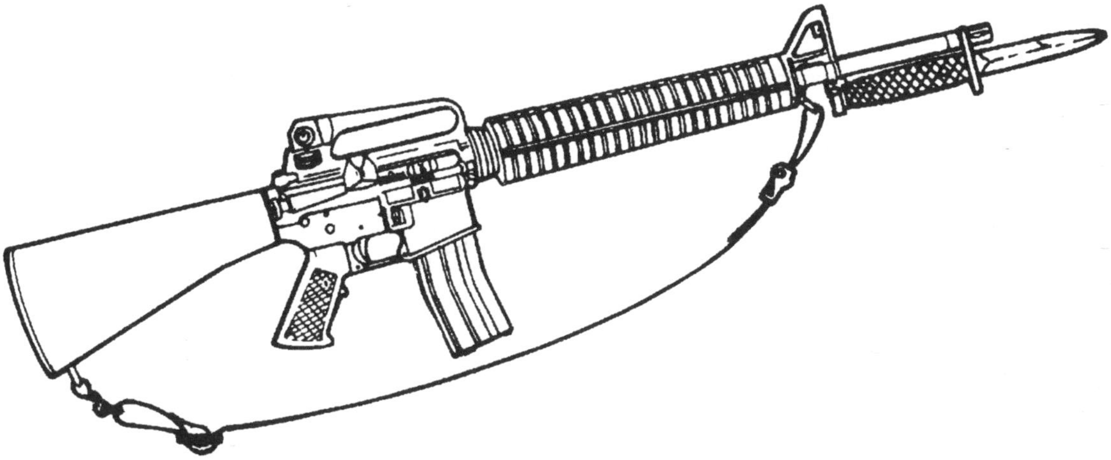

Rifle Manual

Desert Publications
El Dorado, AR 71731-1751 U. S. A.

U. S. Marine Corps M16A2 Rifle Manual

215 S. Washington
El Dorado, AR 71731-1751
501-862-2077

ISBN 0-87947-083-6
12 11 10 9 8 7 6
Printed in U. S. A.

**Desert Publication is a division of
The DELTA GROUP, Ltd.
Direct all inquiries & orders to the above address.**

SSG, STEVEN POUSSON
MILITARY POLICE CORPS
B/5/8 TSG

Organizational and Intermediate Maintenance (Including Repair Parts and Special Tools List) RIFLE, 5.56-MM, M16A2 W/E NSN 1005-01-128-9936

HOW TO USE THIS MANUAL

GENERAL

In order to use this manual efficiently, you need to know:

1. Illustrations for the maintenance procedures show only those parts affected by the operation being performed.
2. Whenever the male gender is mentioned in the manual (i.e., crewmen, repairman), it also pertains to females.

INDEXES

This manual is organized to help you find the information you need quickly. There are several useful indexes and lists.

1. Table of Contents. Lists, in order, all chapters, sections, and appendices, gives page references.
2. Nomenclature Cross-Reference List.
3. Chapter Overviews. A summary of the chapter content is located at the beginning of each chapter.
4. Symptom Index. Located before the troubleshooting table in each maintenance chapter, they list possible rifle malfunctions and the page which describes the troubleshooting procedures.
5. Alphabetical Index. Located at the end of the manual. It is a subject-to-page list of everything in the manual.

REPORTING ERRORS AND RECOMMENDING IMPROVEMENTS

You can help improve this manual. If you find any mistakes, or if you know of a way to improve the procedures, please let us know. MARINE CORPS USERS, submit NAVMC 10772 (Recommended Changes to Technical Publications) to: Commanding General, Marine Corps Logistics Base (Code 850) Albany, Georgia 31704- 5000. A reply will be furnished direct to you. ARMY USERS, mail your letter, DA Form 2028 (Recommended Changes to Publications and Blank Forms), or DA Form 2028-2 direct to: Commander, US Army Armament, Munitions and Chemical Command, ATTN: AMSMC-MAS, Rock Island, IL 61299-6000. A reply will be furnished to you.

REPORTING EQUIPMENT IMPROVEMENT RECOMMENDATION (EIR)

If your rifle needs improvement, let us know. Send us an EIR. You, the user, are the only one who can tell us what you don't like about your equipment. Let us know why you don't like the design. MARINE CORPS PERSONNEL, submit EIRs in accordance with MCO 1650.17. ARMY PERSONNEL, submit a SF 368 (Quality Deficiency Report). Mail to Commander, US

Army Armament, Munitions and Chemical Command, ATTN: AMSMC-QAD, Rock Island, IL 61299-6000. A reply will be furnished to you.

EXTERNAL VIEW OF 5.56-MM RIFLE M16A2

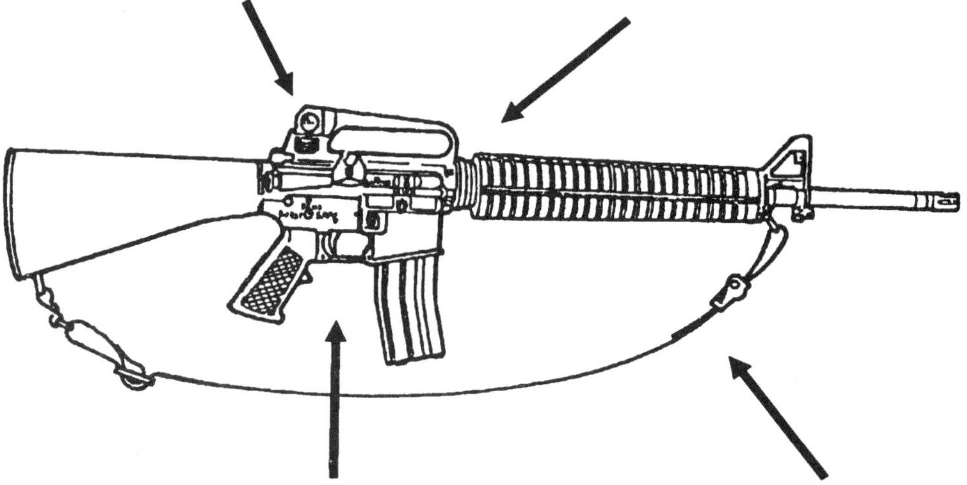

RIGHT SIDE

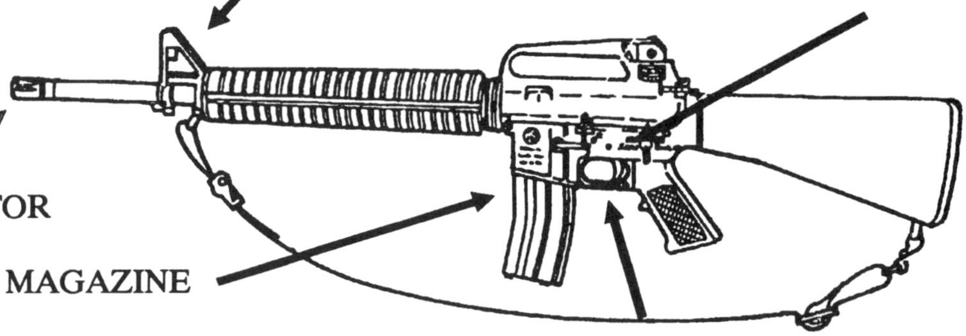

LEFT SIDE

CHAPTER 1
INTRODUCTION

CHAPTER OVERVIEW
This chapter contains general information, equipment description and data, and principles of operation for the M16A2 rifle.

Section I. GENERAL INFORMATION

1-1. SCOPE.

a. *Type of Manual.* Organizational and Intermediate Maintenance.

b. *Model Number and Equipment Name.* 5.56-mm Rifle M16A2.

c. *Purpose of Equipment.* Provides personnel an offensive/defensive capability to engage targets with small arms fire.

1-2. MAINTENANCE FORMS, RECORDS, AND REPORTS.

Refer to: TM 4700- 15/1 (Marine Corps), DA PAM 738-750, (ARMY).

1-3. DESTRUCTION OF MATERIEL TO PREVENT ENEMY USE.

Refer to: TM 750-244-7.

1-4. PREPARATION FOR STORAGE OR SHIPMENT.

Refer to: MCO P4450.7 (Marine Corps), TM 740-90-1 (ARMY).

1-5. NOMENCLATURE, CROSS-REFERENCE LIST.

Common Name/*Nomenclature*
Action Spring/*Compression Helical Spring* (8448629)
Bolt Catch Spring/*Compression Helical Spring* (8448633)
Burst Disconnector/*Lock-Release Lever* (9349113)
Cam Clutch Spring/*Helical Spring* (9349109)
Charging Handle Assembly/*Handle Assembly* (8448517)
Disconnector Springs/*Compression Helical Spring* (9349116)
Ejector Spring/*Helical Spring* (8448516)
Extractor Spring Assembly/*Spring Assembly* (8448755)
Hammer Spring/*Torsion Helical Spring* (9349107)
Magazine Catch Spring/*Compression Helical Spring* (8448637)
Peel Washer/*Shim* (9349051)
Pivot Pin Detent/*Takedown Pin Detent* (8448585)
Rifle Barrel Assembly/*Barrel Assembly* (9349124)
Semiautomatic Disconnector/*Lock-Release Level* (9349114)
Trigger Spring/*Torsion Helical Spring* (8448593)
Weapon/*Rifle, 5.56-mm, M16A2*

1-6. REPORTING OF UNSATISFACTORY EQUIPMENT.

Refer to: MCO 4855.10.

Section II. EQUIPMENT DESCRIPTION AND DATA

1-7. EQUIPMENT CHARACTERISTICS, CAPABILITIES, AND FEATURES.

a. *Characteristics.*

(1) Lightweight
(2) Air-cooled
(3) Gas-operated
(4) Magazine-fed
(5) Semiautomatic or burst fire

b. *Capabilities.* Provide an offensive/defensive capability to engage targets with direct small arms fire.

c. *Features*

(1) The bolt locking action is one of the mechanical features of the weapon. The bolt and barrel extension contain locking lugs which engage and lock the bolt firmly in the barrel extension. The initial force of the explosion of the cartridge is absorbed by the barrel, barrel extension, and bolt.

(2) The trigger guard is easily adaptable to winter operations. A spring-loaded retaining pin is depressed to allow ready access to the trigger when wearing arctic mittens.

(3) The ejection port cover prevents dirt or sand from getting into the ejection port. The cover must be closed during periods when firing is not anticipated. It opens automatically by the forward or rearward movement of the bolt carrier.

1-8. DESCRIPTION OF MAJOR COMPONENTS.

A **CARTRIDGE MAGAZINE.** 30 cartridge capacity.

B **SMALL ARMS SLING.** The small arms sling is adjustable and provides a means to carry the weapon.

C **BOLT CARRIER ASSEMBLY.** Carries bolt to chamber and fires the weapon. Contains the firing pin, extractor, bolt, ejector, and cam pin.

D **HANDLE ASSEMBLY.** Provides a means of charging the weapon.

E **UPPER RECEIVER AND BARREL ASSEMBLY.** Upper receiver contains rear sight, ejection port, ejection port cover, and a housing for the bolt carrier and bolt assembly. Rifle barrel assembly is aircooled, contains compensator and front sight assembly, and holds the two handguards and the sling swivel.

F **LOWER RECEIVER AND BUTTSTOCK ASSEMBLY.** Lower receiver contains the trigger assembly, sear, hammer assembly, selector lever, rifle grip, bolt catch, and buttstock assembly. The buttstock assembly houses the action spring, buffer assembly, and extension assembly.

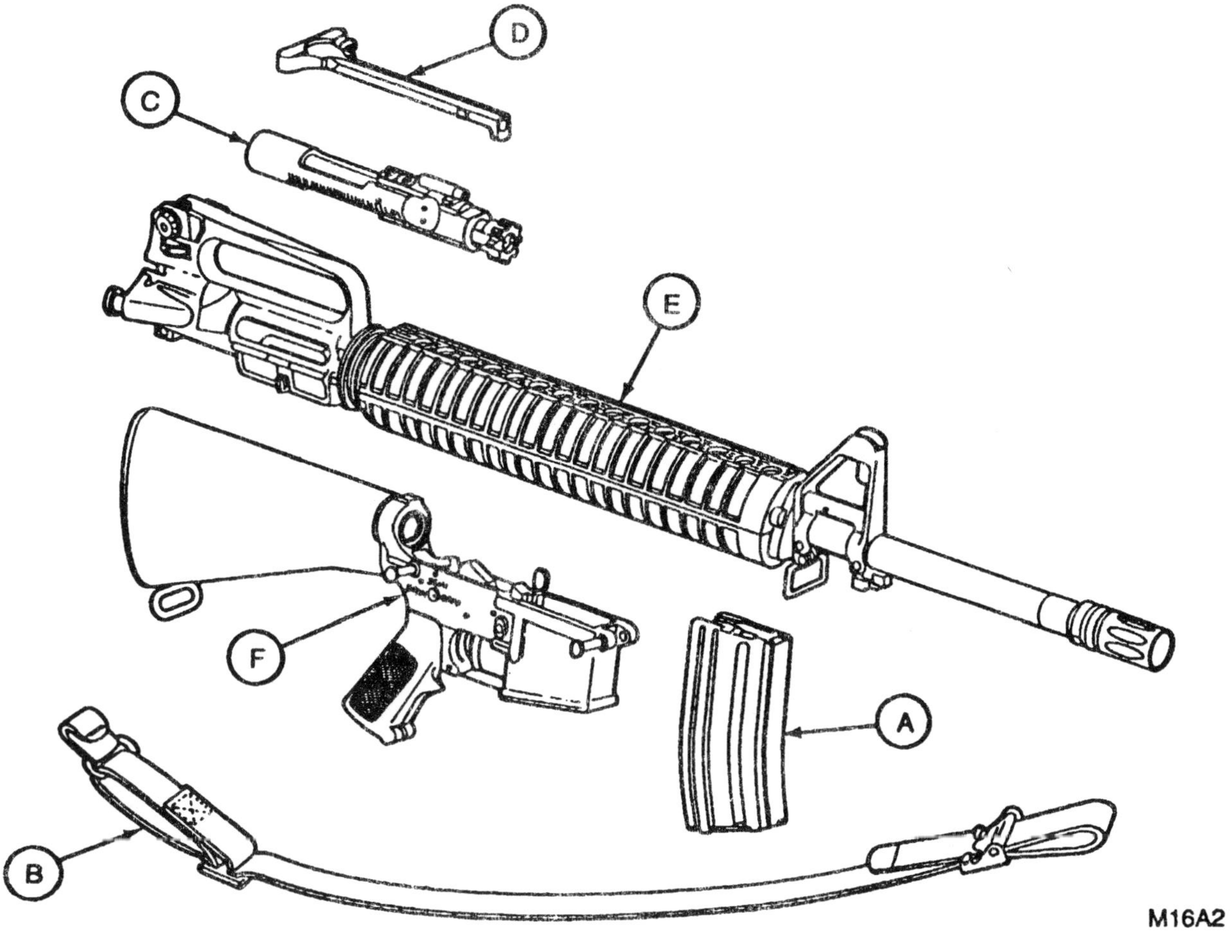
D
C
E
F
A
B
M16A2

1-9. EQUIPMENT DATA.

Weight:

Rifle M16A2 without magazine and sling	7 1/2 lb
Sling, Adjustable.	4 oz
Empty magazine.	4 oz
Loaded magazine	1 lb 1 oz
Rifle M16A2 w/sling and loaded magazine.	8 3/4 lb
Bayonet-Knife M7	10 1/2 oz
Scabbard M8A1	5 oz

Length:

Rifle w/compensator	39 5/8 in
Rifle w/bayonet-knife.	44 7/8 in
Barrel	20 in
Barrel with compensator	21 in

Mechanical features:

Rifling.	right-hand twist
	6 grooves-1 turn
	in 7 inches
Method of operation	direct gas
Type of breech mechanism	rotating bolt
Method of feeding.	magazine
Cooling	air
Trigger pull	5 to 8 1/2 lb

Ammunition:

Caliber	5.56-mm
Type.	ball, blank,
	dummy, and
	tracer

Firing characteristics:

Muzzle velocity (approximate)	3,100 fps
Muzzle energy	1,322 ft-lb
Chamber pressure	52,000 psi
Cyclic rate of fire (approximate)	800 rds/m

Maximum rate of fire:

Semiautomatic .... 45 rds/m
Burst .... 90 rds/m

Sustained rate of fire .... 12/15 rds/m

Maximum range .... 3,534 meters

Maximum effective range:

Individual/point targets .... 550 meters
Area targets .... 800 meters

NOTE

Some weights and measures are approximations using M855 ammunition.

Whenever the term "Cleaner Lubricant and Preservative" (CLP) or the words "lubricant", "lube", "LSA", or "LAW" are cited in this TM, they are to be interpreted to mean that CLP, LSA and LAW can be utilized as applicable. The following constraints must be adhered to:

a. Under all but the coldest arctic conditions, LSA or CLP are the lubricants to use on your weapon. Either may be used at - 10°F and above. However, do not use both on the same weapon at the same time.

b. LAW is the lubricant to use during cold arctic conditions, +10°F and below.

c. Any of the lubricants may be used from -10°F to +10°F.

d. Do not mix lubricants on the same weapon. The weapon must be thoroughly cleaned during change from one lubricant to another. Dry Cleaning Solvent (SD) is recommended for cleaning during change from one lubricant to another.

Rifle Bore Cleaner (RBC) may be used to remove carbon buildup in the bore and other portions of the weapon.

Section III. PRINCIPLES OF OPERATION

1-10. GENERAL. The weapon:

a. *Is gas-operated.* It fires in either the semiautomatic or burst mode.

b. *Has positive locking of the bolt.* Firing pin is part of the bolt and carrier assembly and cannot strike the primer until the bolt is fully locked.

1-11. PRINCIPLES OF OPERATION.

A **CARTRIDGE MAGAZINE.** Holds cartridges ready for feeding and provides a guide for positioning cartridges for stripping . Provides quick reload capabilities for sustained firing.

B **SMALL ARMS SLING.** Provides the means for carrying the weapon.

C **BOLT AND CARRIER ASSEMBLY.** Provides stripping, chambering, locking, firing, extraction, and ejection of cartridges using the drive springs and projectile propelling gases for power.

D **HANDLE ASSEMBLY.** Provides initial charging of the weapon. The charging handle latch locks the handle in the forward position during sustained fire to prevent injury to the operator.

E **UPPER RECEIVER AND BARREL ASSEMBLY.** Provides support for the bolt carrier assembly. The barrel chambers the cartridge for firing and directs the projectile.

F **LOWER RECEIVER AND BUTTSTOCK ASSEMBLY.** Provides firing control for the weapon and provides storage for basic cleaning materials.

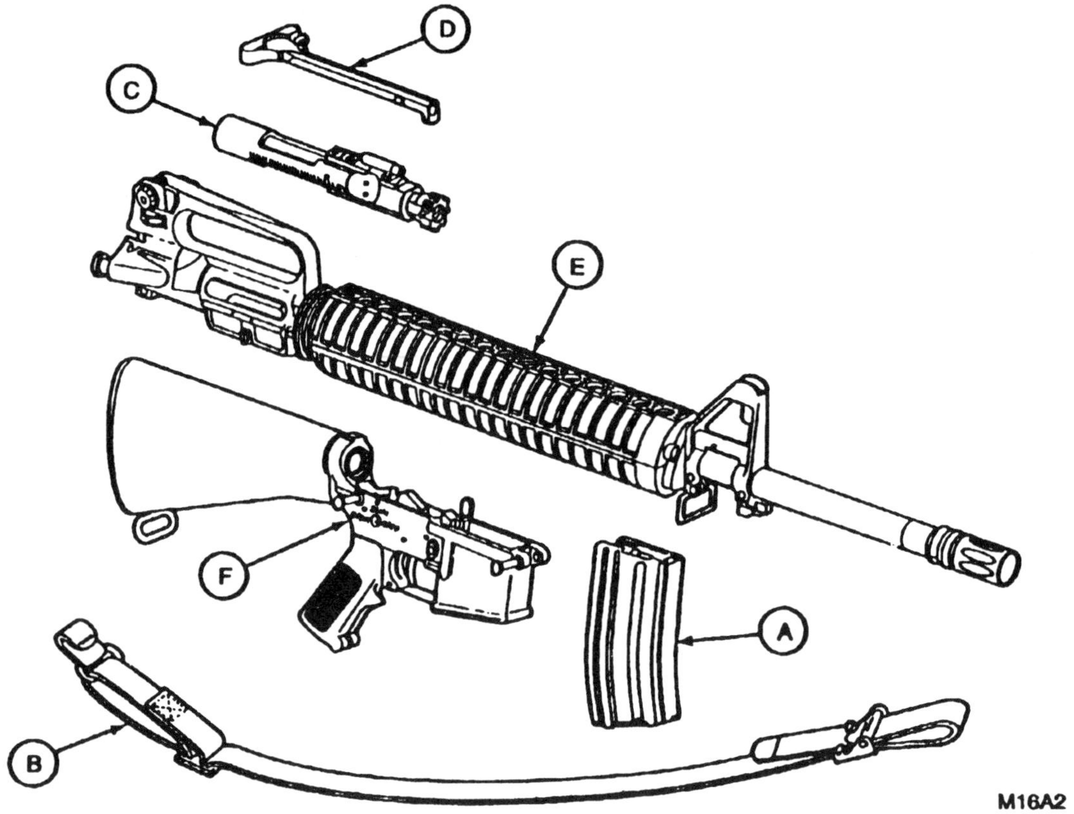

CHAPTER 2
ORGANIZATIONAL MAINTENANCE INSTRUCTIONS

CHAPTER OVERVIEW

This chapter provides information and instructions to help keep the rifle in good repair and contains the following sections:

I. Repair Parts and Special Tools
II. Service Upon Receipt
III. Organizational Preventive Maintenance Checks and Services (PMCS)
IV. Organizational Troubleshooting
V. Organizational Maintenance Procedures
VI. Decontamination of Rifles and Arms Rooms

Section I. REPAIR PARTS AND SPECIAL TOOLS

2-1. COMMON TOOLS AND EQUIPMENT. For authorized common tools and equipment, see (MC) SL-3-00607A.

For Army authorized common tools and equipment refer to the Modified Table of Organization and Equipment (TOE/MTOE) applicable to your unit.

2-2. SPECIAL TOOLS. Special tools required for organizational support are listed in appendix C. Fabricated tools are listed and illustrated in appendix E.

2-3. REPAIR PARTS. Repair parts are listed and illustrated in appendix C of this manual.

Section II. SERVICE UPON RECEIPT

2-4. GENERAL.

a. **(MC ONLY)** Check the weapon against the packing slip to see if the shipment is complete. Report all discrepancies in accordance with MCO P4610.19C.

b. Check to see if all modification instructions have been applied.

c. Inspect the rifle for shipping damage. If it has been damaged, submit an SF 364, Report of Discrepancy (ROD).

d. **(ARMY ONLY)** Report all discrepancies in accordance with DA PAM 738-750.

2-5. ORGANIZATIONAL SERVICE UPON RECEIPT OF MATERIAL. Refer to the following table.

Table 2-1

SERVICE UPON RECEIPT - M16A2 RIFLE

LOCATION	ITEM	ACTION	REMARKS
M16A2 Rifle	a. Charging handle assembly (1)	Clear the weapon	Reference TM 05538C-10/1.

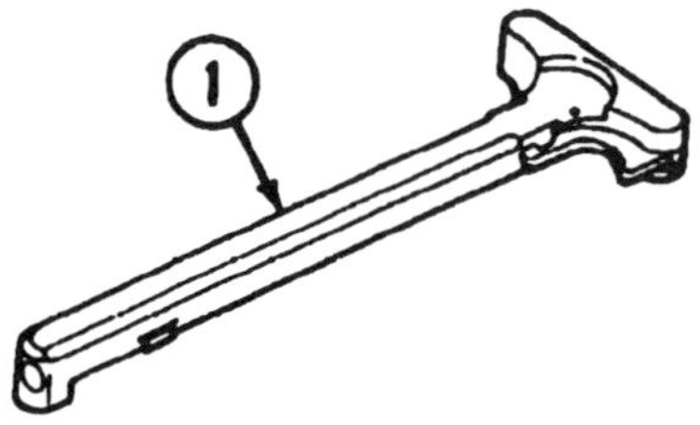

LOCATION	ITEM	ACTION	REMARKS
	b. Bolt carrier assembly and bolt assembly (2)	Remove	Reference TM 05538C-10/1.

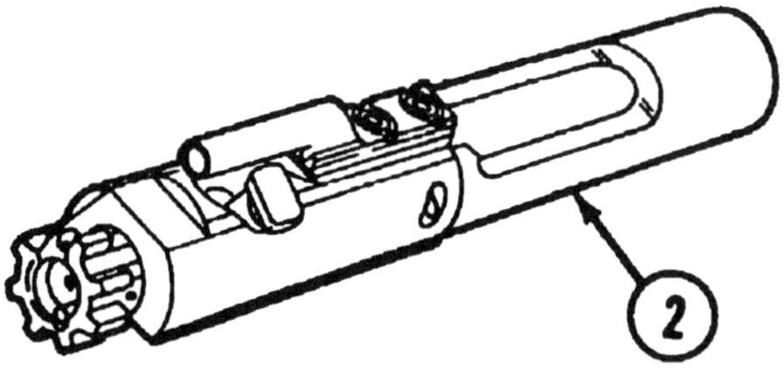

LOCATION	ITEM	ACTION	REMARKS
	c. All components	Visually inspect for proper assembly, damage, or for missing parts. Clean and lubricate.	Reference TM 05538C-10/1.

NOTE

Wipe excess oil from bore and chamber. Particular attention should be given to cleaning the bolt carrier key with a pipe cleaner (item 8, app D).

LOCATION	ITEM	ACTION	REMARKS
	d. Bolt carrier assembly and bolt assembly	Reassemble.	Reference TM 05538C-10/1.
		Hand function to assure proper operation.	Reference TM 05538C-10/1.
	e. Cartridge magazine	Check for positive retention and functioning of bolt catch.	Reference TM 05538C-10/1.

Section III. ORGANIZATIONAL PREVENTIVE MAINTENANCE CHECKS AND SERVICES (PMCS)

2-6. GENERAL. This section contains the procedures and instructions necessary to perform organizational preventive maintenance checks and services. These services are to be performed by organizational maintenance personnel..

2-7. PREVENTIVE MAINTENANCE CHECKS AND SERVICES.

WARNING

Before starting an insepction, be sure to clear the weapon. Do not keep live ammunition near the work area.

a. *General.* The PMCS procedures are contained in table 2-2. They are arranged in logical sequence requiring a minimum amount of time and motion on the part of the persons performing them and are arranged so that there will be minimum interference between persons performing checks simultaneously on the same end item.

b. *Item Number Column.* Checks and services are numbered in disassembly sequence.

c. *Item To Be Inspected Column.* The items listed in this column are divided into groups indicating the portion of the equipment of which they are a part, for example, "Cartridge Magazine," "Bolt Carrier Assembly."

d. *Procedures Column.* This column contains a brief description of the procedure by which the check is to be performed. It contains all the information required to accomplish the checks and services.

Table 2-2

ORGANIZATIONAL PREVENTIVE MAINTENANCE CHECKS AND SERVICES QUARTERLY SCHEDULE

Item No.	Item To Be Inspected	Procedures

WARNING

Before starting an inspection, be sure to clear the rifle. Do not actuate the trigger until the rifle has been cleared. Inspect the chamber to ensure that it is empty and no ammunition is in position to be chambered. Do not keep live ammunition near work area.

NOTE

Whenever the term "Cleaner Lubricant and Preservative" (CLP) or the words "lubricant", "lube", "LSA", or "LAW" are cited in this TM, they are to be interpreted to mean that CLP, LSA or LAW can be utilized as applicable. Follow constraints noted on page 1-5.

1.	Cartridge Magazine (3) (serviceability check)	Disassemble as in TM 05538C-10/1. Inspect tube for bulges, dents, or damaged feeder lips. Inspect spring and follower for kinks or damage. Replace the magazine if any of the above conditions exist. Floor plate must be positively retained when reassembled.

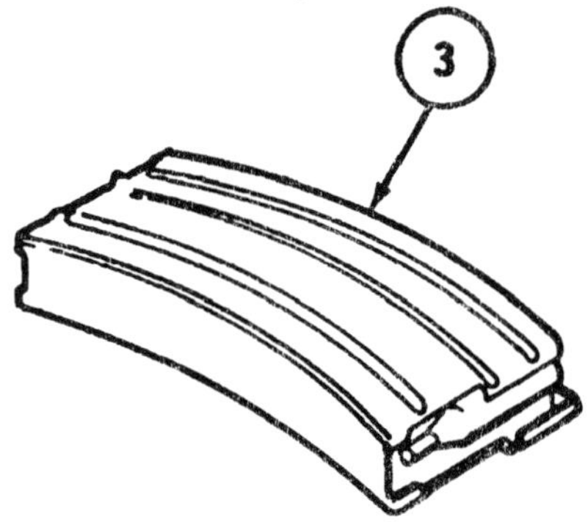

WARNING

Do not interchange bolt assemblies or components from one weapon to another. Doing so may result in injury to, or death of, personnel.

2.	Bolt carrier assembly and bolt assembly (serviceability check)	Disassemble. Visually inspect bolt assembly (4) for cracks, especially in the area of the cam pin hole. Check for cracks on locking lugs (5), for a pitted or chipped bolt face, and for an elongated firing pin hole. If defects are found, evacuate to intermediate maintenance for repair.

Item-No.	Item To Be Inspected	Procedures
	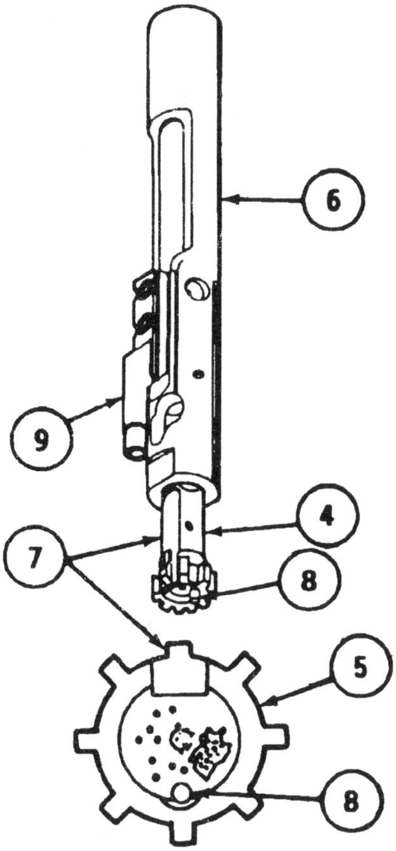	Check for worn bolt rings. Insert the bolt assembly (4) into the bolt carrier (do not insert cam pin) and exercise in and out to check for binding. Turn bolt carrier assembly (6) so the bolt assembly (4) points down. The bolt must not drop out. If the bolt assembly drops out of the bolt carrier due to its own weight, evacuate to intermediate maintenance for repair (usually bolt ring replacement). Check extractor (7) and spring and ejector (8) and spring for serviceability. Check carrier key (9) for damage and looseness. If bolt carrier (6) or carrier key (9) are damaged, evacuate to intermediate maintenance. Clean ejector (8) and spring. Lubricate and assemble or repair as necessary. Some dented carrier keys (9) can be repaired by using the fabricated key tool (Fig E-4). See page E-3.

NOTE

Refer to TM 05538C-10/1 for "buddy system" procedure for removing handguards.

Do not attempt to remove the heat shield, which is permanently attached to the inside surface of the handguard, for any reason. To do so will damage the heat shield and the handguard will have to be replaced.

3.	Upper receiver group (handguards) 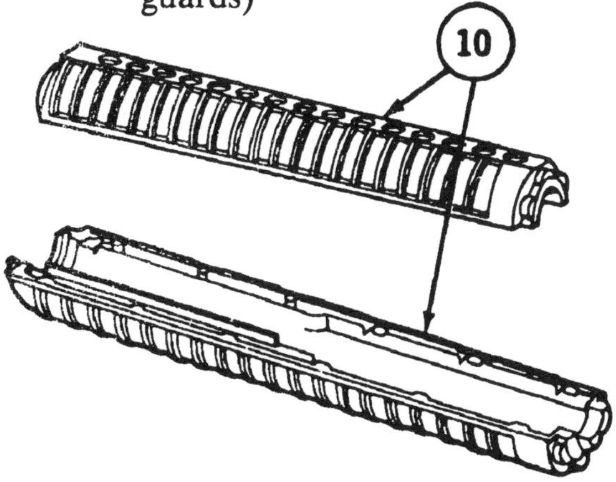	Remove and inspect handguards (10) internally and externally for cracks and/or damage. Cracks up to one inch in length are acceptable providing they do not extend into the handguard retaining flange. Discard and replace the hand guard (10) if the heatshield is loose enough to rattle.

Item No.	Item To Be Inspected	Procedures
4.	Upper receiver group (serviceability check)	Hand check compensator (11) for looseness on barrel (12), then hand check barrel for looseness on upper receiver. The third and middle slot of the compensator must be straight up or at Top Dead Center (TDC). A minor variation of one-half the width of the slot on either side of TDC is allowed. Check gas tube, forward assist (13), and rear sight (14) for damage.

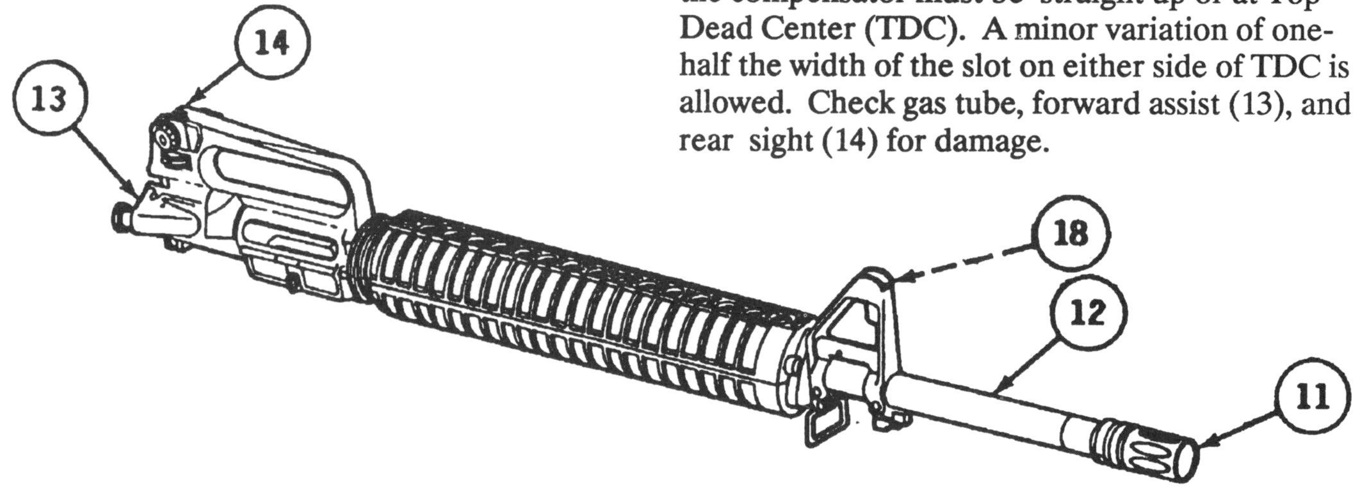

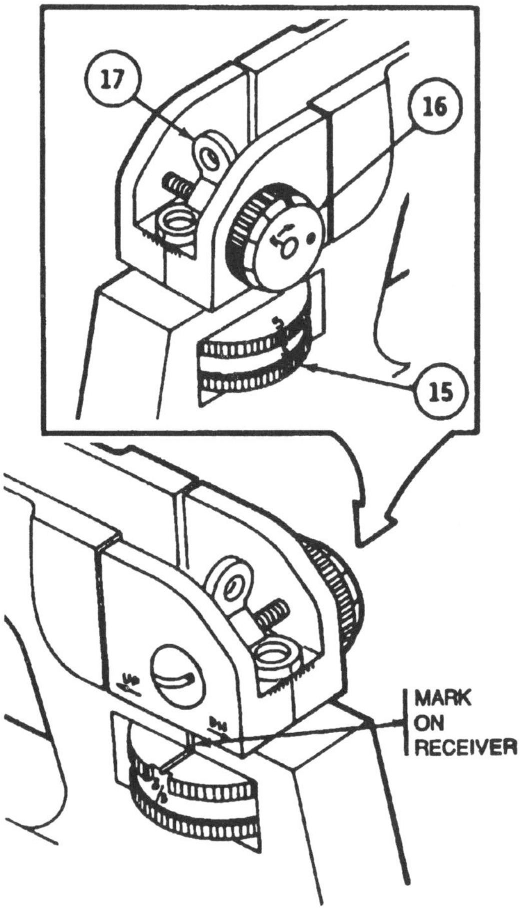

Rear sight elevation (15) and windage (16) knobs must rotate freely with distinct "clicks". Rotate elevation knob counter clockwise until the rear sight is all the way down. If a whole click is not felt as the sight stops, the sight has bottomed out and will not pivot freely.

Position elevation knob back slightly to its last whole click so the rear sight base is under tension of the bearing ball and helical spring. Now, rotate the elevation knob clockwise three clicks. The 300 meter mark should aline with the mark on the receiver. If the 300 meter mark is not aligned with the mark on the receiver, slip the range scale in the following manner. Position the 300 meter mark with the mark on the receiver. Insert a 1/16" Allen wrench through the access hole of the rear sight base and into the index screw (see paragraph 3-13). Loosen the index screw three turns and leave the wrench in place. Rotate the lower portion of elevation knob counter-clockwise until it stops (range

Item No.	Item To Be Inspected	Procedures
		scale should not have moved). Knob should be positioned on its last whole click. Now, rotate lower portion of elevation knob clockwise three clicks. Tighten index screw. Do not attempt to remove the index screw as this is an intermediate maintenance function.

ARMY (NOTE)

If the rear sight fails the above inspection, forward the weapon to Intermediate Maintenance for repair.

		Check front sight plunger and spring (18) for damage and corrosion. Clean and lubricate.
		Check charging handle assembly, ejection port cover, sling swivel and pin/rivet for damage and proper functioning. Replace defective components as necessary.

WARNING

Dry cleaning solvent is flammable and toxic and should be used in a well-ventilated area. The use of rubber gloves is necessary to protect the skin when washing rifle parts.

CAUTION

Do not use wire brush to roughen surfaces. Use a well-ventilated area during cleaning and application of solid film lubricant (item 8, app D). If solid film lubricant comes in contact with recoiling parts of functioning surfaces of the rifle, remove lubricant immediately by washing with dry cleaning solvent (item 3, app D).

5.	Upper receiver group	Inspect upper receiver finish. If scratched or worn shiny in spots, disassemble and remove all lubricant from surface with dry cleaning solvent (item 13, app D) and let dry. Always wear rubber gloves (item 15, app D) when using dry cleaning solvent. Roughen the surface using abrasive cloth (item 10, app D) and apply solid film lubricant (item 18, app D). Allow 16 to 24 hours to dry before handling. Release takedown pin

Item No.	Item To Be Inspected	Procedures
		and open receiver. Hold barrel at 40-degree angle (muzzle down). Pull charging handle assembly to rear. Hold bolt carrier to rear and push charging handle forward. Release bolt carrier. The bolt carrier should close and lock under its own weight. If it does not, remove the bolt from the carrier and slide the carrier and key assembly (without bolt) back and forth in the upper receiver and barrel assembly.
6.	Upper receiver group (bent gas tube extension)	If the gas tube hits the carrier key, or if the gas tube binds in the carrier key, try to correct the malfunction by adjusting (slightly bending) the gas tube in the area of the handguards. If this does not correct the malfunction, evacuate to Intermediate Maintenance.
7.	Lower receiver group (serviceability check)	Remove buffer (19) and action spring (20). Check buffer for cracks. Replace if cracked. Check action spring for kinks and free length. Free length should be 11 3/4 minimum to 13 1/2 maximum inches; if not, replace. Do not attempt to adjust the length by stretching the spring.

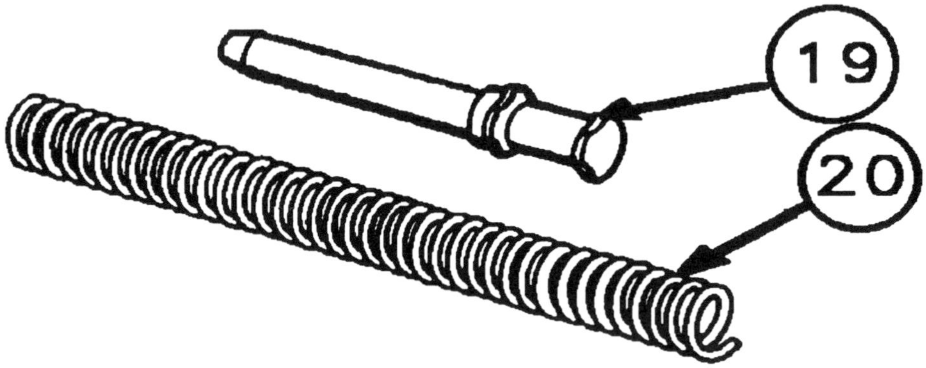

Item No.	Item To Be Inspected	Procedures

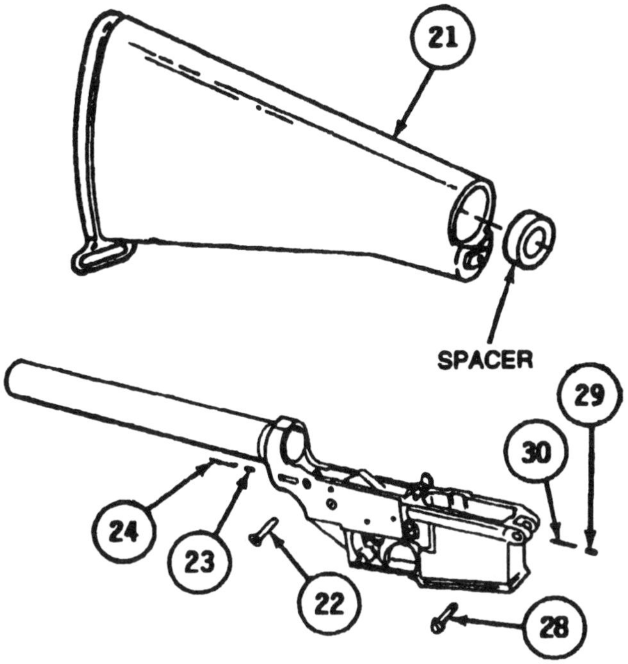

Remove butt cap screw and buttstock assembly (21), taking care not to lose the takedown pin (22), detent (23), and spring (24). Clean and lubricate the takedown pin, detent, spring, and hole in the receiver. Check buttstock assembly components for damage. Replace damaged components as necessary. A cracked buttstock can be repaired at Intermediate Maintenance. Check the amount of gap between the buttstock assembly and the lower receiver. If a gap of 1/32" exists or a forward to rear movement is noticeable, remove the buttstock assembly and hand check lower receiver extension for looseness and corrosion. If loose, evacuate to Intermediate Maintenance. Clean and lubricate the extension. Remove pistol grip (25), spring (26), and safety detent (27). Clean and lubricate pivot pin (28), detent (29), spring (30), and receiver holes.

Replace defective components as necessary. Clean and lubricate selector lever (31). Reassemble.

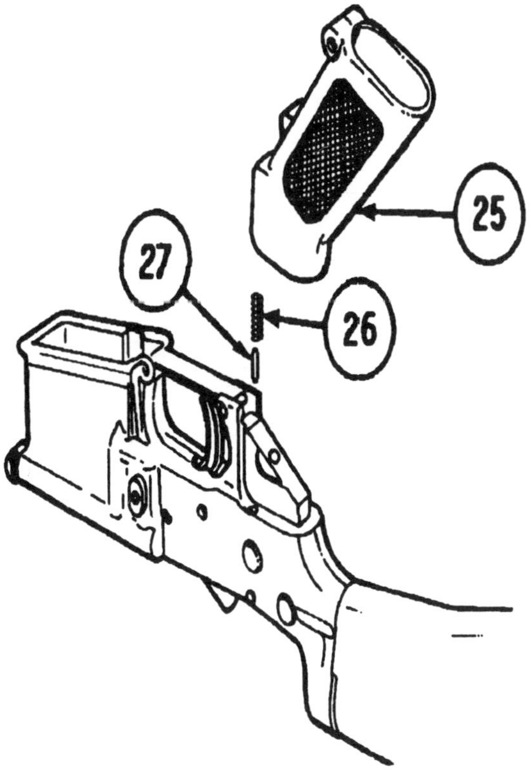

Item No.	Item To Be Inspected	Procedures

NOTE

If the buttcap screw is removed, it must be replaced with a new one.

Function check the magazine catch, bolt catch, automatic sear, hammer, trigger, and disconnectors. If defective, evacuate to intermediate maintenance. Check lower receiver finish. If scratched or worn shiny in spots, repair in the same manner as outlined for upper receiver.

Item No.	Item To Be Inspected	Procedures
8.	Bayonet and scabbard (serviceability check)	Remove grips (32). Clean and lubricate the bayonet. Check release for retention and release on rifle bayonet stud (33). Bayonet blade (34) should not be broken and blade should be free of nicks. Blades with blunt points and any nicks can be restored by stoning. Check scabbard (35) for cracks,splits, worn fabric, and missing thong (36).

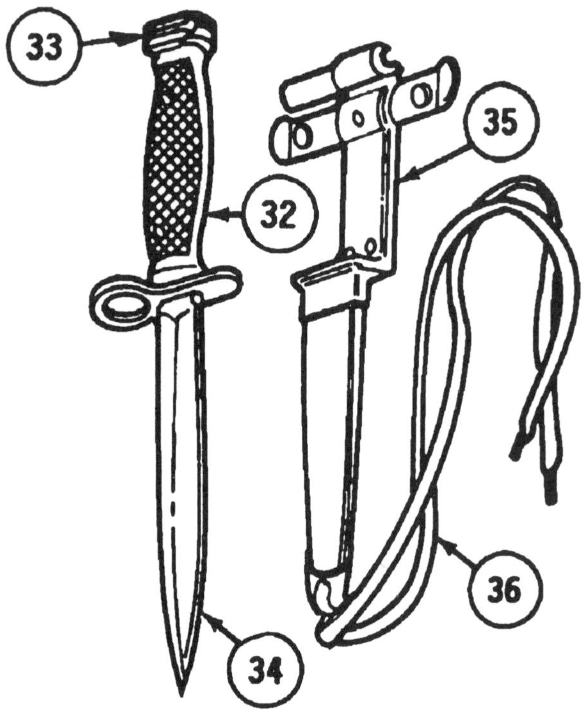

NOTE

Inactive weapons should receive quarterly PMCS unless inspection reveals more frequent servicing is necessary.

An inactive weapon is a weapon which has been stored in an arms room for a period of 90 days without use. The weapon may or may not have been assigned to an individual.

Section IV. ORGANIZATIONAL TROUBLESHOOTING

2-8. GENERAL.

a. This section contains organizational level troubleshooting information for locating and correcting most of the operating troubles which may develop in the weapon. Each malfunction for the individual part or assembly is followed by a list of tests or inspections which will help you to determine the corrective actions to take. You should perform the tests/inspections and corrective actions in the order listed.

b. This manual cannot list all malfunctions that may occur, nor all tests or inspections and corrective actions. If a malfunction is not listed or is not corrected by listed corrective actions, see individual repair sections for maintenance instructions on each major assembly.

2-9. TROUBLESHOOTING PROCEDURES. Refer to Table 2-4 for malfunctions, tests, and corrective actions. The following symptom index, Table 2-3, is provided for a quick reference of the malfunctions covered in Table 2-4.

Table 2-3

SYMPTOM INDEX

Table 2-4

ORGANIZATIONAL TROUBLESHOOTING

MALFUNCTION	TEST OR INSPECTION	CORRECTIVE ACTION
1. BOLT FAILS TO LOCK TO REAR AFTER FIRING LAST ROUND.	Step 1. Broken bolt catch (37) and/or spring.	Evacuate to Intermediate Maintenance.
	Step 2. Magazine follower (38) worn or broken.	Replace magazine.
	Step 3. Magazine spring (39) weak or broken.	Replace magazine.
	Step 4. Magazine feeder lips (40) bent or broken.	Replace magazine.

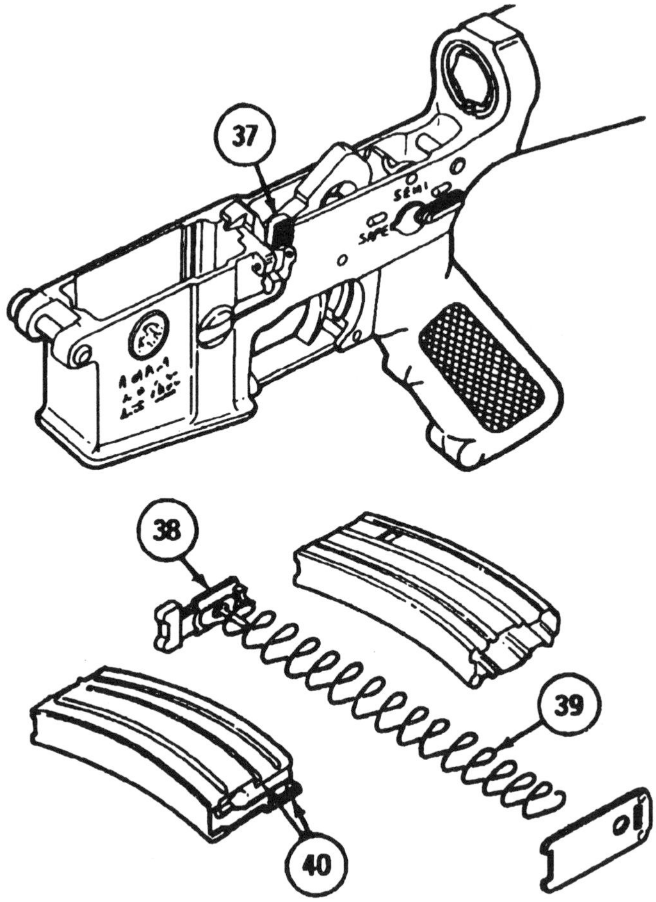

MALFUNCTION	TEST OR INSPECTION	CORRECTIVE ACTION
2. FAILURE TO FIRE.	Step 1. Broken or short firing pin (41).	Evacuate to Intermediate Maintenance.
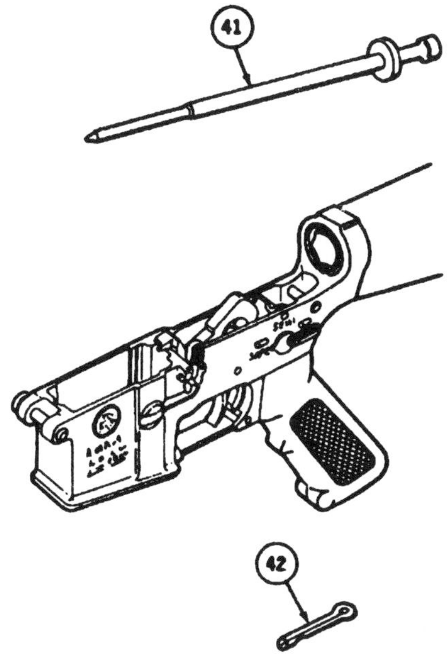	Step 2. Carbon buildup in firing pin track inside bolt.	Remove extractor and clean track with pipe cleaner (item 8, app D).
	Step 3. Firing mechanism and/or lower receiver improperly assembled or has worn, broken, or missing parts.	a. Inspect for proper assembly. Assemble properly. b. Evacuate to Intermediate Maintenance.
	Step 4. Broken, defective, or improperly assembled retaining pin (42).	a. Assemble properly. b. Replace.
3. FAILURE TO EXTRACT.	Step 1. Defective extractor pin (43), extractor (44), and/or extractor spring assembly (45).	Replace extractor pin (43), extractor (44), and/or extractor spring assembly (45).
	Step 2. Short recoil.	Refer to page 2-17.

NOTE

Rubber insert and spring are an assembly. Illustration shows insert out of assembly for clarification only.

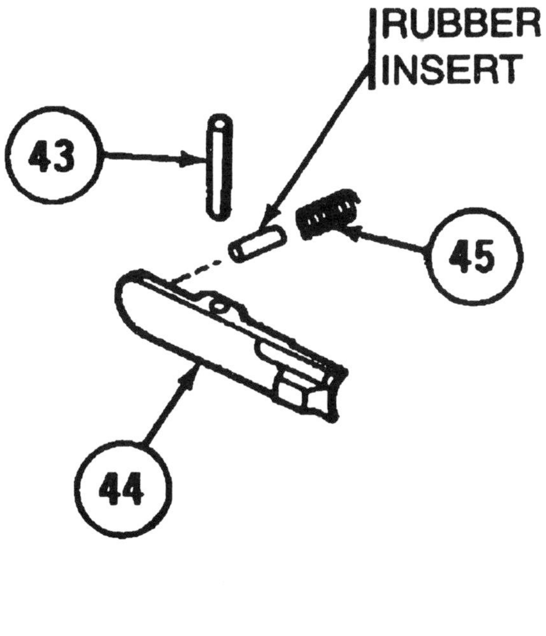

MALFUNCTION	TEST OR INSPECTION	CORRECTIVE ACTION
4. FAILURE TO EJECT.	Step 1. Broken ejector (46).	Replace.
	Step 2. Ejector (46) stuck in bolt body (47).	Disassemble and clean.
	Step 3. Weak or broken ejector spring (48).	Replace .
	Step 4. Short recoil.	Refer to page 2-17.

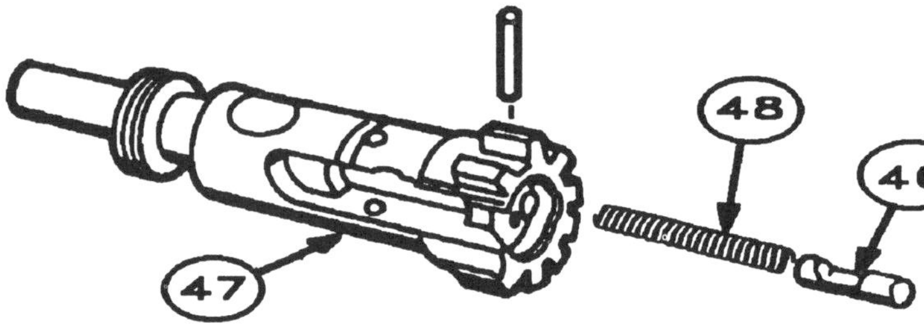

MALFUNCTION	TEST OR INSPECTION	CORRECTIVE ACTION
5. FAILURE TO COCK.	Step 1. Worn, broken, or missing parts of firing mechanism.	Evacuate to intermediate maintenance.
	Step 2. Short recoil.	Refer to page 2-17.
6. FAILURE TO FEED.	Step 1. Magazine catch spring weak or broken. (Used with item 49)	Evacuate to intermediate maintenance.

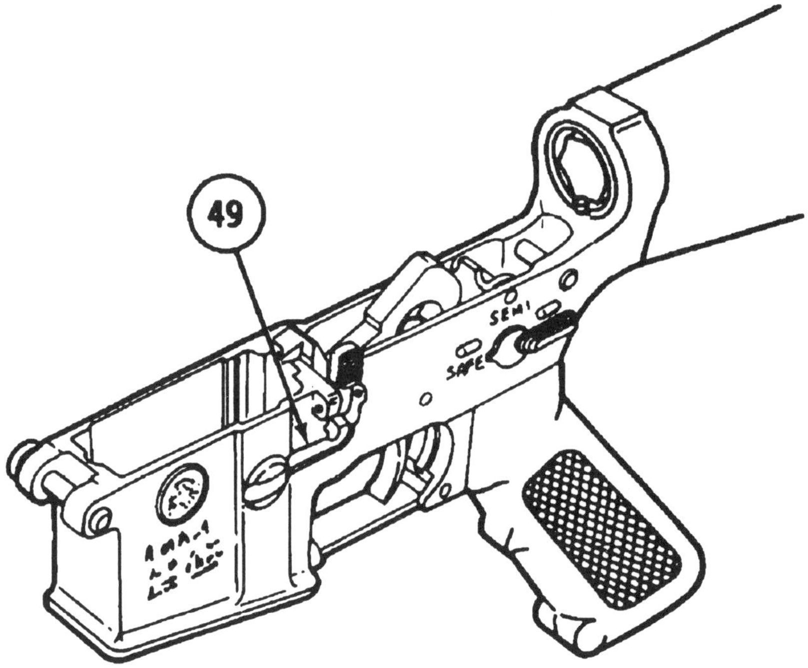

MALFUNCTION	TEST OR INSPECTION	CORRECTIVE ACTION
	Step 2. Magazine catch (49) defective.	Evacuate to intermediate maintenance.
	Step 3. Magazine catch notch (50) defective.	Replace magazine.
	Step 4. Magazine lips (51) burred or broken.	Replace magazine.
	Step 5. Magazine follower (52) defective.	Replace magazine.
	Step 6. Magazine spring weak (53) or broken.	Replace magazine.
	Step 7. Magazine tube (54) dented.	Replace magazine.
	Step 8. Magazine catch (49) out of adjustment (will not retain magazine).	Refer to paragraph 3-15.
	Step 9. Short recoil.	Refer to page 2-17.

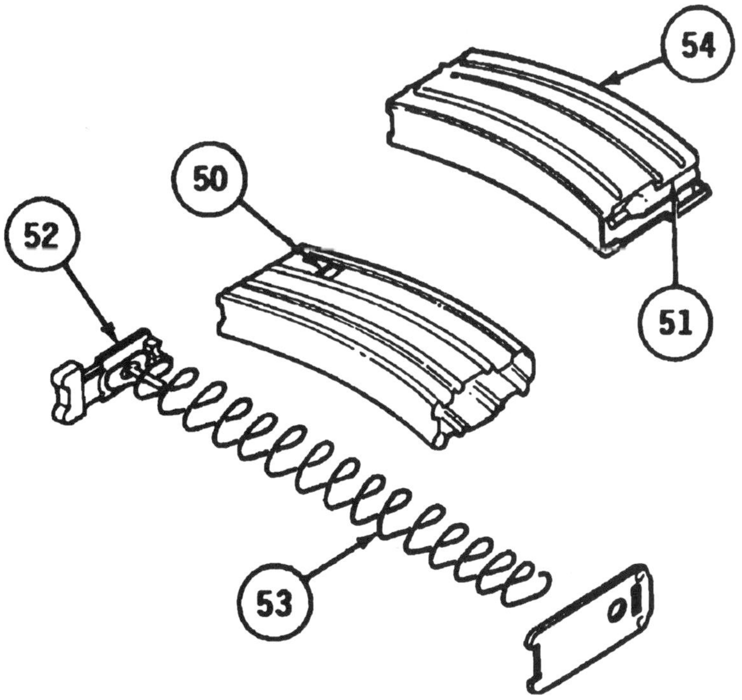

MALFUNCTION	TEST OR INSPECTION	CORRECTIVE ACTION
7. FAILURE TO CHAMBER.	Step 1. Weak or broken action spring 55) (free length 11 3/4 inches minimum to 13 1/2 inches maximum).	Replace action spring .

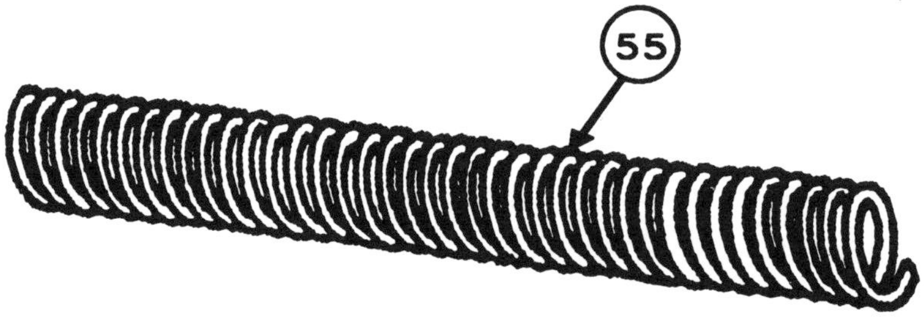

MALFUNCTION	TEST OR INSPECTION	CORRECTIVE ACTION
	Step 2. Short recoil.	Refer to page 2-17.
8. FAILURE TO LOCK.	Step 1. Bolt cam pin (56) missing.	Replace.
	Step 2. Loose or damaged bolt carrier key (57).	Evacuate to intermediate maintenance.
	Step 3. Improperly assembled extractor spring assembly (58).	Assemble correctly.
	Step 4. Bent gas tube (59).	a. Adjust by bending in area of handguard. b. Evacuate to intermediate maintenance.
	Step 5. Weak or broken action spring.	Replace action spring.

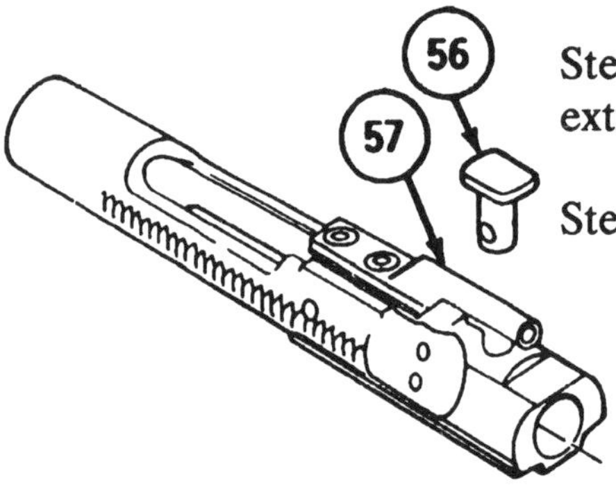

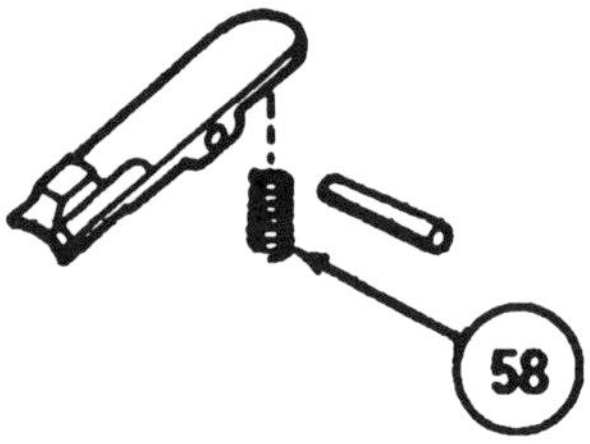

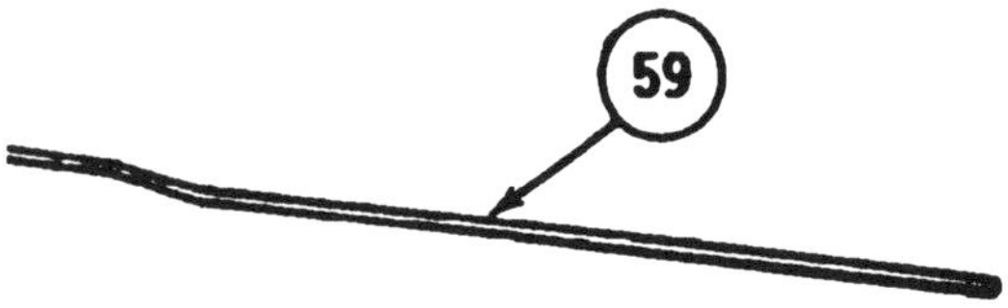

MALFUNCTION	TEST OR INSPECTION	CORRECTIVE ACTION
9. SHORT RECOIL.	Step 1. Weak or broken action spring (60).	Replace action spring.
	Step 2. Unlubricated or dirty action spring and receiver extension.	Clean and lubricate.

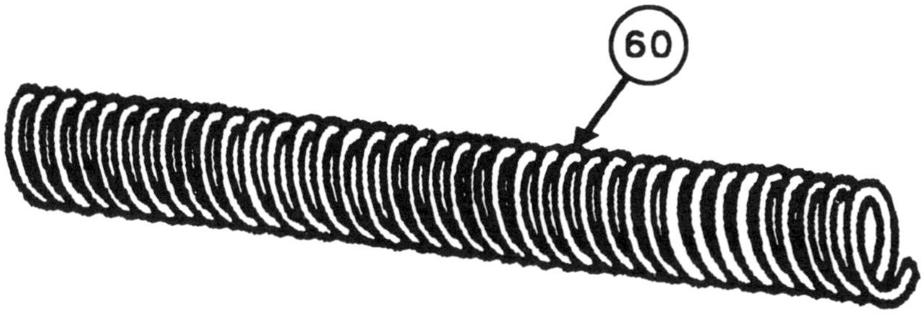

MALFUNCTION	TEST OR INSPECTION	CORRECTIVE ACTION
	Step 3. Improper gap space or worn, missing, or broken rings (61).	Evacuate to Intermediate Maintenance if rings are worn, broken or missing.

MALFUNCTION	TEST OR INSPECTION	CORRECTIVE ACTION
	Step 4. Gas leakage caused by broken or loose gas tube (62) around front sight base.	Evacuate to Intermediate Maintenance.
	Step 5. Improper alinement of gas tube and carrier key.	Evacuate to Intermediate Maintenance.

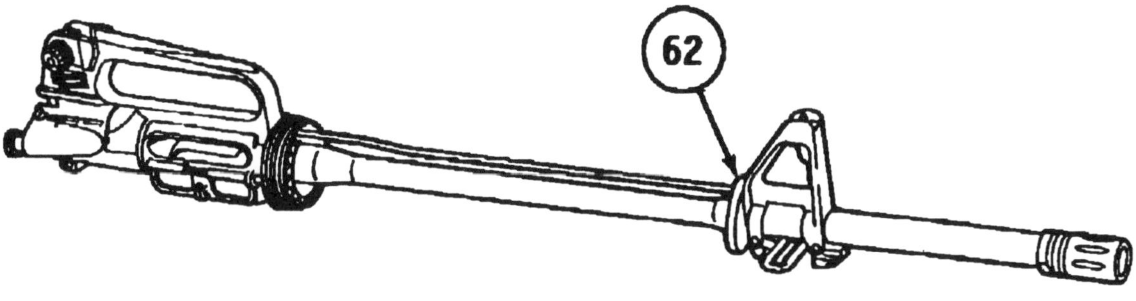

MALFUNCTION	TEST OR INSPECTION	CORRECTIVE ACTION
10. FAILURE TO CYCLE WITH SELECTOR LEVER SET ON BURST.	Faulty selector lever (63), broken cam, cam clutch spring, or burst disconnector (64).	Evacuate to Intermediate Maintenance.

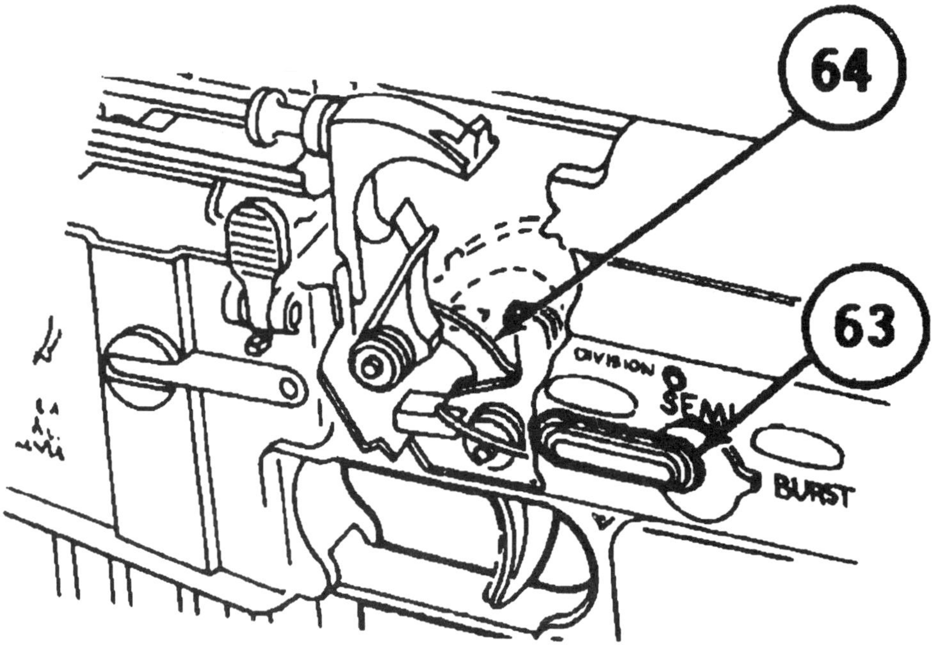

11. FIRES WITH SELECTOR LEVER (63) ON SAFE OR WHEN TRIGGER IS RELEASED WITH SELECTOR LEVER ON SEMI.	Worn, broken, or missing parts of firing mechanism.	Evacuate to Intermediate Maintenance.

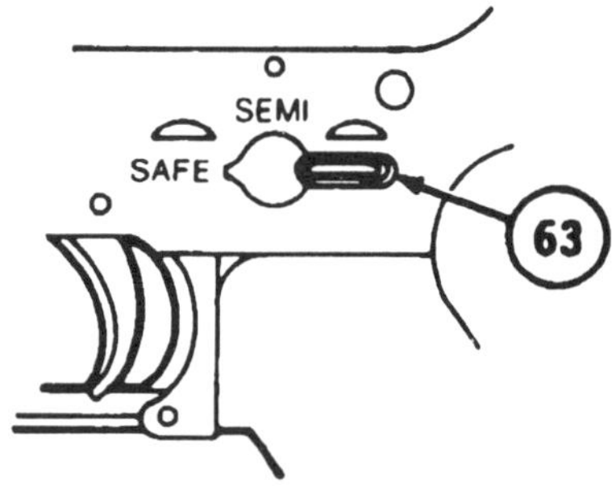

12. FIRES TWO ROUNDS WITH ONE SQUEEZE OF TRIGGER WITH SELECTOR LEVER (63) SET ON SEMI (DOUBLE FIRING).	Perform function test.	If any part of function test (paragraph 2-19) fails, evacuate to Intermediate Maintenance.

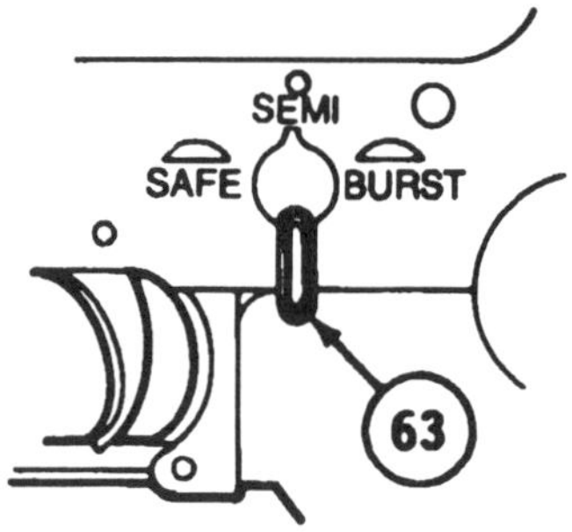

Section V. ORGANIZATIONAL MAINTENANCE PROCEDURES

2-10. INITIAL SETUP. The following will reduce the space required for the initial setup portion of the maintenance procedures.

a. Resources required are not listed unless they apply to the procedure.

b. **Personnel Required** is listed only if the task requires more than one person. If **Personnel Required** is not listed, it means one person can do the job.

c. The normal standard equipment condition is that the item is removed from the end item or next higher assembly and is in the assembled condition. **Equipment Condition** is not listed unless some other condition is required.

d. The approximate time required is listed on the applicable Maintenance Allocation Chart (MAC) in Appendix B.

2-11. MAJOR COMPONENTS OF M16A2 RIFLE.

This task covers disassembly.

INITIAL SETUP

References

TM 05538C-10/1

Equipment Condition

Weapon assembled.

General Safety Instructions

Before starting an inspection, be sure to clear the weapon. Do not keep live ammunition near the work area.

To avoid injury to your eyes, use care when removing and installing spring-loaded parts.

Do not intcrchangc bolt assemblies or components from one weapon to another. Doing so may result in injury to, or death of, personnel.

LOCATION	ITEM	ACTION	REMARKS
DISASSEMBLY			
Weapon	Cartridge magazine (65), small arms sling (66), bolt carrier assembly (67), charging handle assembly (68), upper receiver and barrel assembly (69), and lower receiver and buttstock assembly (70).	Remove.	Refer to TM 05538C-10/1

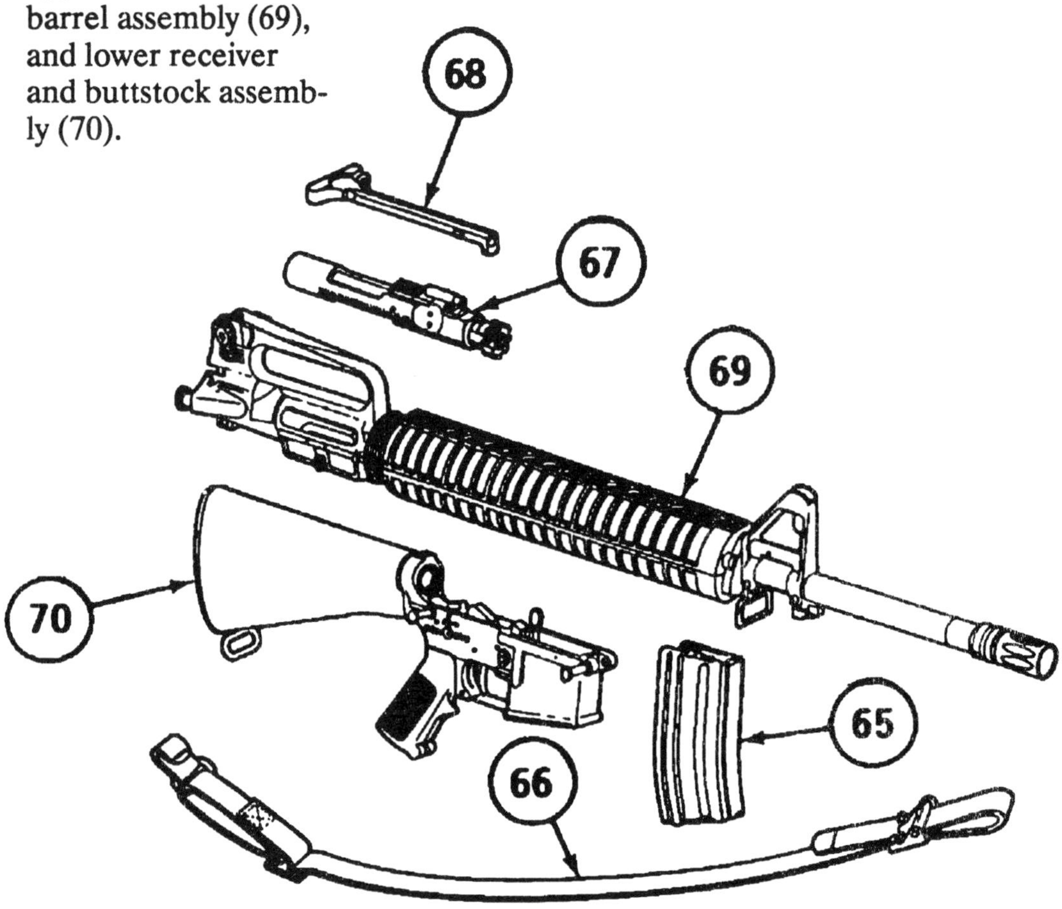

2-12. BOLT CARRIER ASSEMBLY (ORGANIZATIONAL).

This task covers
a. Disassembly
b. Cleaning
c. Inspection
d. Repair
e. Lubrication
f. Reassembly

INITIAL SETUP

Tools

(MC) Small Arms Repairman Tool Kit
NSN 5180-00-357-7770/SL-3-00607A
Key tool (E-4, app E)
(ARMY) Small Arms Repairman Tool Kit
SC 5180-95-CL-A07 (app B)

Materials/Parts

Cleaner, lubricant, and preservative (CLP) (item 6, app D)

General Safety Instructions

Bolt cam pin must be installed or weapon will blow up while firing the first round. If the bolt cam pin is not installed, injury to, or death of, personnel may result.

Do not interchange bolt assemblies or components from one weapon to another. Doing so may result in injury to, or death of, personnel.

LOCATION	ITEM	ACTION	REMARKS
DISASSEMBLY			
Bolt Carrier Assembly	a. Firing pin retaining pin (71).	Remove.	Do not spread or close legs of firing pin retaining pin
	b. Firing pin (72).	Catch firing pin (72) as it drops out.	
	c. Bolt cam pin (73).	Rotate bolt cam pin (73) 1/4 turn and lift straight up.	

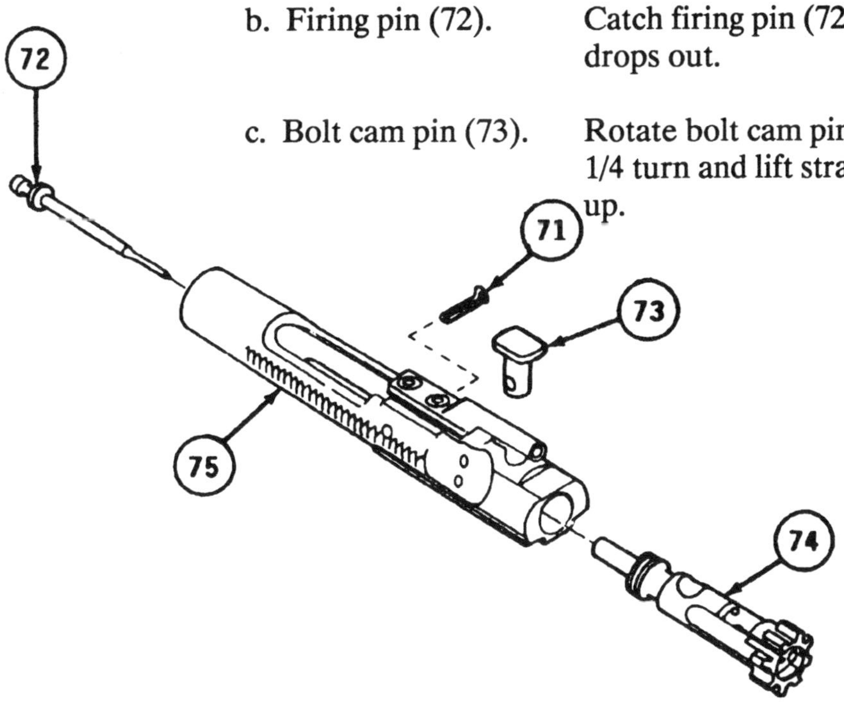

LOCATION	ITEM	ACTION	REMARKS
	d. Bolt assembly (74) and key and bolt carrier assembly (75).	Remove.	
CLEANING			
Bolt Carrier Assembly	All items	Remove carbon using CLP (item 6, app D).	
INSPECTION			
Bolt Carrier Assembly	a. Bolt Assembly	Check for worn rings by holding the bolt carrier assembly with the bolt assembly down. Check ring spacing.	If bolt assembly falls out of carrier after retaining pin and cam pin are removed, the rings are worn. Evacuate to Intermediate Maintenance.
	b. All items	Check for serviceability.	
REPAIR			
Bolt Carrier Assembly	a. Firing pin retaining pin and cam pin	Replace if unserviceable.	Items are unserviceable if cracked or mutilated.
	b. Bolt assembly	See paragraph 2-13.	
	c. Firing pin	Notify Intermediate Maintenance if unserviceable.	Firing pin is unserviceable if broken or if tip is mutilated.

CAUTION

Extreme care must be exercised during the following procedure to assure that the striking force is not directed to the attaching screws and that the tube portion is not enlarged or flared beyond original requirements as such enlargement would permit loss of gas pressure when the key and gas tube come together during function.

	d. Carrier key	Repair small dents and/or distortions using fabricated key tools (E-4, app E) as follows:	

LOCATION	ITEM	ACTION	REMARKS
		Place the key and bolt carrier assembly in a vertical position, supported in a manner that contact is made with the rear surface of the key.	
		Insert the small end of the key tool (E-4, app E) into the tube portion of the key.	
		Strike the large end of the key tool (E-4, app E) lightly with a 3-ounce, soft-brass hammer.	
		Repeat striking (gently) until the carrier key is reformed to original configuration.	

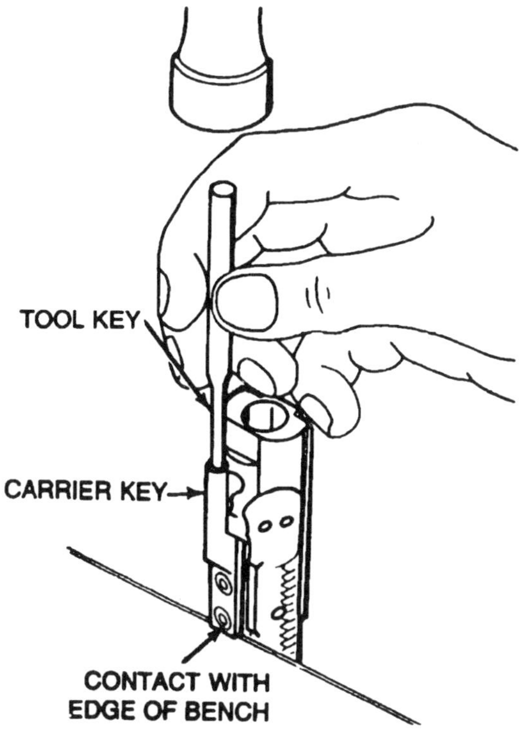

LUBRICATION

LOCATION	ITEM	ACTION	REMARKS
Bolt Carrier Assembly	All items	Lubricate using CLP (item 6, app D).	

REASSEMBLY

WARNING

Do not interchange bolt assemblies of components from one weapon to another. Doing so may result in injury to, or death of , personnel.

Bolt cam pin must be installed or weapon will blow up while firing the first round. If the cam pin is not installed, injury to, or death of, personnel may result.

LOCATION	ITEM	ACTION	REMARKS
Bolt Carrier Assembly	a. Key and bolt carrier assembly (76), bolt assembly (77), and bolt cam pin (78).	Install bolt in carrier and key and secure with cam pin.	Before installing bolt assembly, check to see that the ring gaps are staggered to prevent loss of gas pressure.

LOCATION	ITEM	ACTION	REMARKS
	b. Firing pin (79) and firing pin retaining pin (80).	Install.	Firing pin retaining pin must be installed from the left side only.

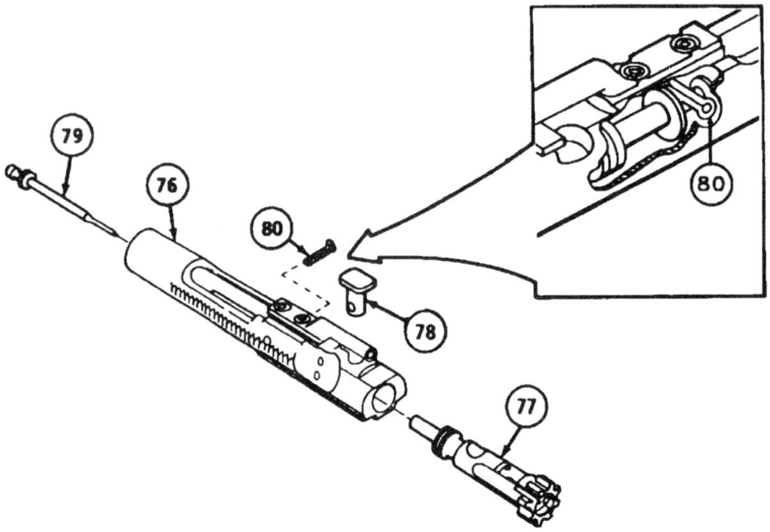

2-13. BOLT ASSEMBLY (ORGANIZATIONAL).

This task covers:
- a. Disassembly
- b. Cleaning
- c. Lubrication
- d. Repair
- e. Reassembly

INITIAL SETUP

Tools

(MC) Small Arms Repairman Tool Kit
NSN 5180-00- 357-7770/SL-3-00607A
(ARMY) Small Arms Repairman Tool Kit
SC 5180-95-CL-A07 (app B)

Materials/Parts

Cleaner, lubricant, and preservative (CLP)(item 6, app D)

General Safety Instructions

Do not interchange bolt assemblies or other components from one weapon to another. Doing so may result in injury to, or death of, personnel.
To avoid injury to your eyes, use care when removing and installing spring-loaded parts.

LOCATION	ITEM	ACTION	REMARKS

DISASSEMBLY

CAUTION

If firing pin is used as a tool to push out extractor pin, use extreme care not to damage its tip.

LOCATION	ITEM	ACTION	REMARKS
Bolt assembly	a. Extractor pin (81), cartridge extractor (82), and extractor spring assembly (83).	Push out extractor pin and remove cartridge extractor and spring assembly as unit.	Do not separate cartridge extractor and spring assembly unless replacement of either or both is required.
	b. Cartridge extractor (82) and extractor spring assembly (83).	Twist spring assembly counterclockwise to remove from cartridge extractor.	

NOTE:

Do not remove rubber insert from spring assembly.

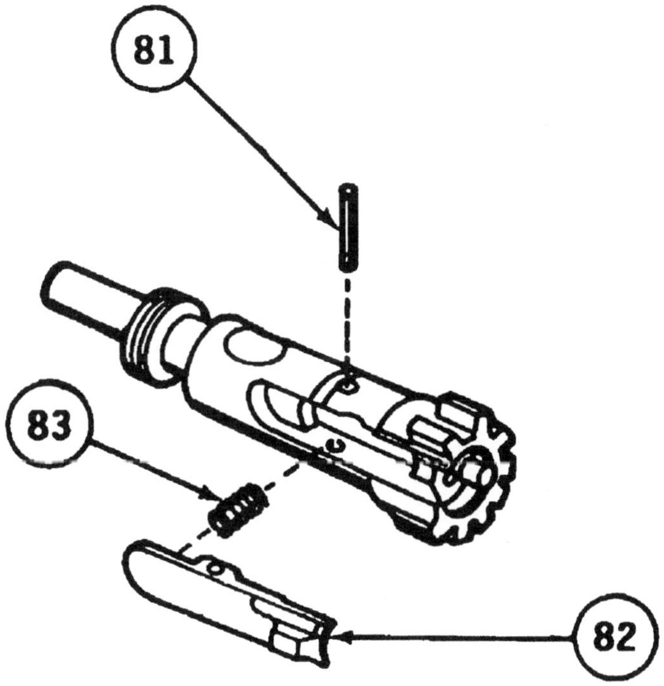

CAUTION

Be sure to use vise jaw protective caps.

LOCATION	ITEM	ACTION	REMARKS
	c. Spring pin (84)	Hold bolt body in vise and remove spring pin using a 1/16" punch and hammer.	

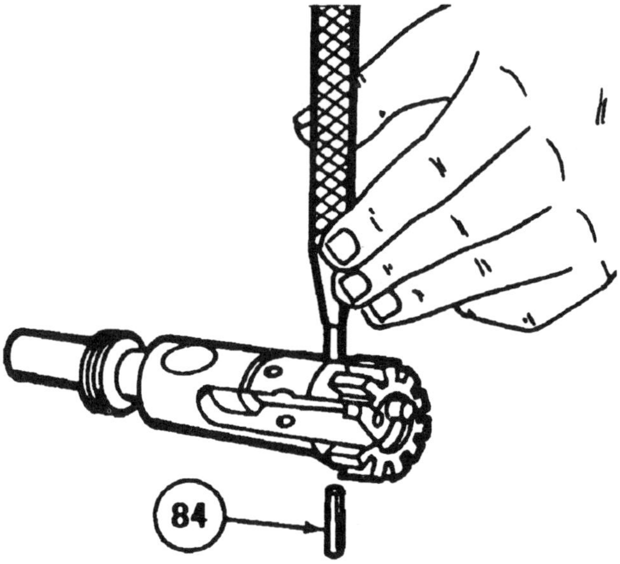

WARNING

To avoid injury to your eyes, use care when removing and installing spring-loaded parts.

LOCATION	ITEM	ACTION	REMARKS
	d. Cartridge ejector (85) and helical spring (86).	Catch cartridge ejector and helical spring as punch is withdrawn to prevent loss.	

CLEANING

CAUTION

Do not distort spring during cleaning.

LOCATION	ITEM	ACTION	REMARKS
Bolt Assembly	All items	Remove carbon with CLP (item 6, app D).	

LOCATION	ITEM	ACTION	REMARKS
LUBRICATION			
Bolt Assembly	All items	Cover with light coat of CLP (item 6, app D).	
REPAIR			
Bolt Assembly	All authorized items	Replace if unserviceable.	
REASSEMBLY			

WARNING

Do not interchange bolt assemblies or other components from one weapon to another. Doing so may result in injury to, or death of personnel.

LOCATION	ITEM	ACTION	REMARKS
REASSEMBLY			
Bolt Assembly	a. Helical spring (86) and cartridge ejector (85).	Install. Align the groove on the cartridge ejector so that the spring pin can be installed. Hold in place with a 1/16" punch inserted from below.	

CAUTION

Be sure to use vise jaw protective caps.

LOCATION	ITEM	ACTION	REMARKS
	b. Spring pin (84)	Use a new spring pin (84), if available. Hold bolt body in vise. Start spring pin in hole. Compress and hold the helical spring and cartridge ejector in place with a 3/8" punch and then complete the installation of spring pin (84) using hammer. Using a 1/16" punch, install pin so the ends are flush with the outside of the bolt body.	

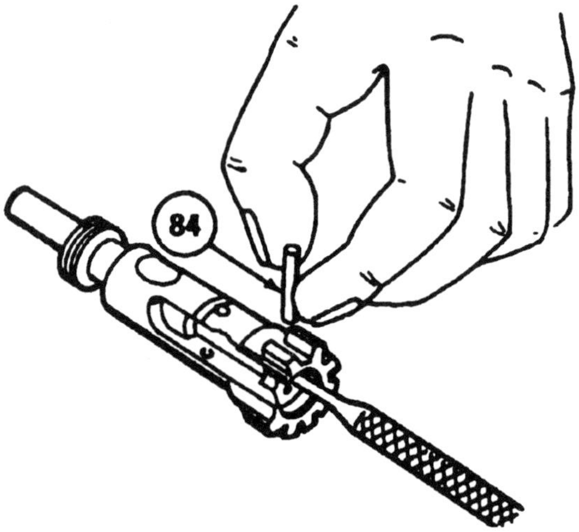

LOCATION	ITEM	ACTION	REMARKS
	c. Cartridge extractor (87) and extractor spring assembly (88).	Insert large end of spring assembly into extractor and seat by turning clockwise.	

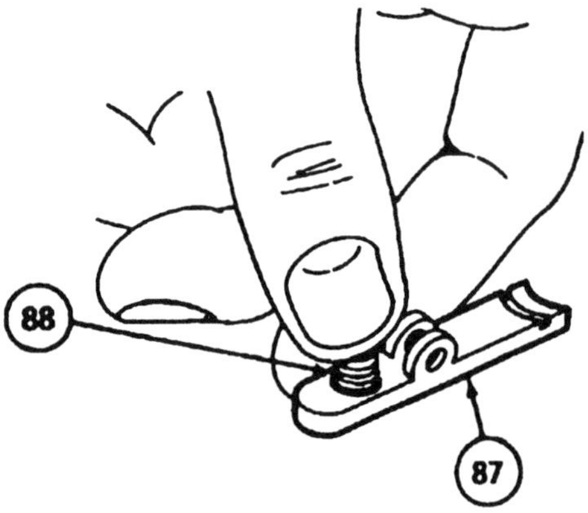

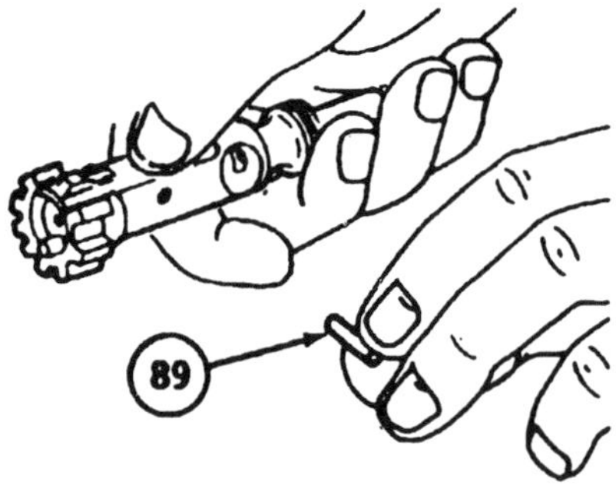

LOCATION	ITEM	ACTION	REMARKS

NOTE

Do not disassemble rubber insert from spring assembly.

	d. Cartridge extractor (87), extractor spring assembly (88), and extractor pin (89).	Position cartridge extractor and spring assembly on the bolt and compress spring and cartridge extractor to align holes. Install extractor pin by hand.	

2-14. CHARGING HANDLE ASSEMBLY (ORGANIZATIONAL).

This task covers:

a. Disassembly
b. Inspection/Repair
c. Lubrication
d. Reassembly

INITIAL SETUP

Tools

(MC) Small Arms Repairman Tool Kit
NSN 5180-00-357- 7770/SL-3-00607A
(ARMY) Small Arms Repairman Tool Kit
SC 5180-95-CL-A07 (app B)

Materials/Parts

Cleaner, lubricant and preservative (CLP) (item 6, app D)

LOCATION	ITEM	ACTION	REMARKS
DISASSEMBLY			
Charging Handle Assembly	a. Spring pin (90)	Remove using hammer and 1/16" punch.	
	b. Charging handle latch (91), helical spring (92), and handle (93)	As punch is withdrawn, catch charging handle latch and helical spring to prevent loss.	

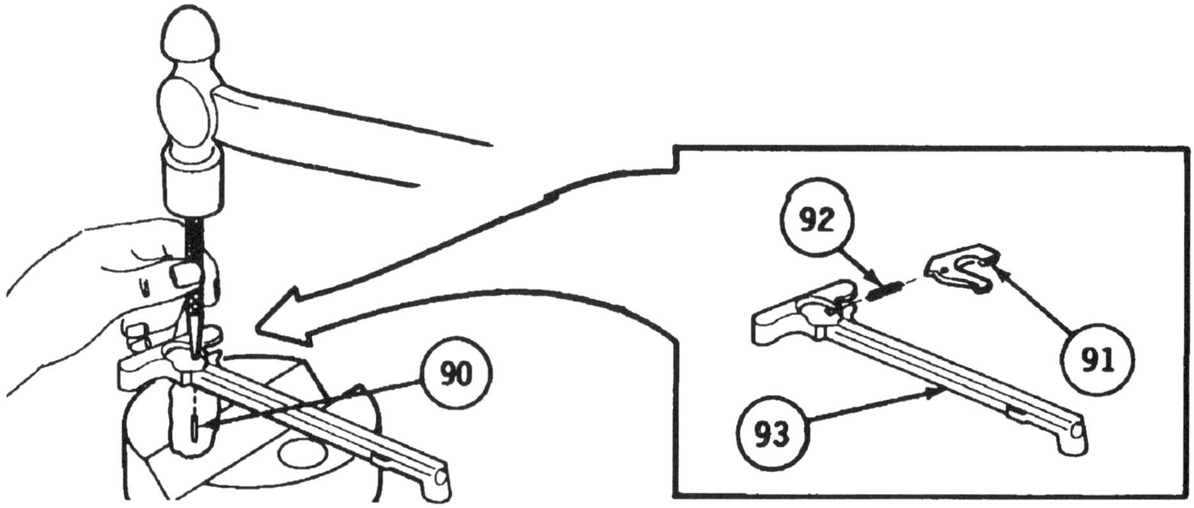

LOCATION	ITEM	ACTION	REMARKS
INSPECTION/REPAIR			
Charging Handle Assembly	All authorized items	Inspect for serviceability. Replace if unserviceable.	Items are unserviceable if broken, cracked, or mutilated.
LUBRICATION			
Charging Handle Assembly	All items	Lightly coat with CLP (item 6, app D.)	

LOCATION	ITEM	ACTION	REMARKS
REASSEMBLY			
Charging Handle Assembly	a. Helical spring (92), charging handle latch (91), and handle (93)	Position helical spring and charging handle latch in handle, align holes, and hold in position.	
	b. Spring pin (90)	Install using hammer. Make pin flush.	

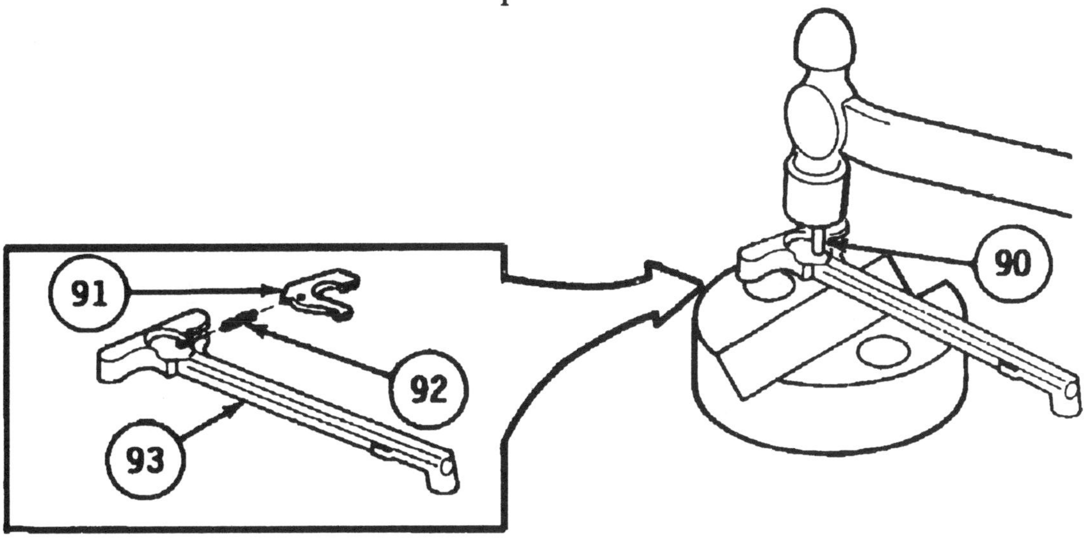

2-15. UPPER RECEIVER AND BARREL ASSEMBLY (HANDGUARD ASSEMBLY) (ORGANIZATIONAL).

This task covers:
- a. Disassembly
- b. Inspection/Repair
- c. Reassembly

INITIAL SETUP

References
TM 05538C-10/1

DISASSEMBLY

NOTE

Refer to TM 05538C-10/1 for "buddy system" procedure on removing handguards.

Do not remove heat shield for any reason. To do so will damage the heat shield and the handguard will have to be replaced.

LOCATION	ITEM	ACTION	REMARKS
Upper Receiver and Barrel Assembly	a. Upper handguard (94)	Push down on the hand-guard slip ring and lift the upper handguard (1) up and out.	
	b. Lower handguard (95)	Push down on the hand-guard slip ring and lift the lower handguard (95) up and out	

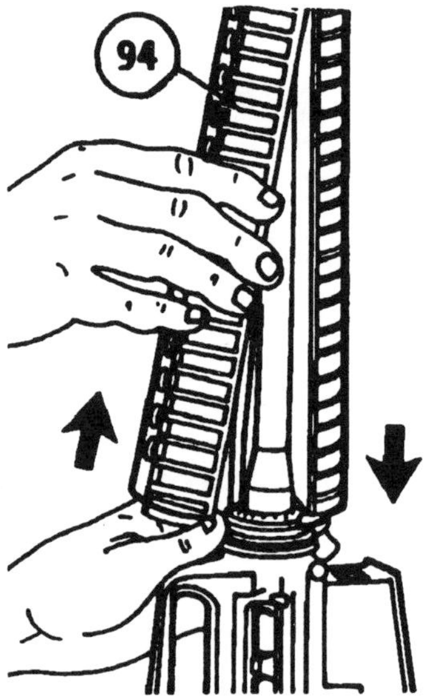

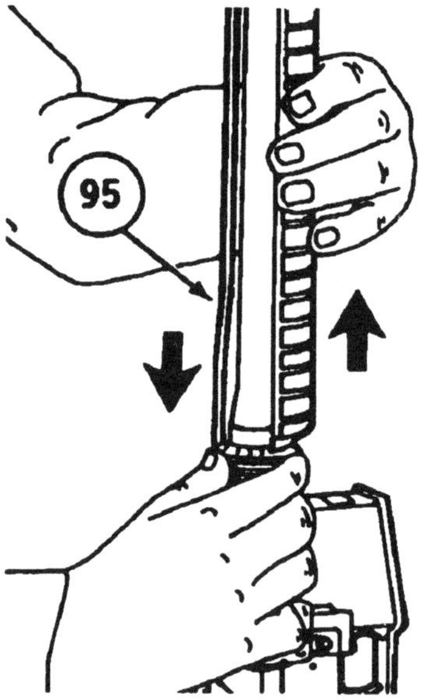

INSPECTION/REPAIR

Upper Receiver and Barrel Assembly	Handguard assembly	Inspect for breaks, separation, and cracks.	Breaks and separations of material which prevent proper retention or interfere with functioning of the weapon will be cause for rejection. Cracks up to one inch in length are acceptable provided they do not extend into the handguard retaining flange..

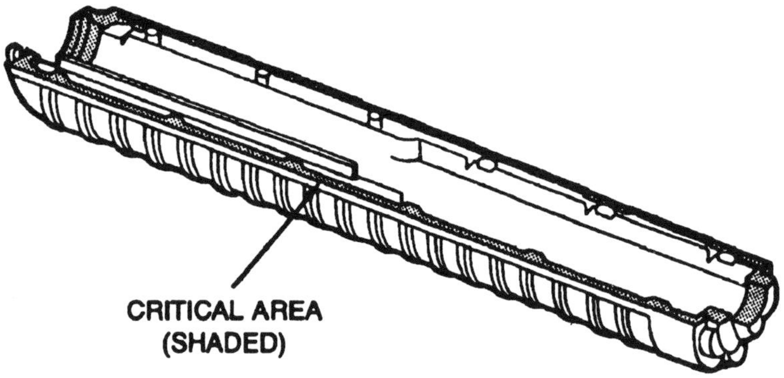

LOCATION	ITEM	ACTION	REMARKS
			Handguards which have a heatshield which is loose enough to rattle will be discarded and replaced.

REASSEMBLY

NOTE

Refer to TM 05538C-10/1 for "buddy system" procedure on installing handguards.

Upper Receiver and Barrel Assembly	a. Upper handguard (96)	Install front of upper handguard in tube cap. Push down on handguard slip ring. Push handguard in place and release handguard slip ring.	

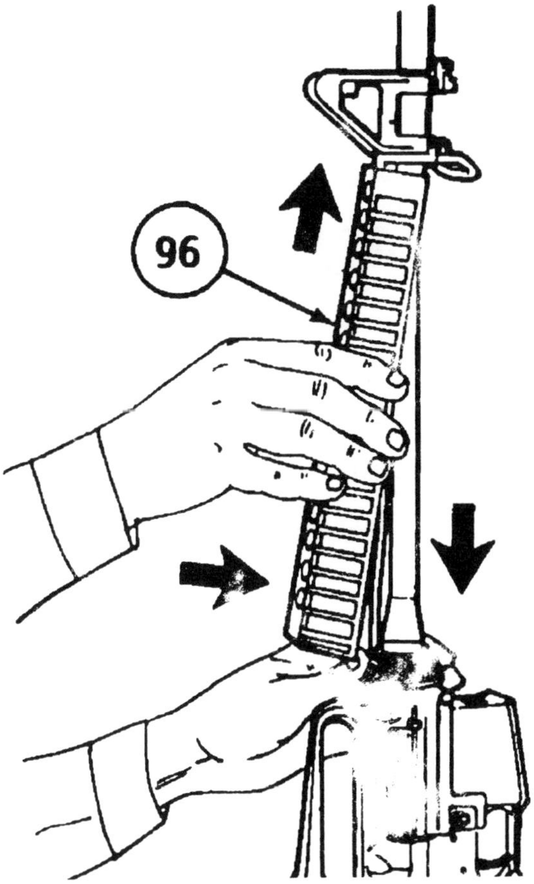

LOCATION	ITEM	ACTION	REMARKS
	b. Lower handguard (97)	Install front of lower handguard in tube cap. Push down on handguard slip ring. Push handguard in place and release handguard slip ring.	

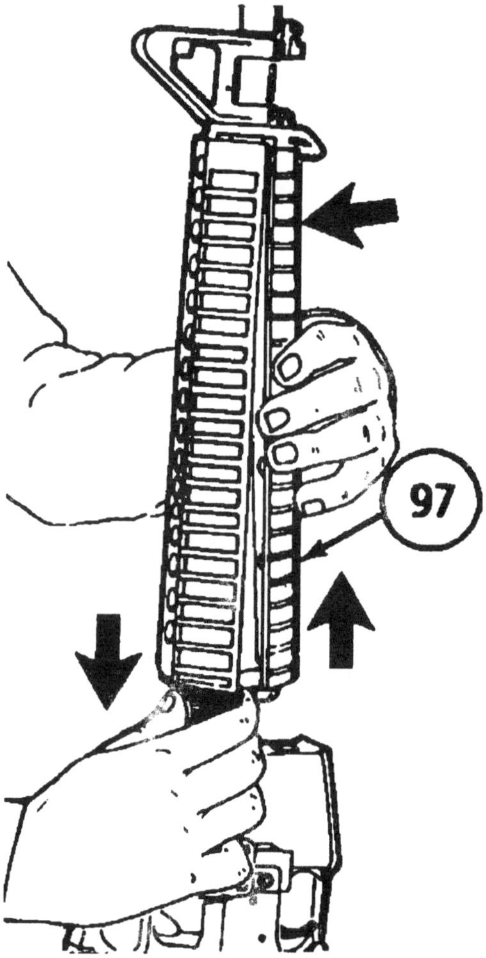

2-16. UPPER RECEIVER AND BARREL ASSEMBLY (ORGANIZATIONAL).

This task covers:

a. Disassembly
b. Cleaning
c. Inspection
d. Repair
e. Lubrication
f. Reassembly

INITIAL SETUP

Tools

(MC) Small Arms Repairman Tool Kit
NSN 5180-00- 357-7770/SL-3-00607A
(ARMY) Small Arms Repairman Tool Kit
SC 5180-95-CL-A07 (app B)
Sight removal tool (E-2, app E)
Front sight detent depressor (E-1, app E)

Materials/Parts

Cleaner, lubricant and preservative (CLP)(item 6, app D)

Equipment Condition

Upper receiver and barrel assembly removed from lower receiver.

General Safety Instructions

To avoid injury to your eyes use care when removing and installing spring-loaded parts.

When using solid film lubricant or dichloromethane, be sure the area is well ventilated.

Do not interchange bolt assemblies or other components from one weapon to another. Doing so may result in injury to, or death of, personnel.

LOCATION	ITEM	ACTION	REMARKS
DISASSEMBLY			
Upper Receiver and Barrel Assembly	a. Front sight post (98)	Using fabricated tool (E-2, app E) and front sight detent depressor (E-1, app E), remove front sight post.	

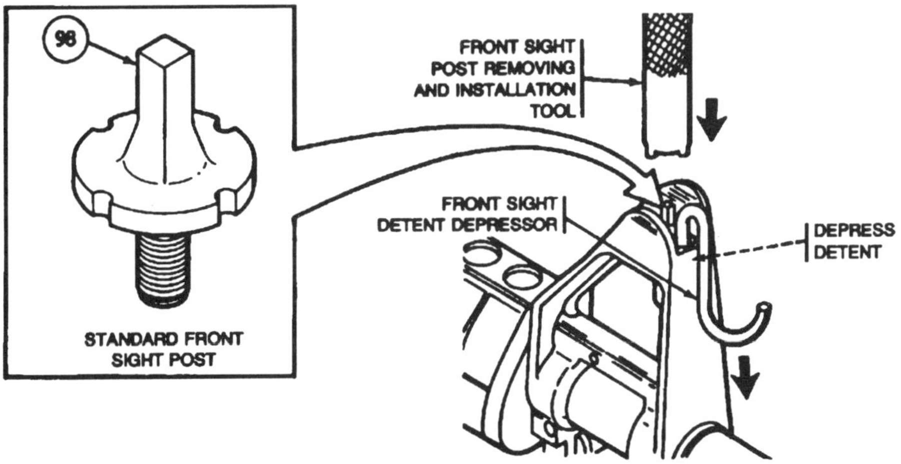

LOCATION	ITEM	ACTION	REMARKS
	b. Front sight detent (99) and helical spring (100)	Catch front sight detent and helical spring to prevent loss.	

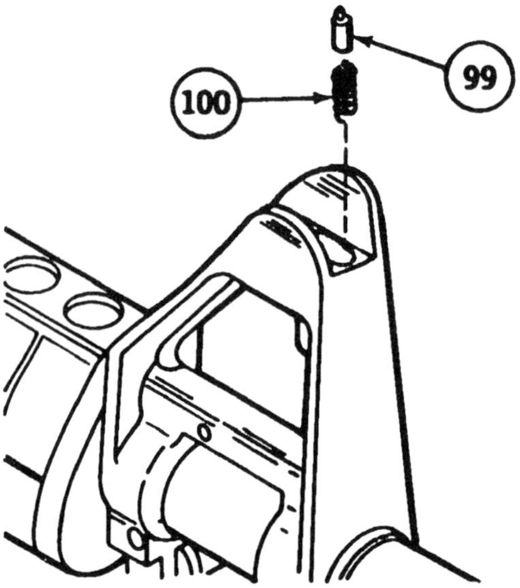

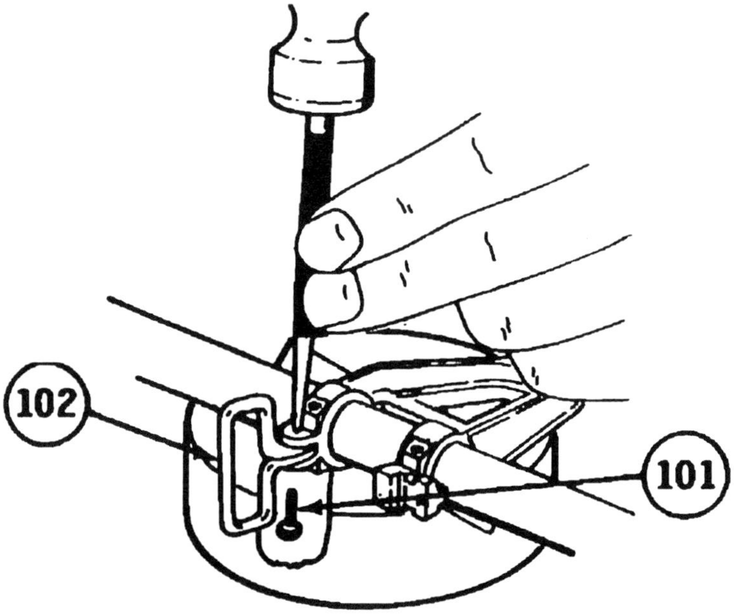

LOCATION	ITEM	ACTION	REMARKS
	c. Tubular rivet (101) and sling swivel (102)	Disassemble only if repair is necessary. If repair is necessary, use hammer and punch to knock out rivet and remove swivel. Discard rivet.	Handguards should be removed to perform this operation.

CLEANING

LOCATION	ITEM	ACTION	REMARKS
Upper Receiver and Barrel Assembly	All items	Clean with CLP (item 6, app D).	

INSPECTION

LOCATION	ITEM	ACTION	REMARKS
Upper Receiver and Barrel Assembly	a. Front sight assembly	Inspect for chips, breaks, bends, and cracks.	
	b. Front sight area	Inspect for evidence of gas leakage around gas tube.	

LOCATION	ITEM	ACTION	REMARKS
	c. Barrel	Clean and inspect for pits in bore, burrs, broken or worn locking lugs, and surface cracks and defects.	Pits no wider than a land or groove and 3/8 inch or less in length are allowable in the bore. Uniformly fine pits in a densely pitted area of the bore are allowable.
		Inspect bore for ringing.	Definitely ringed bores or bores ringed sufficiently to bulge the outside surface of the barrel are cause for rejection. Lands that appear dark due to coating of gliding metal from projectiles are allowable. Stripping of lands and grooves shall not be cause for rejection unless so determined by barrel erosion gage.
		Inspect chamber for pitting.	Fine pits, or fine pits in a densely pitted area, are allowable. Pits 1/8 inch in length are cause for rejection.
	d. Compensator	Check for looseness on barrel. The third, or middle, slot must be straight up or at Top Dead Center (TDC).	TDC may vary as much as one half the width of the slot.

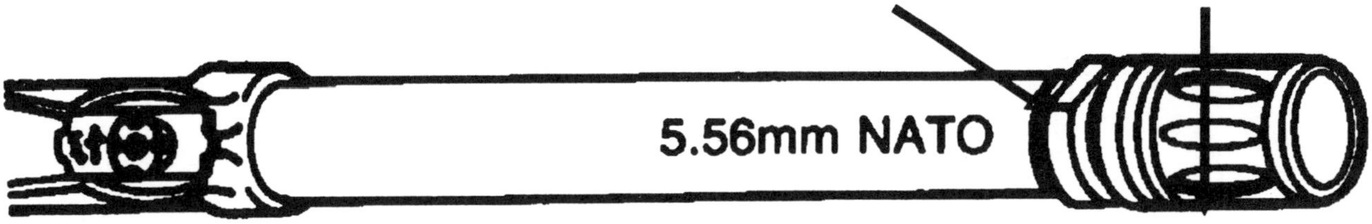

LOCATION	ITEM	ACTION	REMARKS
REPAIR			
Upper Receiver and Barrel Assembly	All authorized items	Replace authorized unserviceable parts.	
LUBRICATION			
Upper Receiver and Barrel Assembly	All items	Cover with a light coat of CLP (item 6, app D).	
REASSEMBLY			
Upper Receiver and Barrel Assembly	a. Sling swivel (103) and tubular rivet (104)	If previously disassembled, position sling swivel and install new tubular rivet using center punch and hammer to spread and flare the hollow head of tubular rivet.	

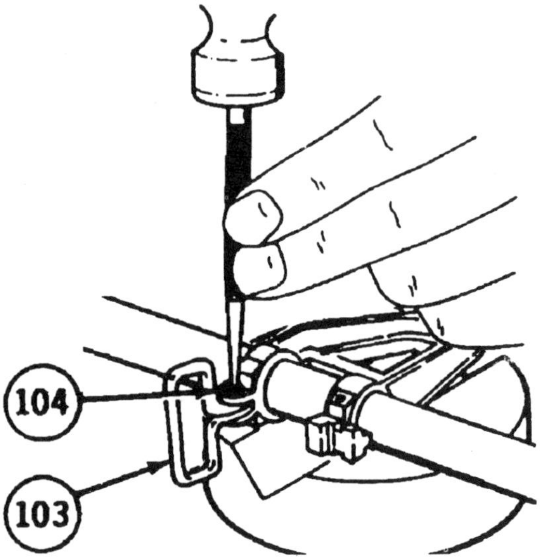

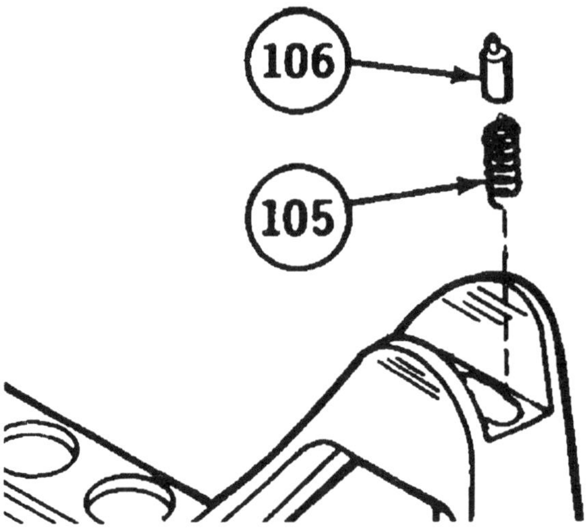

	b. Helical spring (105) and front sight detent (106)	Position and depress helical spring and front sight detent with front sight detent depressor (E-1, app E).	

LOCATION	ITEM	ACTION	REMARKS
	c. Front sight post (107)	Install using sight removal tool (E-2, app E).	

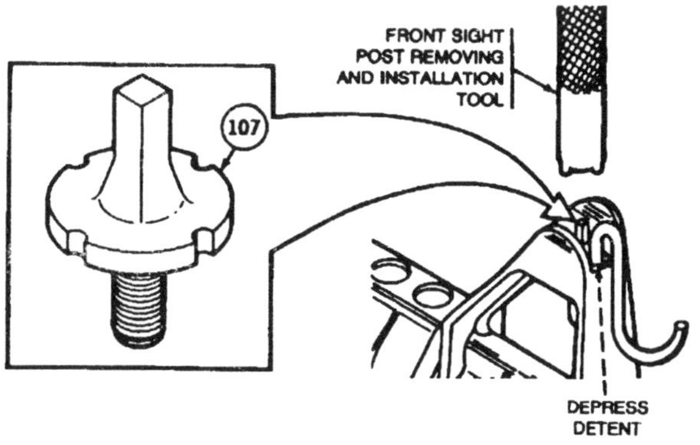

DISASSEMBLY

NOTE

Do not disassemble unless repair is necessary.

LOCATION	ITEM	ACTION	REMARKS
Upper Receiver and Barrel Assembly	Retaining ring (108), ejection port cover pin (109), helical spring (110), and ejection port cover (111)	Using two small punch tips or two small flat tip screwdrivers, remove retaining ring and slide ejection port cover pin out to the rear. Catch helical spring and ejection port cover to prevent loss as pin is withdrawn.	Ejection port cover pin may bind against the forward assist housing on the M16A2 rifle and require some additional force to remove.

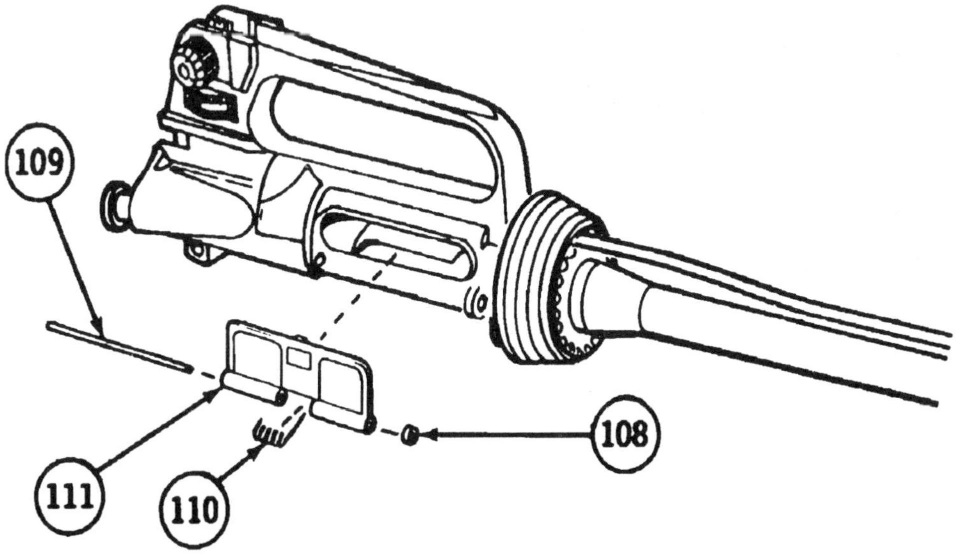

LOCATION	ITEM	ACTION	REMARKS
INSPECTION			
Upper Receiver and Barrel Assembly	All items	Inspect for serviceability in and tightness of latch assembly on ejection port cover.	If items are damaged or nonfunctional, they are unserviceable.
REPAIR			
Upper Receiver and Barrel Assembly	All authorized items	Replace if unserviceable.	
REASSEMBLY			

NOTE

Use a new retaining ring, if available.

LOCATION	ITEM	ACTION	REMARKS
Upper Receiver and Barrel Assembly	Ejection port cover (111), helical spring (110), ejection port cover pin (109), and retaining ring (108)	Position cover and spring. Slide in cover pin and install retaining ring using tweezers or round nose pliers to position ring.	Long leg of spring must be twisted once or pretensioned and positioned before the pin is completely installed. Place short leg to the rear on inside of cover as the pin enters the spring slot of the cover (approximately 1/4 inch). Twist the long leg 1/2 turn (180 degrees) with fingers of the right hand; hold the long leg against the cover (spring now under tension) while pushing on rear of pin to complete installation. Check for proper spring tension on cover before installing retaining ring.

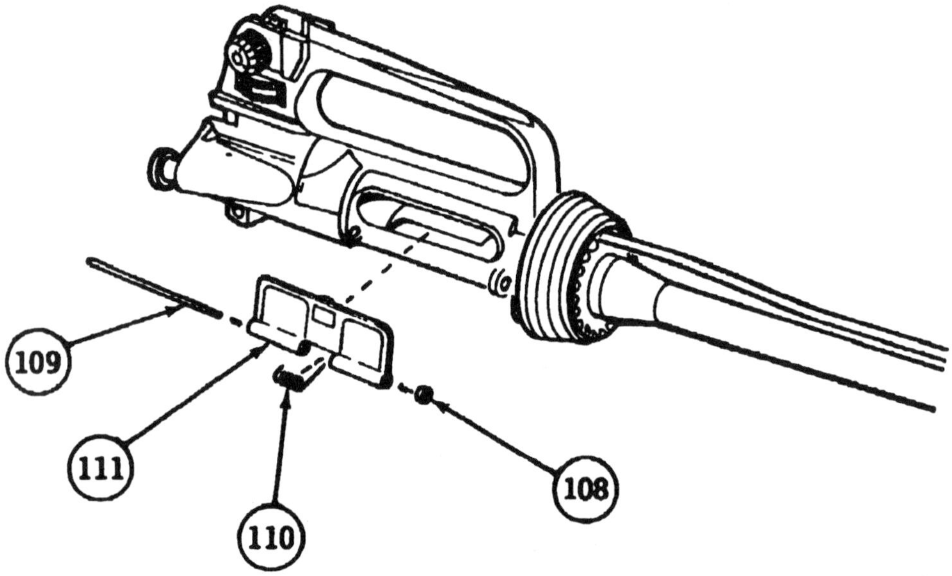

2-17. LOWER RECEIVER AND BUTTSTOCK ASSEMBLY (ORGANIZATIONAL).

This task covers:

a. Disassembly
b. Inspection
c. Repair
d. Lubrication
e. Reassembly

INITIAL SETUP

Tools

(MC) Small Arms Repairman Tool Kit
NSN 5180-00- 357-7770/SL-3-00607A
(ARMY) Small Arms Repairman Tool Kit
SC 5180-95-CL-A07 (app B)
Pivot Pin Removing Tool (E-3, app E)
Pivot Pin Installation Tool (E-6, app E)

Materials/Parts

Cleaner, lubricant and preservative (CLP)(item 6, app D)

General Safety Instructions

To avoid injury to your eyes use care when removing and installing spring-loaded parts.

Do not interchange bolt assemblies or other components from one weapon to another. Doing so may result in injury to, or death of, personnel.

LOCATION	ITEM	ACTION	REMARKS
DISASSEMBLY			
Lower Receiver and Buttstock Assembly	a. Machine screw (112) and lock washer (113)	Using screwdriver, reach inside rifle grip and remove screw and lock washer.	

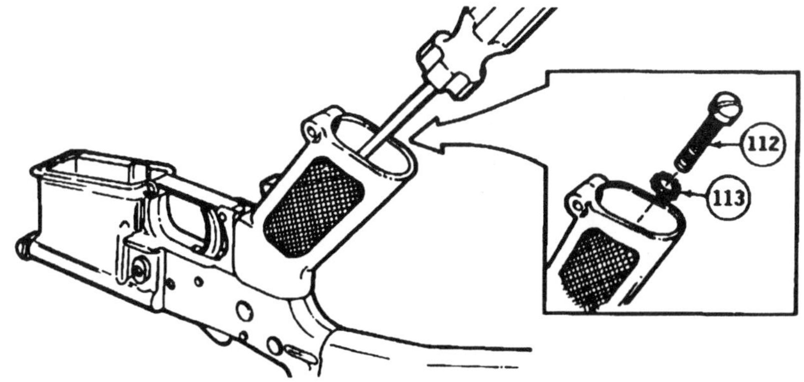

LOCATION	ITEM	ACTION	REMARKS
DISASSEMBLY	b. Rifle grip (114), helical spring (115), and safety detent (116)	Carefully remove rifle grip and catch helical spring and safety detent to prevent loss.	

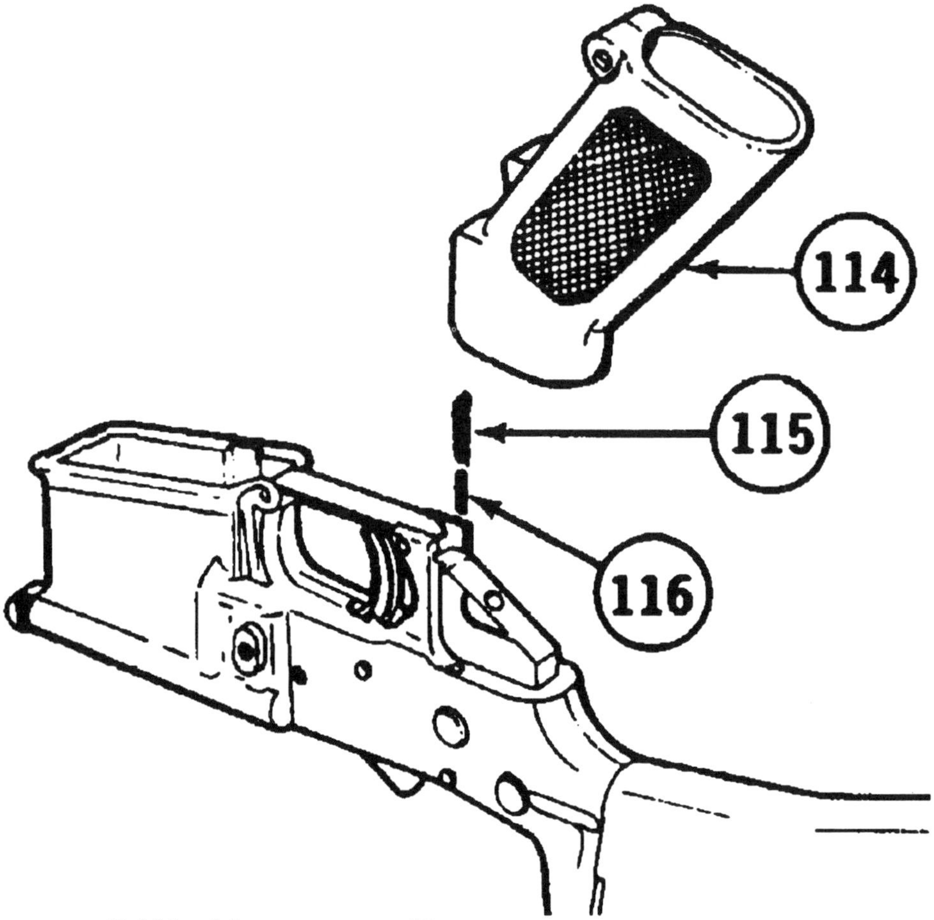

	c. Self-locking screw (117)	Remove.	

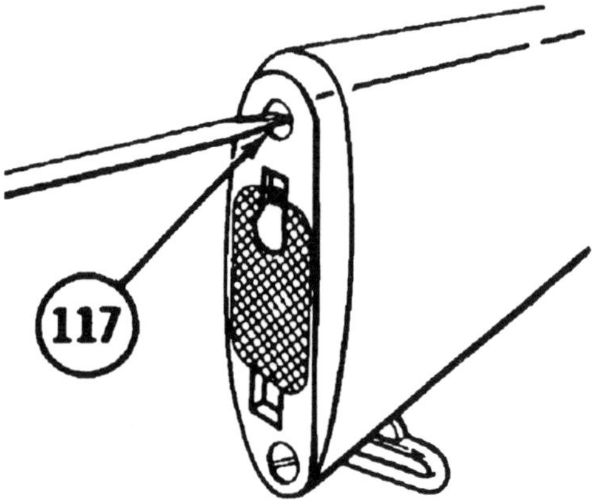

LOCATION	ITEM	ACTION	REMARKS
	d. Buttstock assembly (118), stepped spacer (119), helical spring (120), detent (121), and takedown pin (122)	Remove stock carefully and catch helical spring, detent, and takedown pin to prevent loss.	

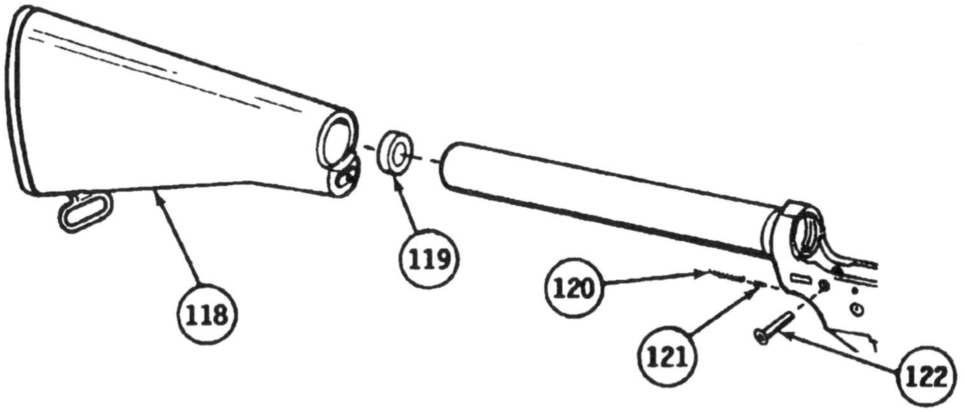

WARNING

To avoid injury to your eyes, use care when removing and installing spring-loaded parts.

LOCATION	ITEM	ACTION	REMARKS
	e. Pivot pin (123)	Insert pivot pin removing tool (E-3, app E) to compress detent. Turn pin a quarter-turn. Remove tool and pin. Catch detent and spring as pivot pin is removed.	

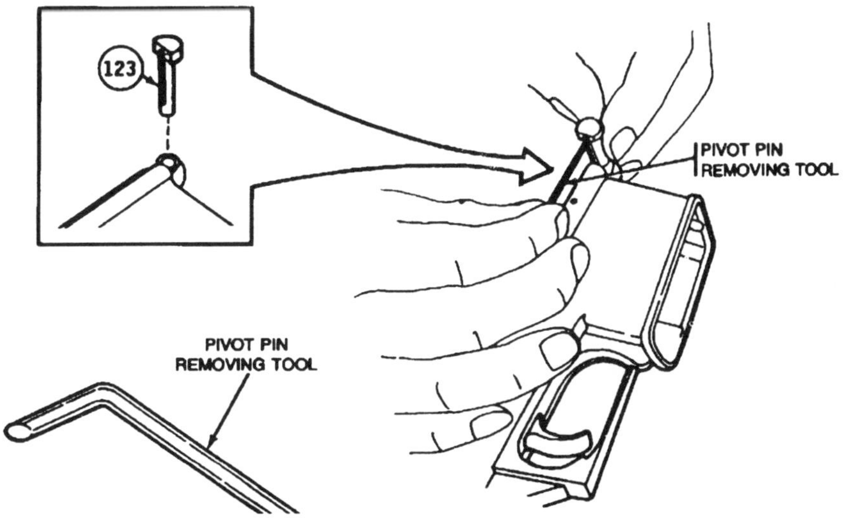

LOCATION	ITEM	ACTION	REMARKS
	f. Pivot pin detent (124) and helical spring (125)	Be sure to hold cupped hand in front of detent and helical spring to prevent loss of detent and spring.	

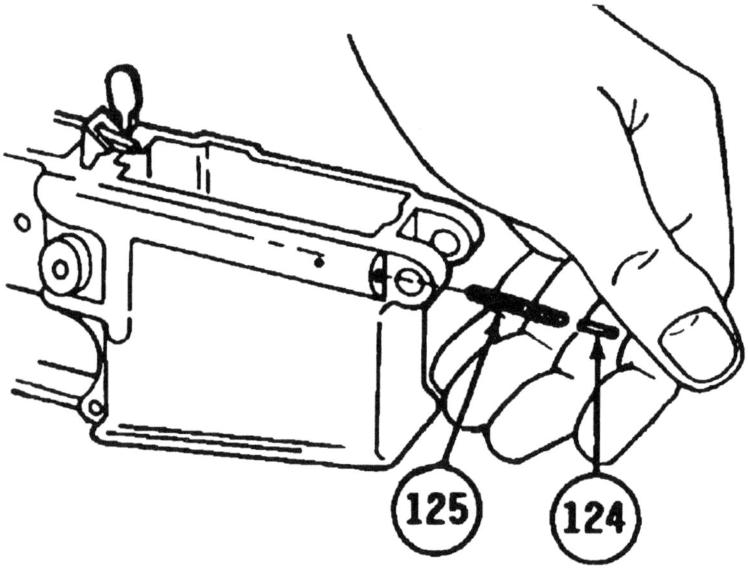

LOCATION	ITEM	ACTION	REMARKS
	g. Buffer assembly (126) and action spring (127)	Press buffer assembly in. Using screwdriver, depress buffer retainer and release buffer (126) and action spring (127). Remove buffer assembly (126) and action spring (127) from receiver while depressing the retainer.	

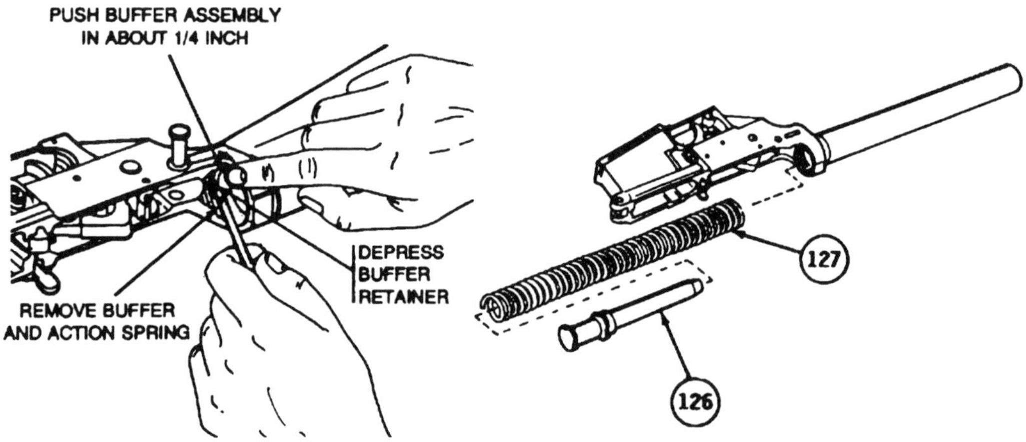

LOCATION	ITEM	ACTION	REMARKS

NOTE

Early type buffer assembly must be replaced.

INSPECTION

LOCATION	ITEM	ACTION	REMARKS
Lower Receiver and Buttstock Assembly	a. Buffer assembly	The buffer assembly must not be cracked between hole and end of housing.	Some old buffers (128) have a pin through hole which protrudes equally on each side approximately 1/32 of an inch. Some buffers (129) have a hole in the housing but no pin. Discard these. New buffers (130) do not have a hole in buffer body or a pin.

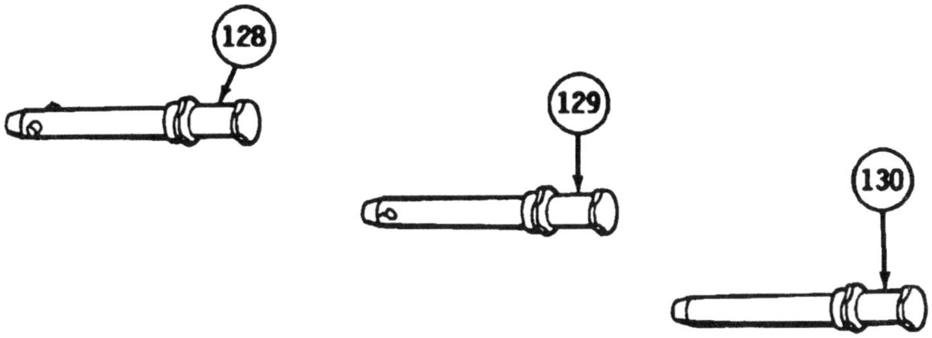

LOCATION	ITEM	ACTION	REMARKS
	b. Action spring	The free length of the action spring must be between 11 3/4 inches minmum and 13 1/2 inches maximum.	

LOCATION	ITEM	ACTION	REMARKS
	c. Lower receiver (without further disassembly)	Inspect serial number for legibility.	If the serial number is hard to read, evacuate to Depot Maintenance. Only Depot Maintenance is authorized to restamp the serial number.

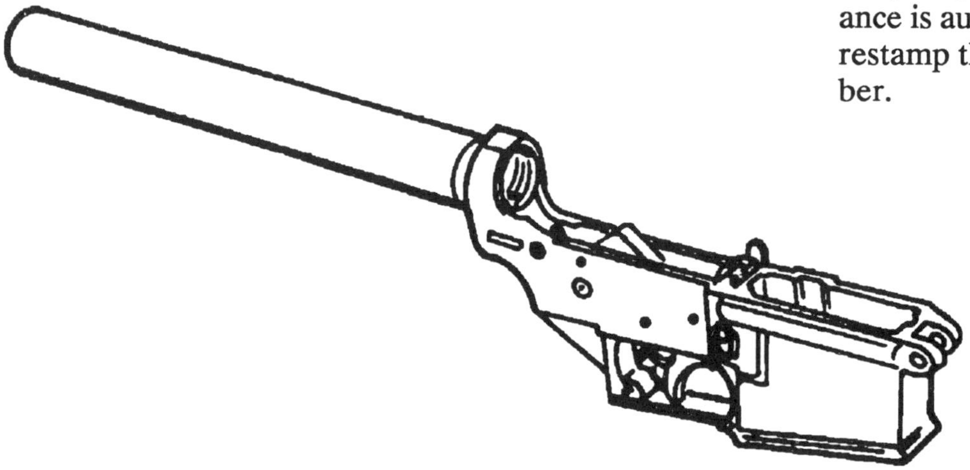

		Inspect for missing or damaged parts. Inspect finish of lower receiver for shiny spots.	Touch up with solid film lubricant.

REPAIR

Lower Receiver and Buttstock Assembly	All authorized items	Replace if unserviceable.	Evacuate any damaged parts to Intermediate Maintenance.

LUBRICATION

Lower Receiver and Buttstock Assembly	All metal parts.	Apply a light coat of CLP (item 6, app D) on all metal components.	

REASSEMBLY

WARNING

To avoid injury to your eyes, use care when removing and installing spring-loaded parts.

Do not interchange bolt assemblies or other components from one weapon to another. Doing so may result in injury to, or death of, personnel.

LOCATION	ITEM	ACTION	REMARKS
Lower Receiver and Buttstock Assembly	a. Action spring (131) and buffer assembly (132)	Press in until retainer snaps up and holds action spring and buffer assembly in place.	

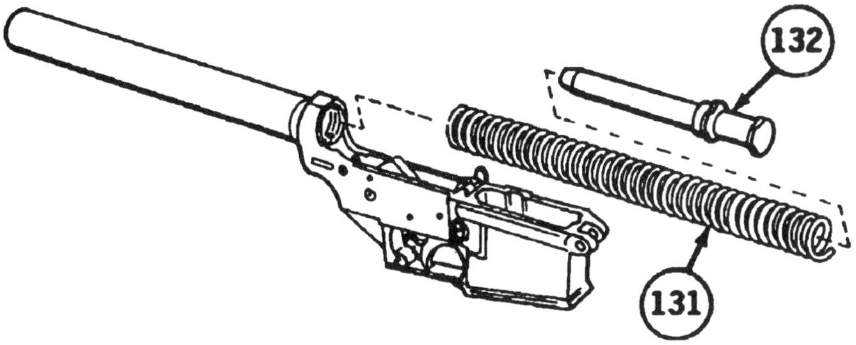

LOCATION	ITEM	ACTION	REMARKS
	b. Helical spring (133), pivot pin detent (134), and pivot pin (135)	Install pivot pin installation tool (E-6, app E). Insert spring and detent. Compress detent in recess with punch and rotate tool.	

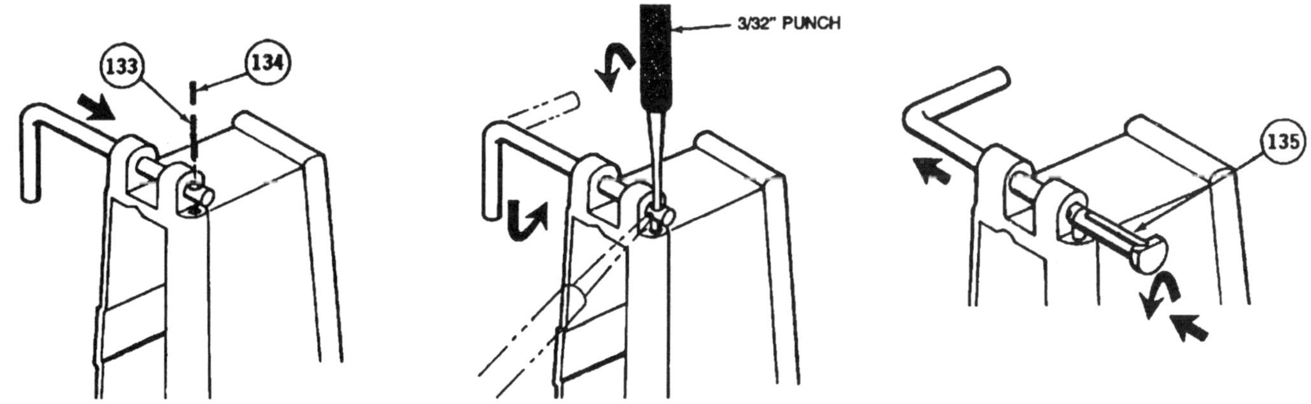

LOCATION	ITEM	ACTION	REMARKS
		Remove punch. Push out tool using pivot pin (135)	Rounded end of detent must be in the groove of the pivot pin when assembly is complete.

LOCATION	ITEM	ACTION	REMARKS
Lower Receiver and Buttstock Assembly	c. Takedown pin (136), takedown pin detent (137), helical spring (138), stepped spacer (139), buttstock assembly (140), and self- locking screw (141)	Install takedown pin with groove to the rear. Install detent and spring from the rear. Install spacer on receiver extension. Begin to install buttstock assembly. Carefully compress the spring with stock and secure the stock in place with the self- locking screw.	

CAUTION:

Do not kink the detent spring (8) during assembly.

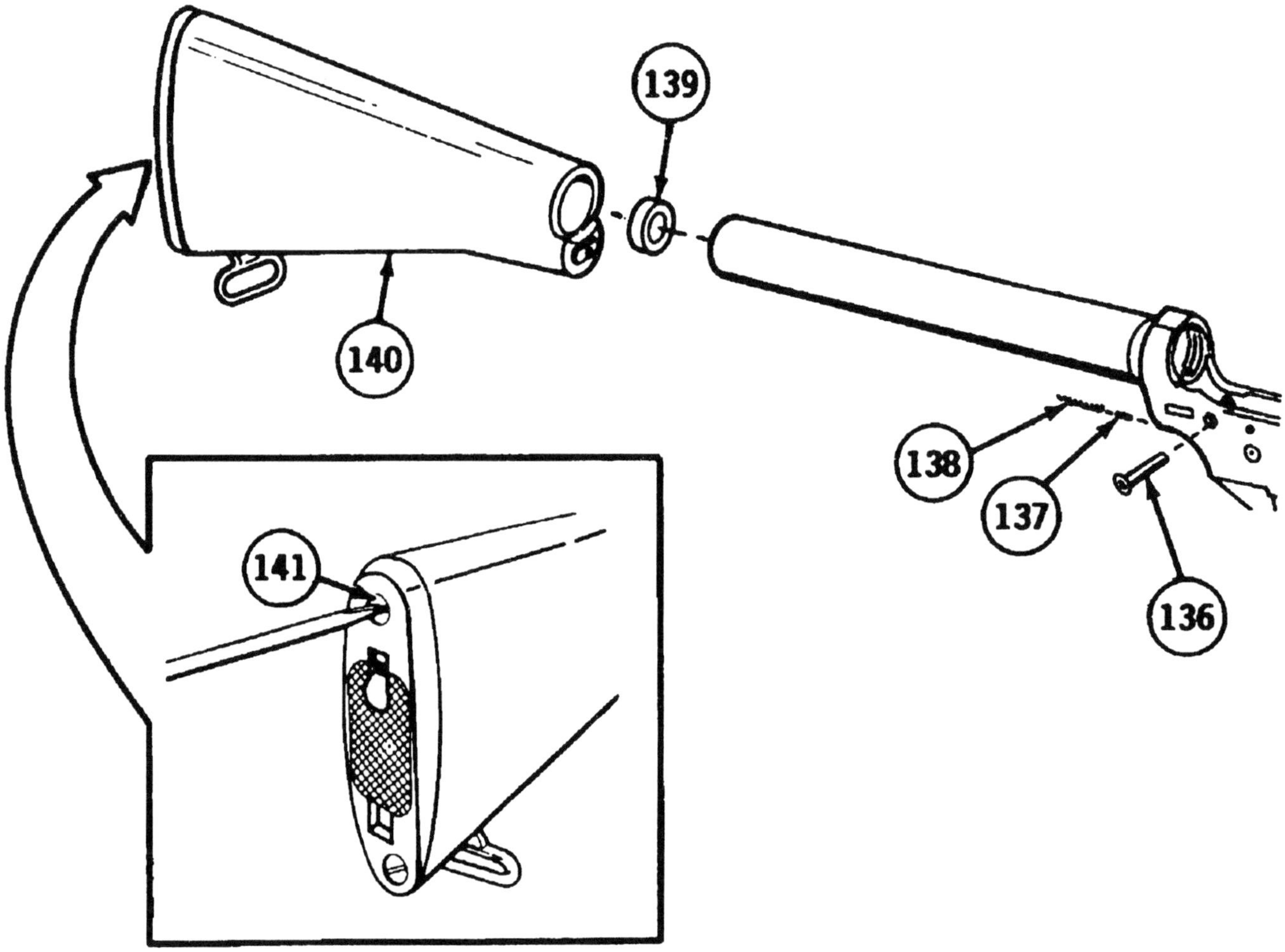

LOCATION	ITEM	ACTION	REMARKS
	d. Safety detent (142), helical spring (143), rifle grip (144), washer (145), and machine screw (146)	Install detent, pointed end first, and spring from the bottom. Carefully compress the spring with the rifle grip and secure the grip in place with the lock washer and screw. The spring is partially housed in a hole formed on top of the grip.	

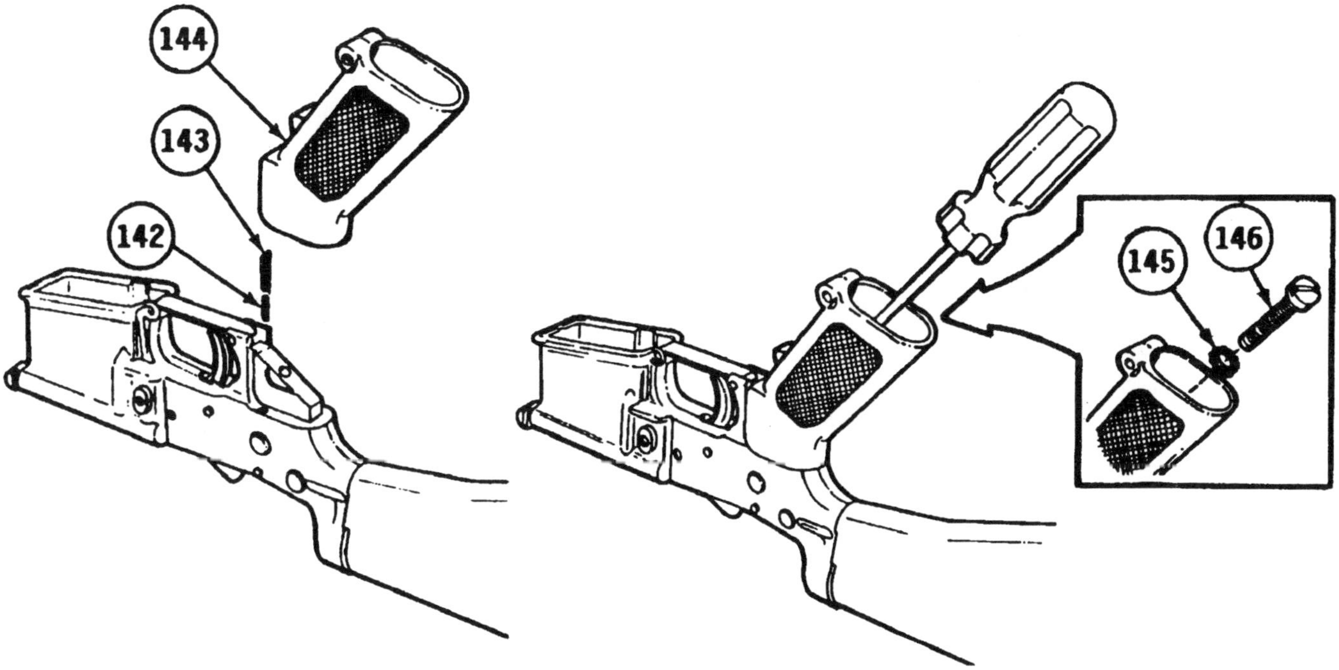

2-18. BUTTSTOCK ASSEMBLY (ORGANIZATIONAL)

This task covers:
a. Disassembly
b. Inspection
c. Repair
d. Lubrication
e. Reassembly

INITIAL SETUP

Tools
(MC) Small Arms Repairman Tool Kit
NSN 5180-00- 357-7770/SL-3-00607A
(ARMY) Small Arms Repairman Tool Kit
SC 5180-95-CL-A07 (app B)

Materials/Parts
Cleaner, lubricant and preservative (CLP)(item 6, app D)

Equipment Condition
Buttstock assembly removed from lower receiver and buttstock assembly.

LOCATION	ITEM	ACTION	REMARKS
DISASSEMBLY			
Buttstock Assembly	a. Self-locking screw (147) and small sling swivel (148)	Using screwdriver, remove self-locking screw, small sling swivel, and butt plate group.	

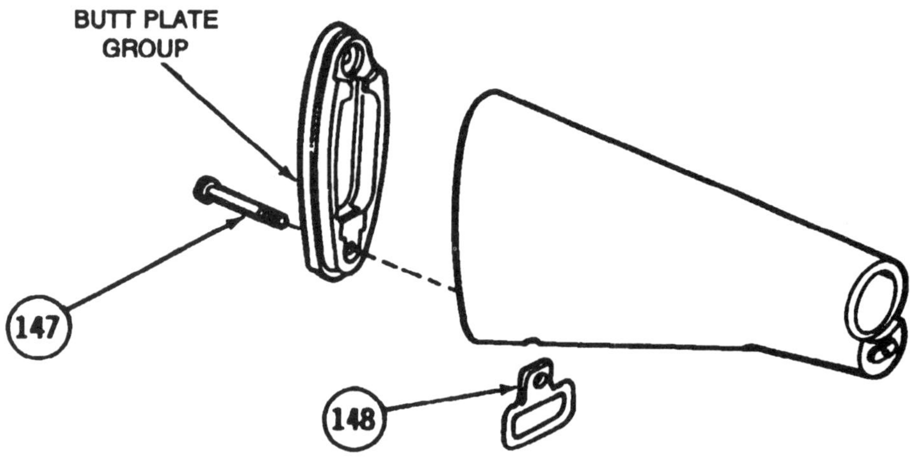

LOCATION	ITEM	ACTION	REMARKS
	b. Butt plate (149)	Push down on plunger and lift door assembly out of butt plate	

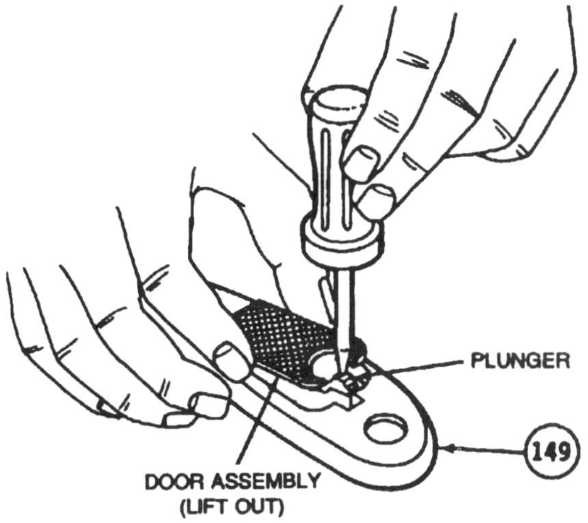

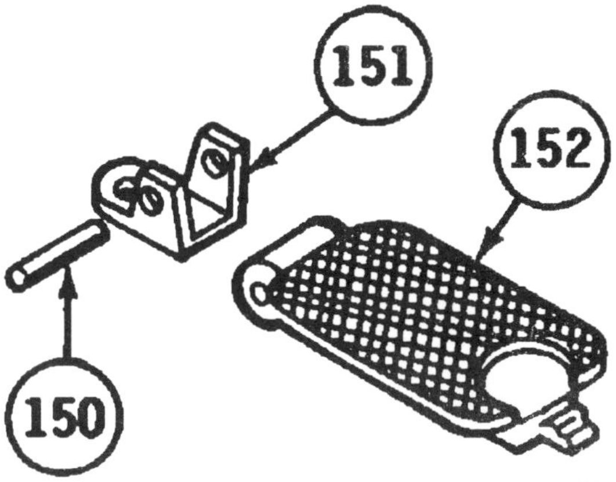

LOCATION	ITEM	ACTION	REMARKS
	c. Straight pin (150), hinge (151), and door assembly (152)	Remove straight pin and separate hinge and door assembly.	

INSPECTION

LOCATION	ITEM	ACTION	REMARKS
Buttstock Assembly	Stock	Inspect stock for cracks. Report cracked stocks and evacuate to intermediate support.	(MC ONLY) Evacuate a cracked stock to Intermediate Maintenance for repair. Also submit SF 368. Quality Deficiency Report.

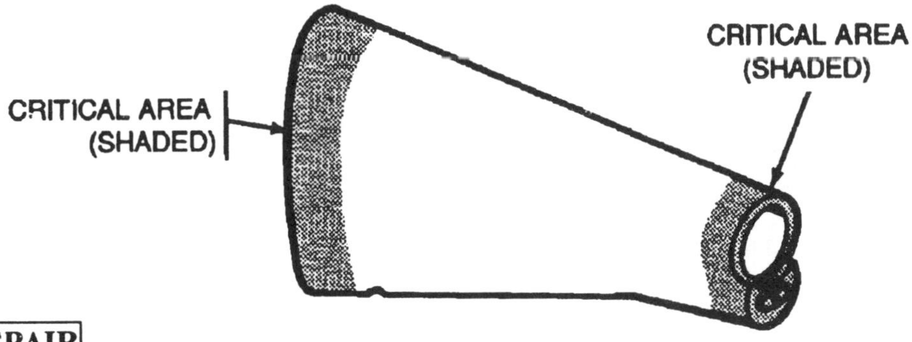

REPAIR

LOCATION	ITEM	ACTION	REMARKS
Buttstock Assembly	All authorized items	Replace unserviceable items.	Unserviceable items are those items which are damaged.

LOCATION	ITEM	ACTION	REMARKS
LUBRICATION			
Buttstock Assembly	Stock	Lubricate all metal components with CLP (item 6, app D).	
REASSEMBLY			
Buttstock Assembly	a. Door assembly (152), hinge (151), and straight pin (150)	Position hinge on door assembly and install straight pin.	
	b. Butt plate (153)	Install door assembly into butt plate and press plunger to lock.	

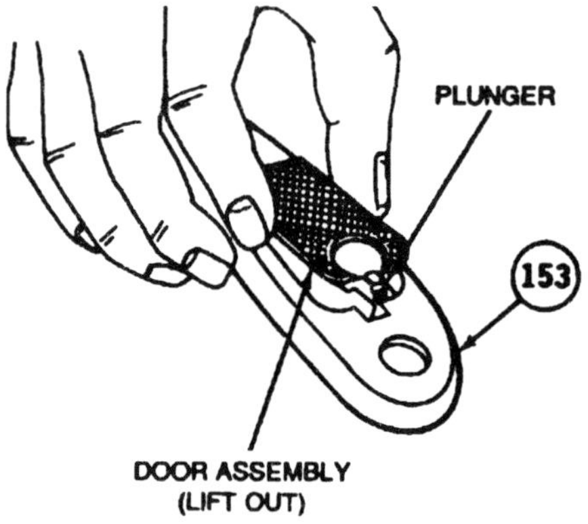

	c. Small sling swivel (154) and self-locking screw (155)	Position butt plate group and rear sling swivel to the buttstock and secure with self-locking screw (155).	See page 2-44 for reassembly of buttstock assembly to lower receiver.

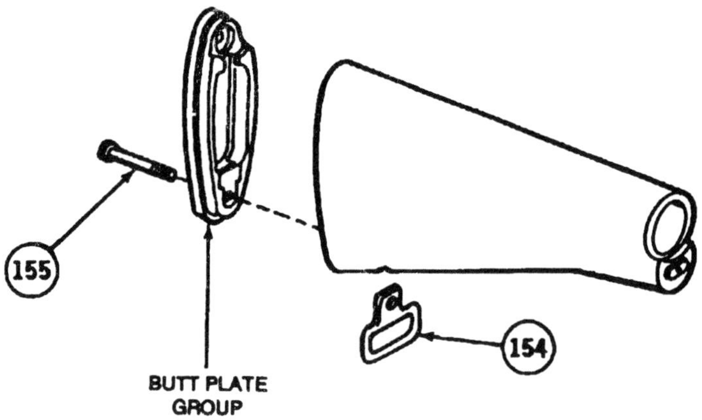

2-19. MAJOR COMPONENTS OF M16A2 RIFLE.

This task covers:

a. Reassembly
b. Organizational Test
c. Organizational Stowage

INITIAL SETUP

References

TM 05538C-10/1

Equipment Condition

Weapon disassembled into major components.

General Safety Instructions

Do not interchange bolt assemblies or components from one weapon to another. Doing so may result in injury to, or death of, personnel.

Do not keep live ammunition near the work area.

LOCATION	ITEM	ACTION	REMARKS
REASSEMBLY			
Weapon	Lower receiver and buttstock assembly (156), upper receiver and barrel assembly (157), charging handle assembly (158), bolt carrier assembly (159), small arms sling (160), and cartridge magazine (161)	Install.	Refer to TM 05538C-10/1.

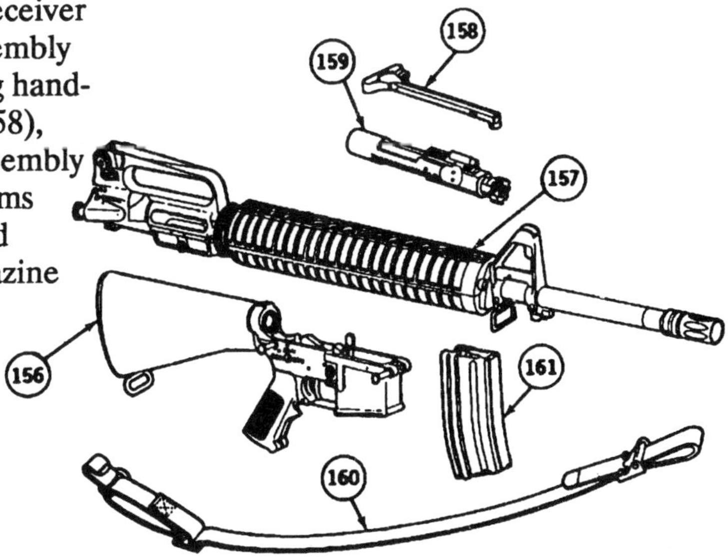

LOCATION	ITEM	ACTION	REMARKS
ORGANIZATIONAL TEST			
Weapon		Function test as follows:	
	a. Charging handle assembly	Pull to rear. Check that chamber is clear. Let bolt and bolt carrier close.	Do not pull trigger. Leave hammer in cocked position.
	b. Selector lever	Place in SAFE position and pull trigger.	Hammer should not fall.

WARNING

If weapon fails the following tests, continued use of weapon could result in injury or death.

NOTE

For the purpose of the following test "SLOW" is defined as 1/4 to 1/2 the normal rate of trigger release.

LOCATION	ITEM	ACTION	REMARKS
	c. Selector lever	Place in SEMI position and pull trigger.	Hammer should fall.
		Hold trigger to rear, charge weapon and release trigger with a slow, smooth motion, without hesitations or stops, until the trigger is fully forward.	Hammer should not fall.
		Repeat the SEMI position test five times, the weapon must not malfunction.	If the weapon malfunctions during any of these five repetitions, evacuate it to Intermediate-Maintenance for repair.
	d. Selector lever	Place in Burst position. Cock weapon and squeeze trigger.	Hammer should fall.

LOCATION	ITEM	ACTION	REMARKS
		While holding the trigger to the rear, pull the charging handle assembly to the rear and release it three times. Release the trigger.	Hammer should not fall. The burst disconnector should have held the hammer to the rear while the trigger was in the squeezed position.
		Squeeze the trigger.	Hammer should fall. This should be the first round of a three- round burst.

Section VI. DECONTAMINATION OF RIFLES AND ARMS ROOMS (ARMY ONLY)

2-20. DECONTAMINATION OF SIGHTS ACTIVATED WITH TRITIUM (h 3).

a. Identification. Tritium sights will be marked with the assembly date and the radiation symbol and stamped H 3, 9mc.

b. Damage Determination. Evidence of a break in the glass container for the H 3 will be a lack of illumination (assuring the expiration date for the sight has not been exceeded). Radiation from the sight is extremely low and CANNOT be detected with standard issue radiation detectors, i.e., AN/PDR-27.

c. Contamination. The tritium isotope used in the low light level sight is in a gaseous state and will rapidly diffuse into the atmosphere in the event of breakage. Very little residual contamination should be left on the rifle. All illumination will cease upon loss of H 3 gas.

WARNING

Dry cleaning solvent is flammable and toxic and should be used in a well ventilated area. The use of rubber gloves is necessary to protect the skin when washing rifle parts.

d. Decontamination. When a broken sight is found, the sight MUST be removed and turned in for disposal in accordance with AR 385-11. After removing the sight, the rifle should be cleaned with dry cleaning solvent (item 13, app D). Wear rubber gloves (item 15, app D) and use a wash pan to apply solvent. Let dry, then lubricate with cleaner, lubricate and preservative (CLP)(item 6, app D).

e. Requirements. Because of its small volume of gas and its low energy of emitted radiation, H 3 does not pose a health hazzard to the user. Current Army regulations, NRC license conditions and Title 10, Code of Federal regulations, Part 20 require that the above actions be carried out.

LOCATION	ITEM	ACTION	REMARKS

2-21. DECONTAMINATION OF SIGHTS ACTIVATED WITH PROMETHIUM (Pm 147).

NOTE

Pm 147 is no longer available for issue. It is being replaced with tritium (H 3).

a. General. When a sight activated with promethium (Pm 147) is found, the sight MUST be removed and turned in for disposal in accordance with AR 385-11. Contact the local RPO

b. Identification. Promethium sights are marked with the assembly date, the radiation symbol, and Pm 147, 1 mc.

c. Decontamination. If a sight activated with promethium (Pm 147) is found, conduct a survey under the direction of the local RPO. Decontaminate as required in accordance with local procedures.

ORGANIZATIONAL STOWAGE

LOCATION	ITEM	ACTION	REMARKS
Weapon	Rifle	Prior to stowing the rifle in arms room, perform the following procedures:	Rifles passed into arms room issue window should be passed butt first with the bolt locked to the rear.
		Clear.	Refer to TM 05538C-10/1.
		Place selector in SEMI. Point in safe direction.	Hammer should fall.
		Squeeze trigger.	
		Close ejection port (dust) cover.	
		Place rifle in rack.	

CHAPTER 3
INTERMEDIATE MAINTENANCE INSTRUCTIONS

CHAPTER OVERVIEW

This chapter provides information and instructions to keep the weapon in good repair and contains the following sections:

I. Repair Parts and Special Tools
II. Service Upon Receipt
III. Intermediate Troubleshooting
IV. Intermediate Maintenance Procedures for the M16A2 Rifle
V. Preparation for Storage or Shipment
VI. Preembarkation Inspection of Material in Units Slated for Overseas Movement

Section I. REPAIR PARTS AND SPECIAL TOOLS

3-1. COMMON TOOLS AND EQUIPMENT. For authorized common tools and equipment, see SL-3-00607A. Army users refer to TOE/MTOE applicable to your unit.

3-1. SPECIAL TOOLS. Special tools required for intermediate maintenance are listed in appendix C and fabricated tools are listed and illustrated in appendix E.

3-3. REPAIR PARTS. Repair parts are listed and illustrated in appendix C.

NOTE

Bolt assemblies, and/or barrel assemblies may be interchanged, at the Intermediate Maintenance level, from one rifle to another under the provisions of the note on page C-3. If these parts are interchanged the weapon must be checked/inspected as depicted in paragraphs 3-9, 3-10, 3-12. While performing these checks and inspections, pay special attention to the headspace requirements on page 3-46.

Section II. SERVICE UPON RECEIPT

3-4. GENERAL.

a. Check the weapon against the packing slip to see if the shipment is complete. Report all discrepancies in accordance with MCO P4610.19C.

b. Check to see if all modification instructions have been applied.

*(***ARMY ONLY***)*

c. Inspect the weapon for damage incurred during shipment. If the equipment has been damaged, report the damage on SF 364, Report of Discrepancy (ROD).

d. Check the weapon against the packing slip to see if the shipment is complete. Report all discrepancies in accordance with the instruction in DA PAM 738-750.

e. Check to see whether the equipment has been modified.
f. Check to see if all MWO's have been applied.

3-5. INTERMEDIATE SERVICE UPON RECEIPT OF MATERIEL. Perform the action noted in Table 3-2.

Table 3-2

SERVICE UPON RECEIPT - M16A2 RIFLE

LOCATION	ITEM	ACTION	REMARKS
M16A2 Rifle	Charging handle assembly	Clear the weapon	Refer to TM 05538C-10/1.

WARNING

To avoid injury to your eyes, use care when removing and installing spring-loaded parts.

LOCATION	ITEM	ACTION	REMARKS
	Bolt carrier assembly and bolt assembly	Remove.	Refer to TM 05538C-10/1.
	All components	Visually inspected for proper assembly, damage, or missing parts.	Refer to TM 05538C-10/1.
	Bolt carrier assembly and bolt assembly.	Reassemble.	Refer to TM 05538C-10/1.
	Hand function to assure proper operation.		
	Cartridge magazine	Insert empty magazine and pull the bolt to the rear. Check magazine for positive retention and check functioning of bolt catch by assuring that bolt locks to the rear with empty magazine inserted.	Refer to TM 05538C-10/1

Section III. INTERMEDIATE MAINTENANCE TROUBLESHOOTING

3-6. GENERAL.

a. This section contains intermediate maintenance troubleshooting information for locating and correcting most of the operating troubles which may develop in the weapon. Each malfunction for the individual component, unit, or system is followed by a list of tests or inspections which will help you to determine the corrective actions to take. You should perform the tests/inspections and corrective actions noted in Table 3-3 in the order listed in the Test & Inspection column for each malfunction.

b. This manual cannot list all malfunctions that may occur, nor all tests or inspections and corrective actions. If a malfunction is not listed or is not corrected by listed corrective actions, see individual repair sections for maintenance instructions on each major assembly.

3-7. TROUBLESHOOTING PROCEDURES.

Refer to troubleshooting table for malfunctions, tests, and corrective actions. The symptom index noted in Table 3-1 is provided for a quick reference of the malfunctions covered in table 3-3.

SYMPTOM INDEX

Table 3-3
INTERMEDIATE TROUBLESHOOTING

MALFUNCTION	TEST OR INSPECTION	CORRECTIVE ACTION
1. FAILURE TO FIRE.	Step 1. Broken hammer (1).	Replace hammer (1).
	Step 2. Weak or broken hammer spring (2).	Replace spring (2).
	Step 3. Hammer spring (2) improperly assembled.	Reassemble correctly (paragraph 3-17).
	Step 4. Burst cam (3) and/or clutch spring (4) frozen or improperly assembled.	Disassemble, clean, lubricate, and reassemble correctly.
	Step 5. Selector lever (5) frozen on SAFE position.	Disassemble and clean.
	Step 6. Broken firing pin (6) or firing pin does not meet gage protrusion requirement.	Replace.

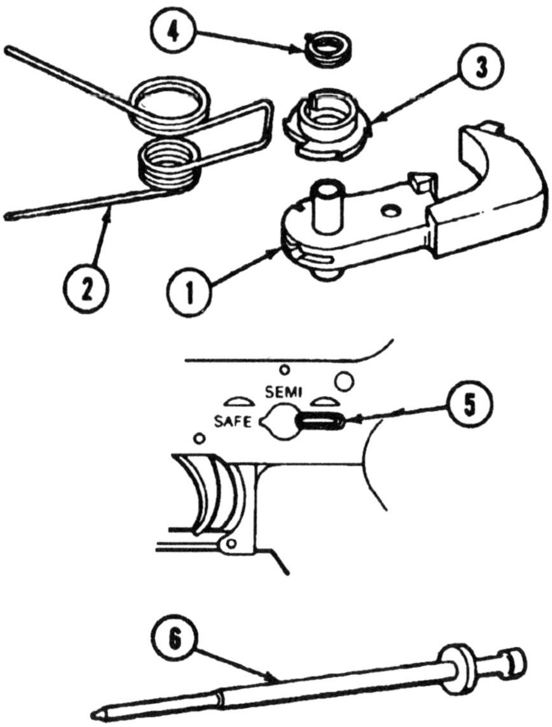

MALFUNCTION	TEST OR INSPECTION	CORRECTIVE ACTION
2. FAILURE TO UNLOCK	Step 1. Burred locking lugs(7) on bolt assembly.	Remove burrs.
	Step 2. Burred lugs (8) on barrel extension.	Remove burrs.
	Step 3. See short recoil.	

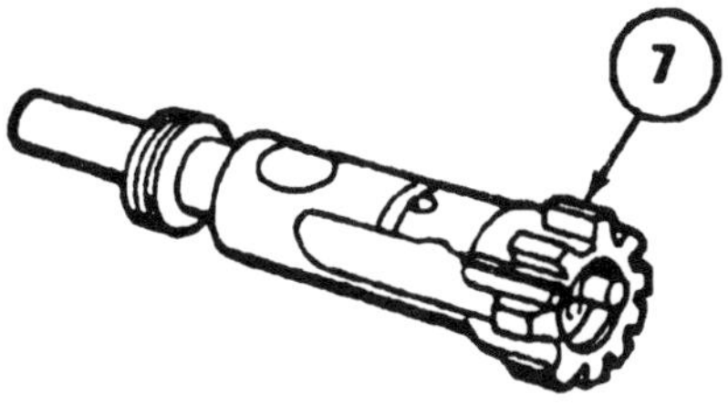

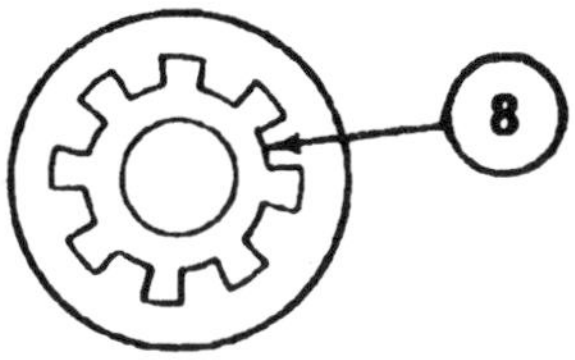

MALFUNCTION	TEST OR INSPECTION	CORRECTIVE ACTION
3. FAILURE TO EXTRACT.	Step 1. Inspect extractor and extractor spring	Replace if cracked or broken.
	Step 2. Inspect badly pitted chamber with reflector tool.	Replace rifle barrel assembly if chamber is badly pitted.
4. FAILURE TO EJECT.	See short recoil.	
5. FAILURE TO COCK IN EITHER SEMI OR BURST MODE.	Step 1. Worn or broken trigger nose (9) or trigger spring (10).	Replace trigger (11) or defective trigger spring (10).
	Step 2. Worn or broken hammer trigger notch (12).	Replace hammer (13).
	Step 3. Worn or broken hammer disconnector hook (14).	Replace hammer (13),

MALFUNCTION	TEST OR INSPECTION	CORRECTIVE ACTION
	Step 4. Worn or broken hammer automatic sear hook (15).	Replace the hammer (13)
	Step 5. Worn or broken disconnector hooks (16).	Replace defective disconnectors (17).
	Step 6. Weak, broken, or missing disconnector springs (18).	Replace springs (18).

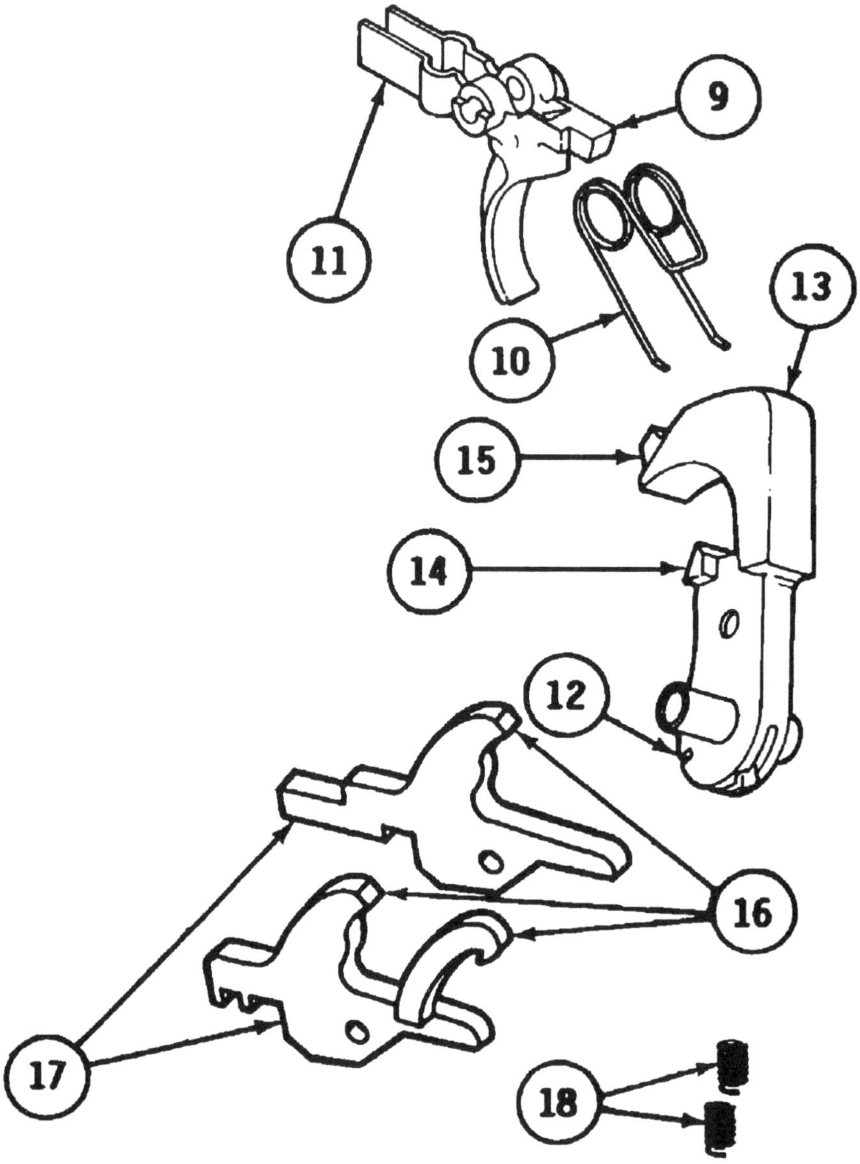

MALFUNCTION	TEST OR INSPECTION	CORRECTIVE ACTION
	Step 7. Worn, broken, or missing automatic sear (19).	Replace automatic sear (19).
	Step 8. Weak or broken automatic sear spring (20).	Replace automatic sear (19).
	Step 9. Long leg of automatic sear spring (21) incorrectly assembled in receiver.	Remove sear (19) and install correctly (paragraph 3-15).
	Step 10. Burst cam (22) or clutch spring (23) frozen or improperly assembled (paragraph 3-17).	Disassemble, inspect, clean, lubricate, or replace as required.

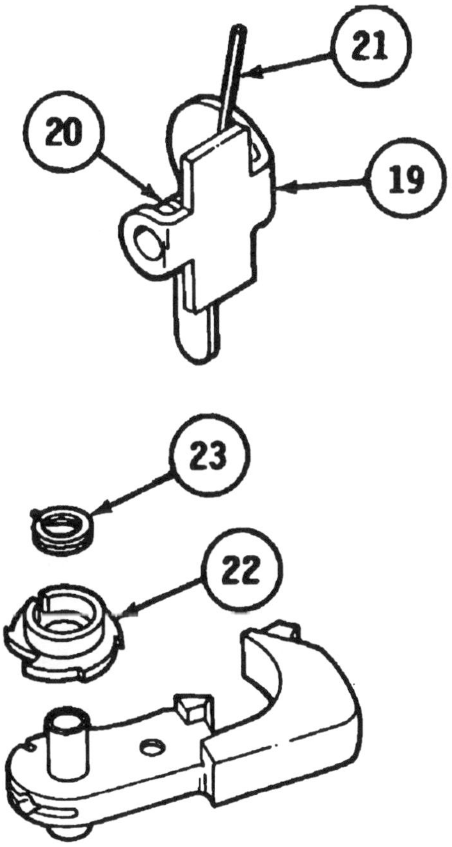

MALFUNCTION	TEST OR INSPECTION	CORRECTIVE ACTION
6. FAILURE OF MAGAZINE TO LOCK IN WEAPON.	Step 1. Dirty or corroded magazine catch (24).	Disassemble and clean.
	Step 2. Defective magazine catch spring (25).	Replace spring (25).
	Step 3. Worn or broken magazine catch (24).	Replace magazine catch (24).
7. FAILURE TO FEED.	Step 1. Magazine catch spring (25) weak or broken.	Replace magazine catch spring (25).
	Step 2. Short recoil.	
8. FAILURE TO CHAMBER.	See short recoil.	

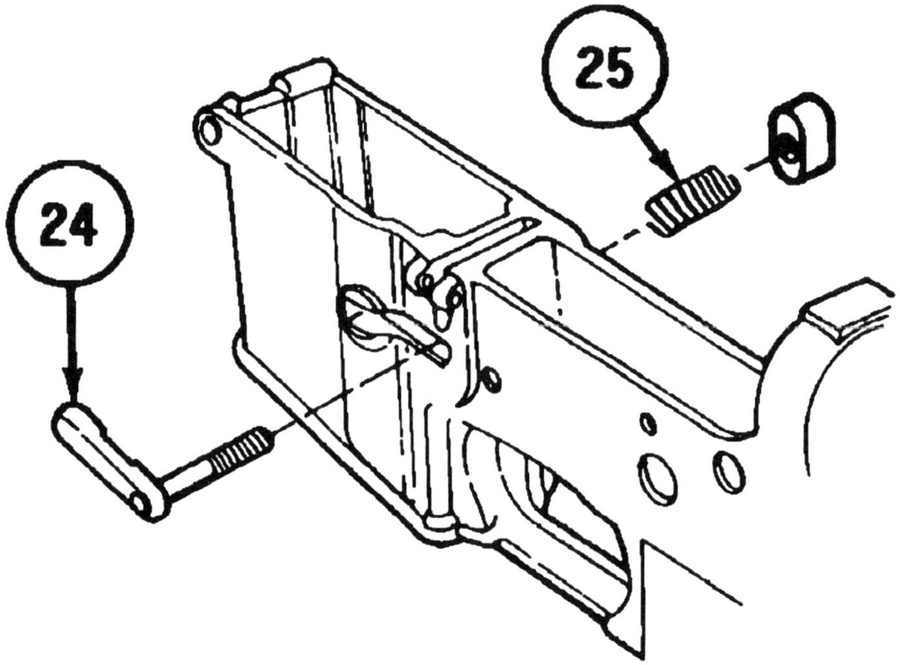

NOTE

See carrier key tool (E-4, app E) and procedures for its use on page 3-27.

MALFUNCTION	TEST OR INSPECTION	CORRECTIVE ACTION
9. FAILURE TO LOCK	Step 1. Damaged bolt carrier key (26).	Repair or replace bolt carrier key (26) and check alignment.
	Step 2. Loose screws (27) on bolt carrier key (26).	Disassemble and repair (paragraph 3-11). Reassemble using new screws.

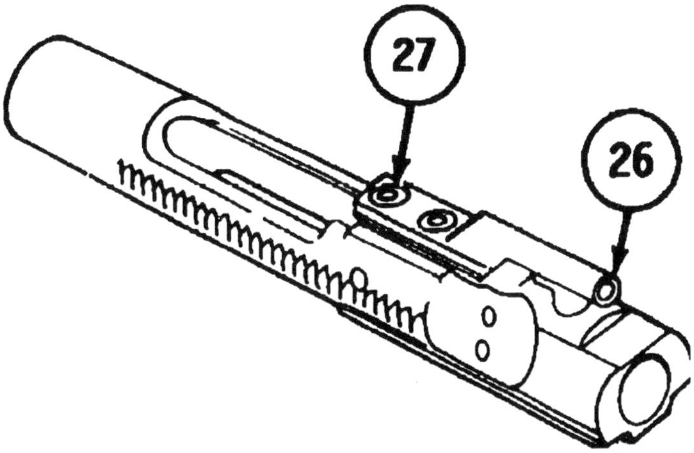

MALFUNCTION	TEST OR INSPECTION	CORRECTIVE ACTION
	Step 3. Bent gas tube (28).	Adjust by bending tube in area of handguards. Replace gas tube (28) and check alignment.
	Step 4. See short recoil.	
10. SHORT RECOIL	Step 1. Improper gap space of worn, missing, or broken bolt rings (29).	Replace bolt rings and stagger gaps.

MALFUNCTION	TEST OR INSPECTION	CORRECTIVE ACTION
	Step 2. Broken or bent gas tube (28).	Adjust by bending in area of handguards or replace gas tube.

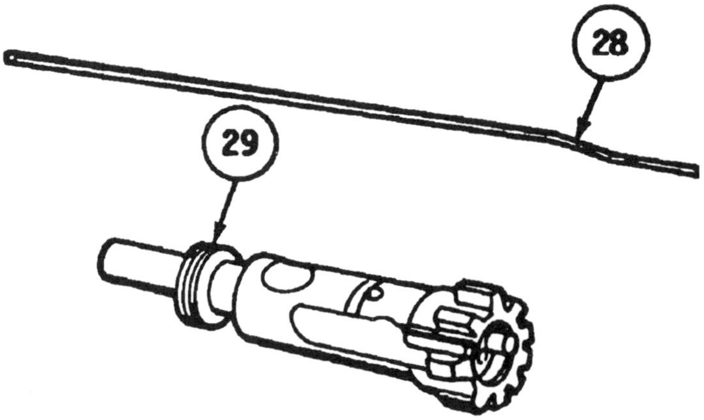

MALFUNCTION	TEST OR INSPECTION	CORRECTIVE ACTION
	Step 3. Gas tube spring pin (30) missing from front sight (31).	Replace spring pin (30).
	Step 4. Partially plugged gas system because of carbon build-up in the gas tube (28).	Replace gas tube (28).
	Step 5. Carbon build-up or foreign matter in the narrow passage of the bolt carrier key (26).	Clean with CLP (item 6, app D) and a pipe cleaner (item 8, app D).

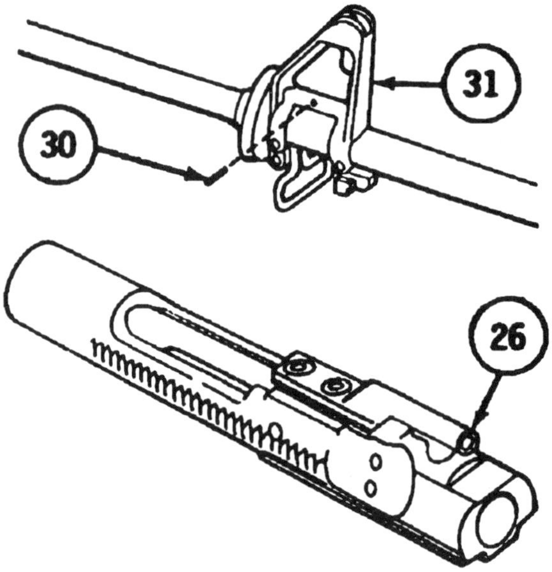

MALFUNCTION	TEST OR INSPECTION	CORRECTIVE ACTION

WARNING

When using P-C-111, avoid skin contact. If it comes in contact with the skin, wash off thoroughly with running water. The use of a good lanolin base cream after exposure to compound is helpful. The use of gloves and protective equipment is required.

	Step 6. Carbon build-up in barrel gas port (32).	Remove carbon build-up by soaking n P-C-111 (item 5, app D). Use rubber gloves (item 15, app D) with P-C-111. Use a small cleaning brush (item 3, app D).

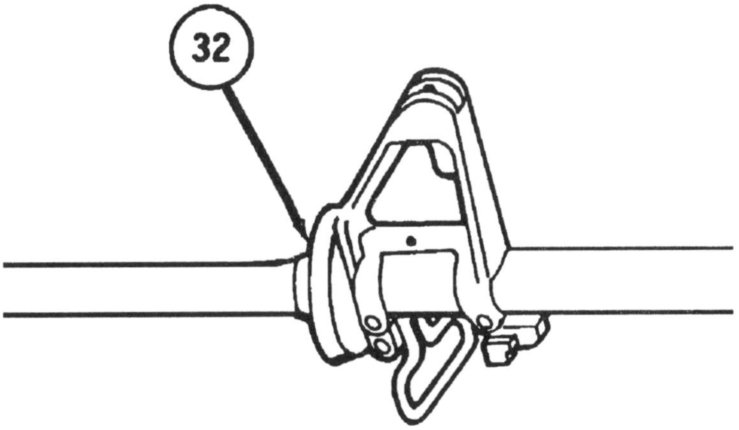

11. BOLT FAILS TO LOCK TO REAR AFTER FIRING LAST ROUND.	Step 1. Broken bolt catch (33).	Replace bolt catch (33).
	Step 2. Weak or broken bolt catch spring (34).	Replace bolt catch spring (34).
	Step 3. Restricted movement of bolt catch (33).	Disassemble and clean.
	Step 4. Weak action on follower by magazine spring.	Replace magazine (35).

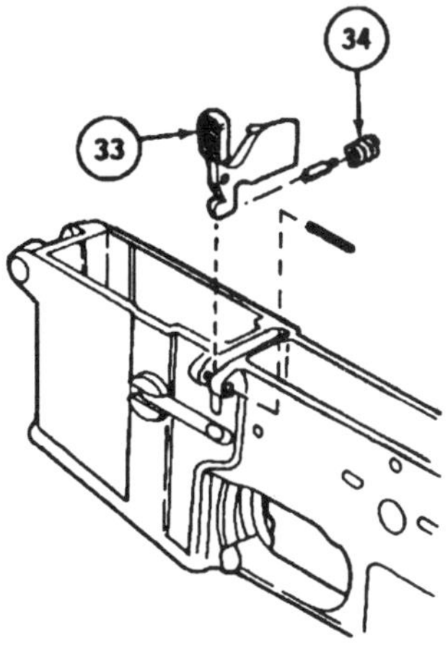

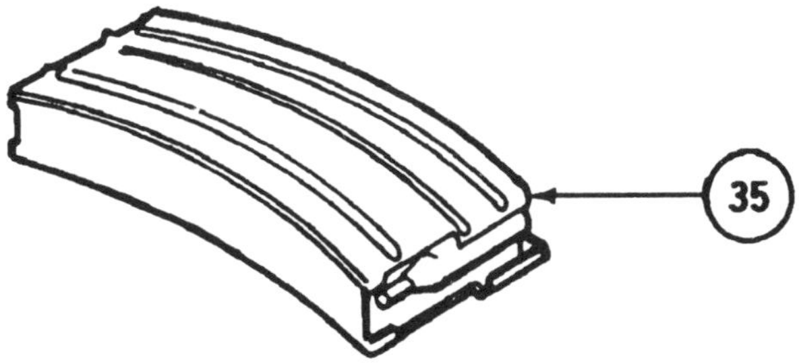

MALFUNCTION	TEST OR INSPECTION	CORRECTIVE ACTION
12. WEAPON CANNOT BE ZEROED.	Step 1. Defective or bent rifle barrel assembly (36).	Replace rifle barrel assembly (36).
	Step 2. (For windage) barrel assembly out of alignment with rear sight on upper receiver.	Align barrel and upper receiver (paragraph 3-12).
	Step 3. (For elevation) corroded front (37) or rear (38) sights.	Disassemble, clean, and lubricate.

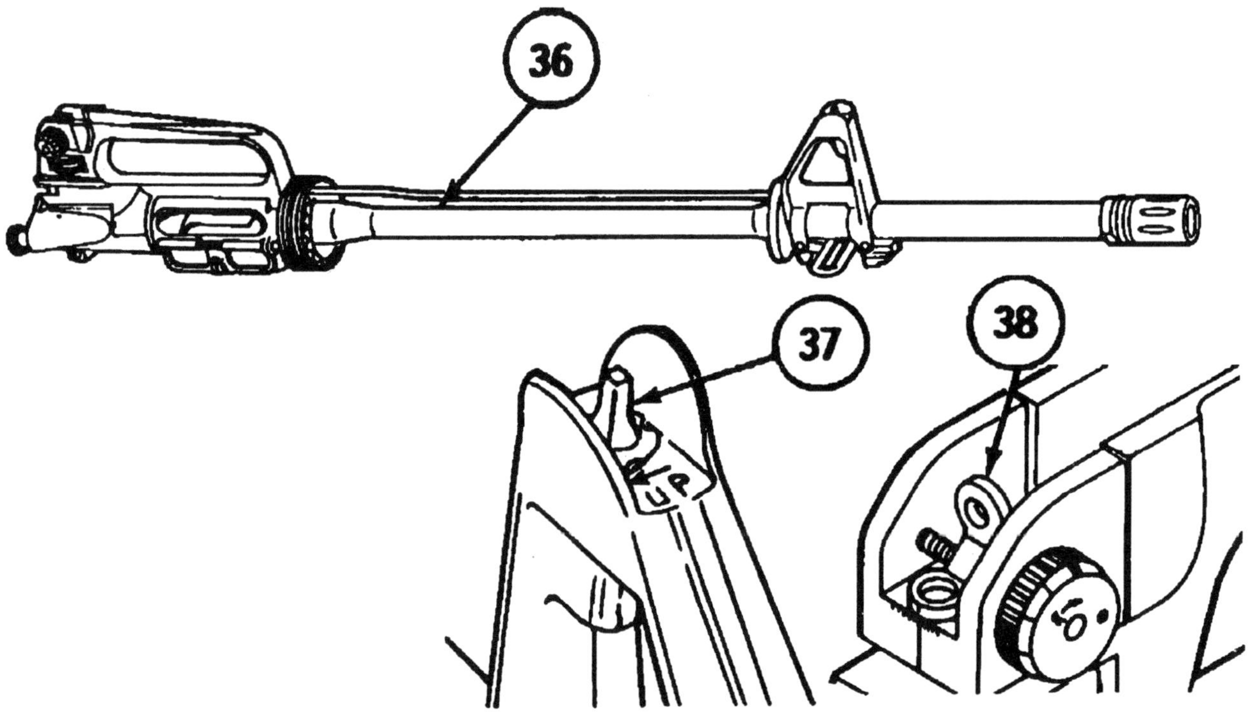

MALFUNCTION	TEST OR INSPECTION	CORRECTIVE ACTION
13. FAILURE TO CYCLE WITH SELECTOR LEVER SET AT BURST.	Step 1. Broken automatic sear (39) or spring (40).	Replace automatic sear (39).
	Step 2. Faulty selector lever (41).	Replace selector lever (41).
	Step 3. Broken tooth on burst cam (42).	Replace burst cam (42).
	Step 4. Broken cam clutch spring (43). Should be bent and properly formed without any sharp edges or corners.	Inspect and replace if required.
	Step 5. The bend in the cam clutch spring (43) installed backwards (toward outside).	Install properly with the bend to the inside.

NOTE

When hammer is rotated back to cocked position, cam should rotate to allow the burst disconnector to latch in the next notch.

	Step 6. Cam clutch spring (43) fails to "clutch" and burst cam (42) fails to rotate back with hammer.	Replace cam clutch spring (43). If problem continues, replace hammer (44) and cam (42).
	Step 7. Short recoil.	See malfunction 10.

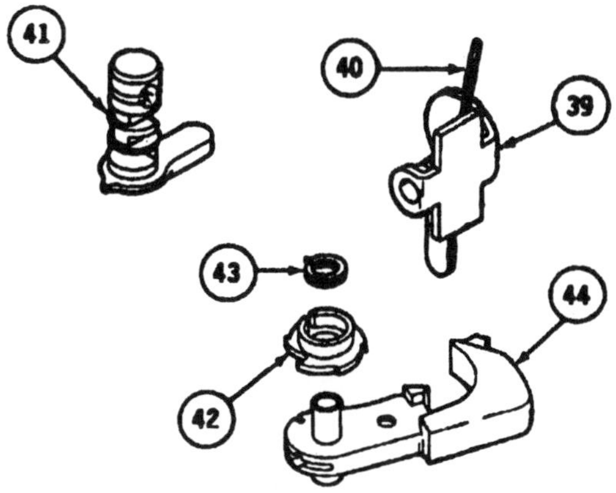

MALFUNCTION	TEST OR INSPECTION	CORRECTIVE ACTION
14. FIRES WITH SELECTOR LEVER ON SAFE OR WHEN TRIGGER IS RELEASED WITH SELECTOR LEVER ON SEMI.	Step 1. Worn or broken hammer trigger nose (45).	Replace trigger (46).
	Step 2. Worn or broken hammer trigger notch (47).	Replace firing hammer (48).
	Step 3. Defective selector.	Replace selector (49).

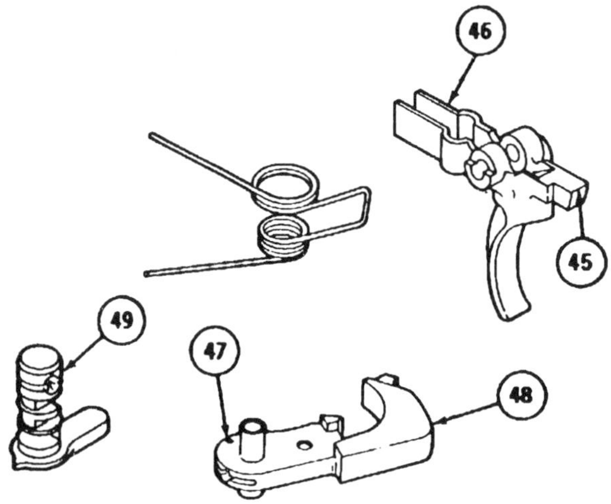

MALFUNCTION	TEST OR INSPECTION	CORRECTIVE ACTION
15. FIRES TWO ROUNDS WITH SELECTOR LEVER ON SEMI (DOUBLING).	Step 1. Check for worn semiautomatic disconnector, hammer, or trigger.	Replace unserviceable parts.
	Step 2. Worn trigger or hammer pin hole. Gage trigger and hammer pin holes.	If gage 12006472 enters any of the four holes (paragraph 3-15), replace weapon.
16. HAMMER PIN "WALKS"	Hammer pin (50) "walks" or works loose during firing or hammer pin is very easy to push out of receiver when hammer is installed.	Replace hammer assembly (paragraph 3-15).

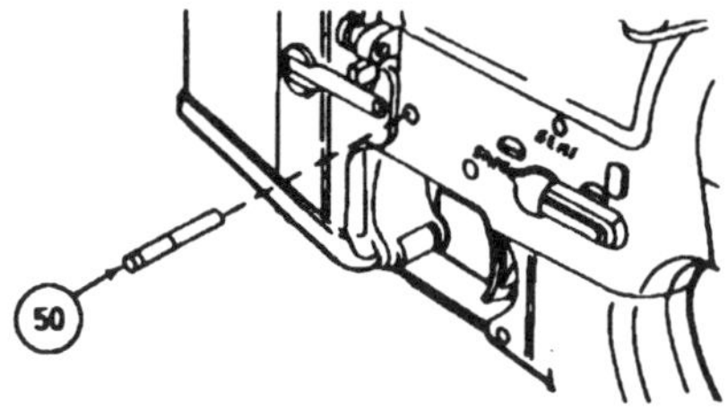

Section IV. INTERMEDIATE MAINTENANCE PROCEDURES FOR THE M16A2 RIFLE

3-8. MAJOR COMPONENTS OF M16A2 RIFLE.

This task covers disassembly.

INITIAL SETUP

Tools

(MC) Small Arms Repairman Tool Kit
NSN 5180-00-357-7770/SL-3-00607A
Tool and Gage Set, Infantry Weapons, M16A2
NSN 4933-00-056-7106/SL-3-06229A
(ARMY) Small Arms Repairman Tool Kit
SC 5180-95-CL-A07 (app B)

References

TM 05538C-10/1

General Safety Instructions

Before starting an inspection, be sure to clear the weapon. Do not pull the trigger until the rifle has been cleared. Inspect the chamber to ensure that it is empty and no ammunition is in position to be chambered. Do not keep live ammunition near work area.

LOCATION	ITEM	ACTION	REMARKS
DISASSEMBLY			
Weapon	Cartridge magazine (51), small arms sling (52), bolt carrier assembly (53), charging handle assembly (54), upper receiver and barrel assembly (65), and lower receiver and buttstock assembly (56).	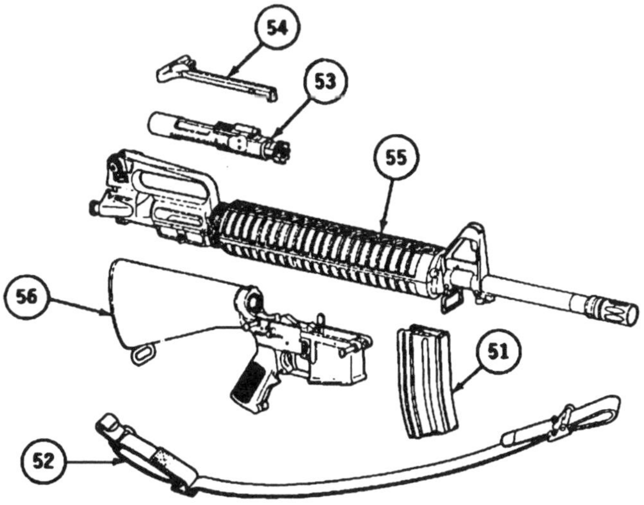 Remove.	

Refer to Tm 05538C-10/1.

3-9. BOLT CARRIER ASSEMBLY (INTERMEDIATE).

This task covers:
- a. Disassembly
- b. Cleaning
- c. Inspection
- d. Test
- e. Repair
- f. Reassembly

INITIAL SETUP

Tools

(MC) Small Arms Repairman Tool Kit
NSN 5180-00-357-7770/SL-3-00607A
Tool and Gage Set, Infantry Weapon, M16A2
NSN 4933-00-056-7160/LS-3-06229A
(ARMY) Small Arms Repairman Tool Kit
SC 5180-95-CL-A07 (app B)

Materials/Parts

Cleaner, lubricant and preservative (CLP) item 6, app D)
Pipe cleaner (item 8, app D)

LOCATION	ITEM	ACTION	REMARKS
DISASSEMBLY			
Bolt Carrier Assembly	a. Firing pin retaining pin (56)	Remove.	
	b. Firing pin (57)	Remove.	**Tip bolt carrier and key allowing firing pin to drop out. Catch the firing pin.**
	c. Bolt cam pin (58)	Remove.	**Rotate bolt cam pin 1/4 turn and lift straight up.**

LOCATION	ITEM	ACTION	REMARKS
	d. Bolt assembly (59) and key and bolt carrier assembly (60).	Remove.	

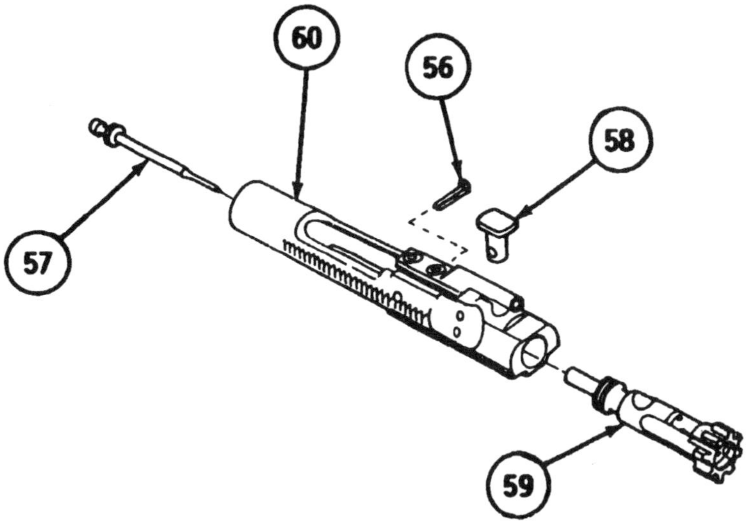

CLEANING

Bolt Carrier Assembly	Key and bolt carrier assembly	Clean carrier key and gas relief ports using CLP (item 6, app D) and pipe cleaner (item 8, app D).	

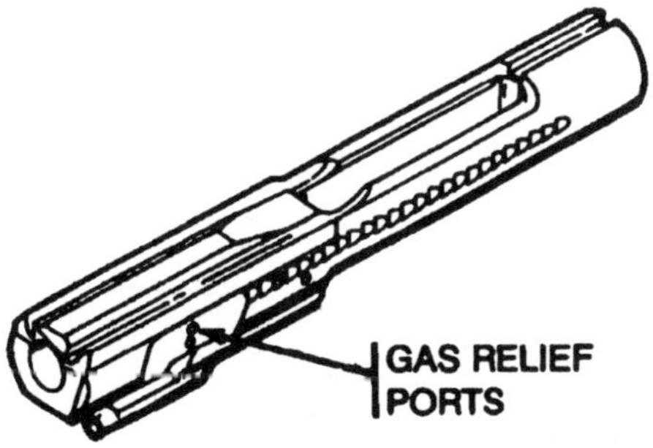

INSPECTION

Bolt Carrier Assembly	a. Key and bolt carrier assembly	Check carrier key and key screws for tightness and for proper staking	

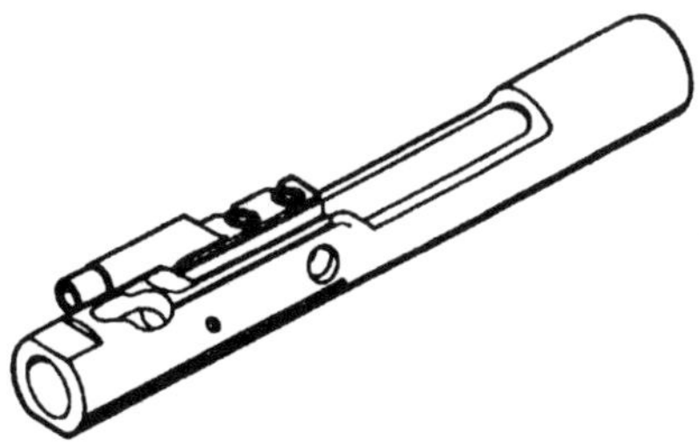

LOCATION	ITEM	ACTION	REMARKS
	b. Firing pin	Inspect tip for proper contour. Inspect for pitting, wear, and burrs.	

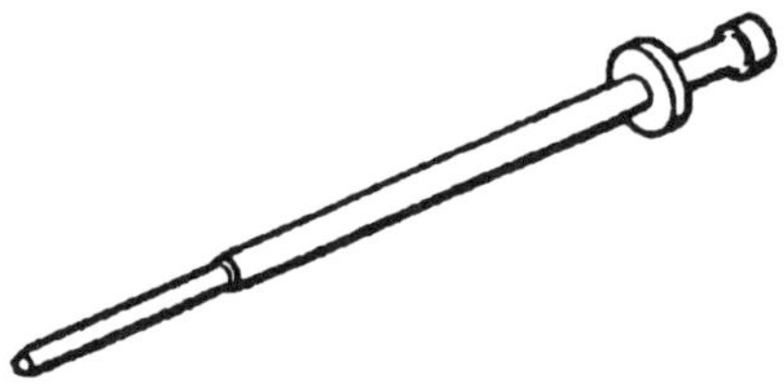

LOCATION	ITEM	ACTION	REMARKS
	c. Bolt assembly	Inspect for wear, burrs, and pits	Replace the bolt assembly if it contains a cluster of pits approximately 1/8 inch in diameter and if the pits appear to be more than 0.010 inch deep. Bolts that contain very small individual pits in a scattered pattern shall not be cause for rejection.

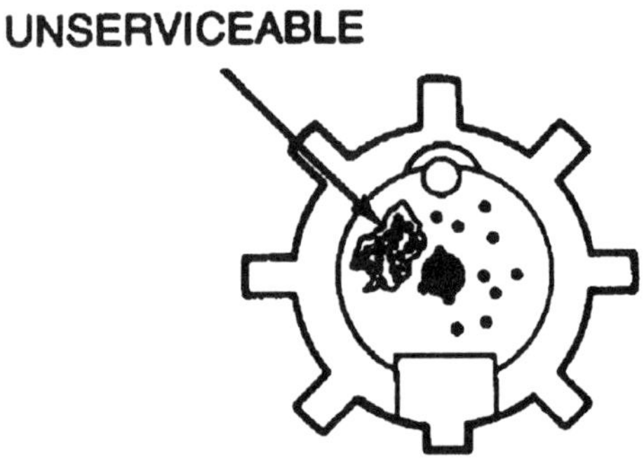

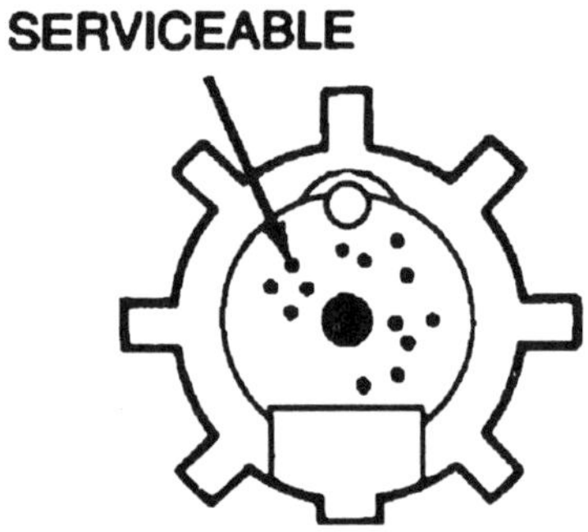

LOCATION	ITEM	ACTION	REMARKS
	d. Bolt carrier assembly and bolt assembly	Exercise bolt in bolt carrier assembly.	Prior to reassembly, insert bolt assembly in bolt carrier assembly (do not insert cam pin) and exercise bolt in and out of bolt carrier assembly. Check for binding.

LOCATION	ITEM	ACTION	REMARKS
		Check for proper fit with cam pin removed. Turn bolt carrier assembly and suspend so the bolt assembly is pointed down.	The bolt must not drop out. If weight of bolt assembly allows it to drop out of carrier assembly, replace bolt rings.

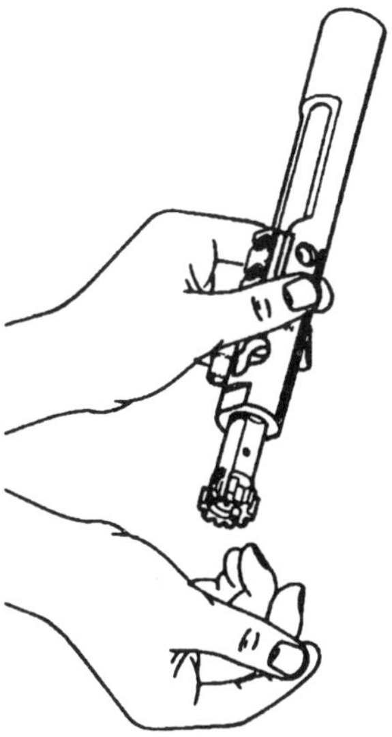

LOCATION	ITEM	ACTION	REMARKS
TEST			
Bolt Assembly	Bolt assembly	Test firing pin hole for elongated and oversize holes.	Bolts that have elongated or oversized holes that permit special no-go plug gage 12620101 to penetrate fully at any position on the circumference of the firing pin hole will be replaced.

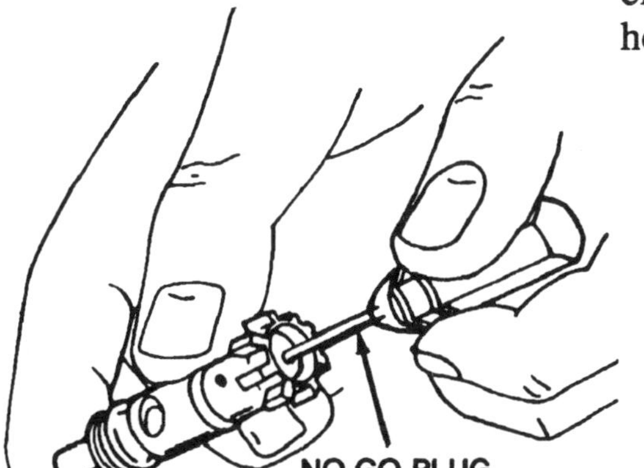

	Bolt assembly	Using firing pin protrusion gage 7799735, check for proper firing pin protrusion.	
		Insert firing pin through bolt assembly.	Large diameter portion of firing pin should contact rear of bolt.

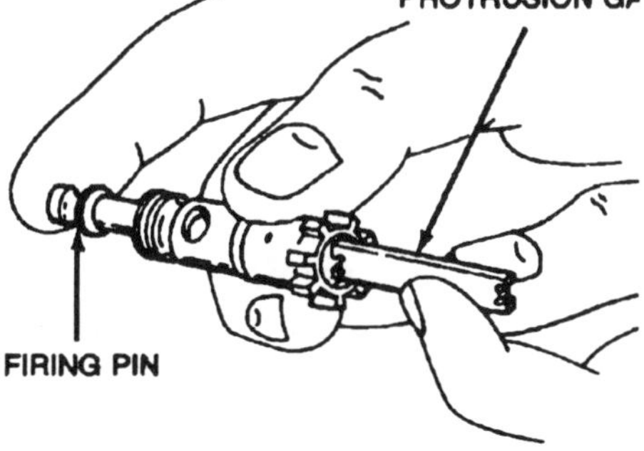

LOCATION	ITEM	ACTION	REMARKS
			Firing pin should touch the gage on minimum but should not touch on maximum.

REPAIR

Bolt Carrier Assembly	All authorized items	Replace if unserviceable. Retest all replaced parts.	

REASSEMBLY

Bolt Carrier Assembly	a. Key and bolt carrier assembly (60) and bolt assembly (59)	Install.	
	b. Bolt cam pin (58)	Install and rotate a quarter turn.	
	c. Firing pin (57)	Install.	Hold carrier with bolt assembly down and drop in firing pin.

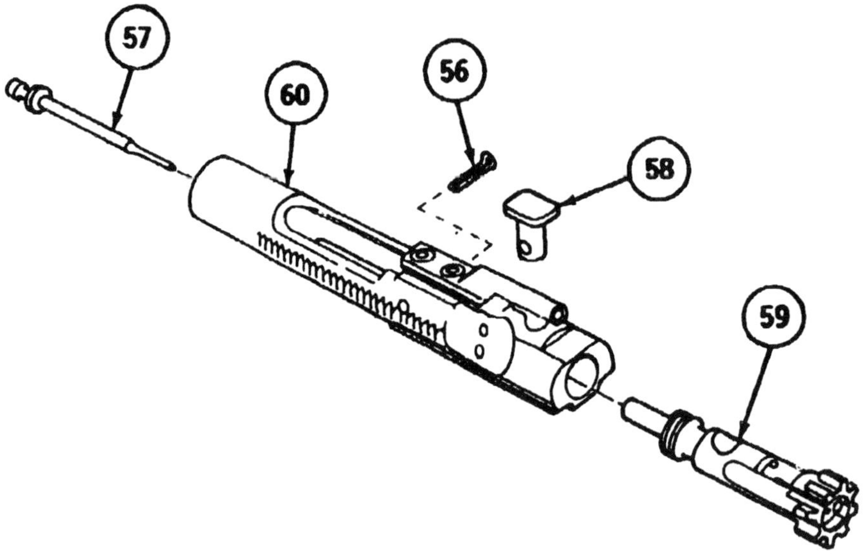

	d. Firing pin retaining pin (56)	Install.	Install from the left side. To ensure proper installation of firing pin retaining pin. Attempt to shake out firing pin.

3-10. BOLT ASSEMBLY (INTERMEDIATE).

This task covers:

a. Disassembly
b. Inspection/Repair
c. Reassembly

INITIAL SETUP

Tools

(MC) small Arms Repairman Tool Kit
NSN 5180-00-357-7770/SL-3-00607A
Tool and Gage Set, Infantry Weapons, M16A2
NSN 4933-00-056-7106/SL-3-06229A
(ARMY) Small Arms Repairman Tool Kit
SC 5180-95-CL-A07 (app B)

Materials/Parts

Penetrant kit (item 21, app D)
Wiping rag (item 22, app D)

LOCATION	ITEM	ACTION	REMARKS
DISASSEMBLY			

NOTE

Do not remove rings unless they require replacement and three new replacement rings are on hand.

LOCATION	ITEM	ACTION	REMARKS
Bolt Assembly	Bolt rings and bolt	Using a small flat tip jeweler's screwdriver, remove the three bolt rings from the bolt.	Replace defective firing pin.

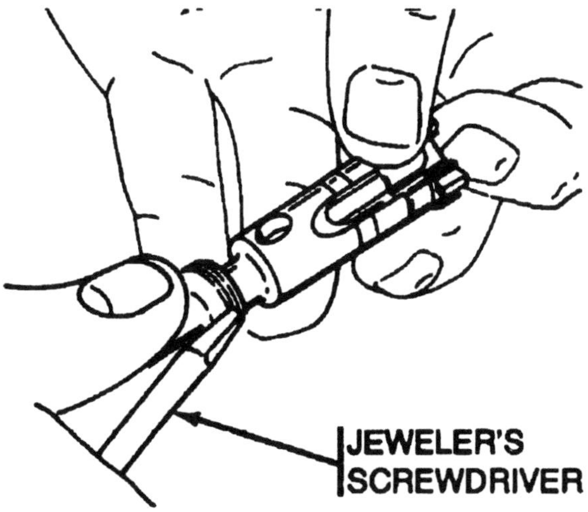

LOCATION	ITEM	ACTION	REMARKS
INSPECTION-/REPAIR			
Bolt Assembly	a. Bolt rings	Visually inspect for cracks, kinks, and bends.	
		Replace if defective.	If one or more bolt rings are damaged, replace all three rings. See paragraph 3-9 for wear check.
	b. Bolt locking lugs and bolt cam pin hole	Inspect for cracks in the locking lugs and cam pin hole area. Use black light if available; otherwise use a glass of no more than 3X magnification or use a penetrant kit (item 21, app D).	
			Pay close attention to the area where the locking lugs meet the body.
			Replace bolt assembly if defective.

NOTE

Replacement of the bolt assembly will require that the headspace be tested.

LOCATION	ITEM	ACTION	REMARKS
REASSEMBLY			
Bolt Assembly	Bolt rings and bolt	Install the three bolt rings one at a time onto the bolt using care not to bend or "spring" new bolt rings. Stagger the bolt ring gaps to prevent loss of gas pressure.	To install a ring, carefully place one end in the bolt ring groove and hold in place with the thumb of one hand. With the index finger of the other hand, gently guide and push the rest of the ring into the groove a little bit at a time until the entire ring is in place.

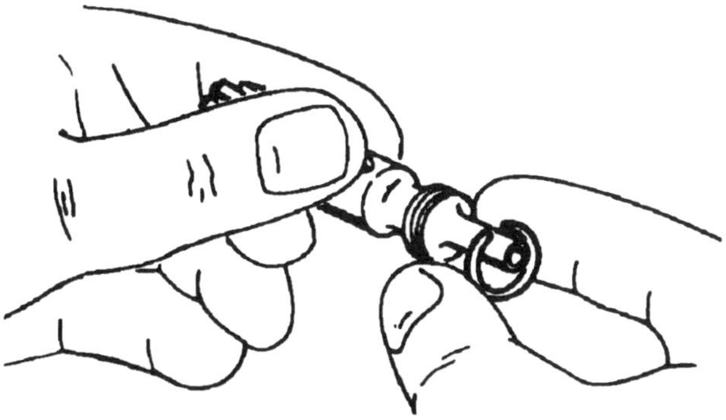

NOTE

Make certain ring gap are staggered to prevent loss of gas pressure. New rings will make installing the bolt in the carrier difficult. Lubricate inside of carrier and use gentle pressure when installing.

3-11. KEY AND BOLT CARRIER ASSEMBLY (INTERMEDIATE).

This task covers:

a. Disassembly
b. Inspection/Repair
c. Reassembly

INITIAL SETUP

Tools

(MC) Small Arms Repairman Tool Kit
NSN 5180-00-357-7770/SL-3-00607A
(ARMY) Small Arms Repairman Tool Kit
SC 5180-95-CL-A07 (app B)
Field Maintenance Basic Less Power Small Arms
Shop Set SC 4933-95-CL-A11 (19204)
Key tool (E-4, app[E)

LOCATION	ITEM	ACTION	REMARKS

NOTE

Do not disassemble the key and bolt carrier assembly unless the bolt carrier key or bolt carrier is defective as determined by inspection procedures described in section III, preceeding.

DISASSEMBLY

LOCATION	ITEM	ACTION	REMARKS
Key and Bolt Carrier Assembly	a. Carrier and key screws (61)	Using socket wrench handle and 1/8" socket head screw socket wrench attachment, remove the two socket head screws.	
	b. Bolt carrier key (62) from bolt carrier (63)	Remove.	Use a tight fitting 1/8" wrench as key screws are difficult to remove. The heads and part of the key may be ground off in order to remove key from carrier if screw cannot be otherwise removed.

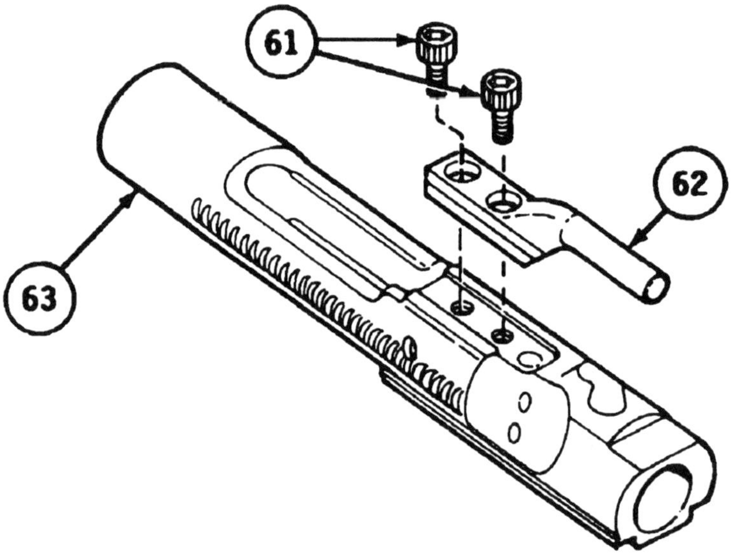

LOCATION	ITEM	ACTION	REMARKS
INSPECTION/REPAIR			
Key and Bolt Carrier Assembly	a. Carrier and key screw	Visually inspect the carrier and key screws for looseness and proper staking.	Do not retorque carrier and key screws if staking marks do not indicate loosening screws.

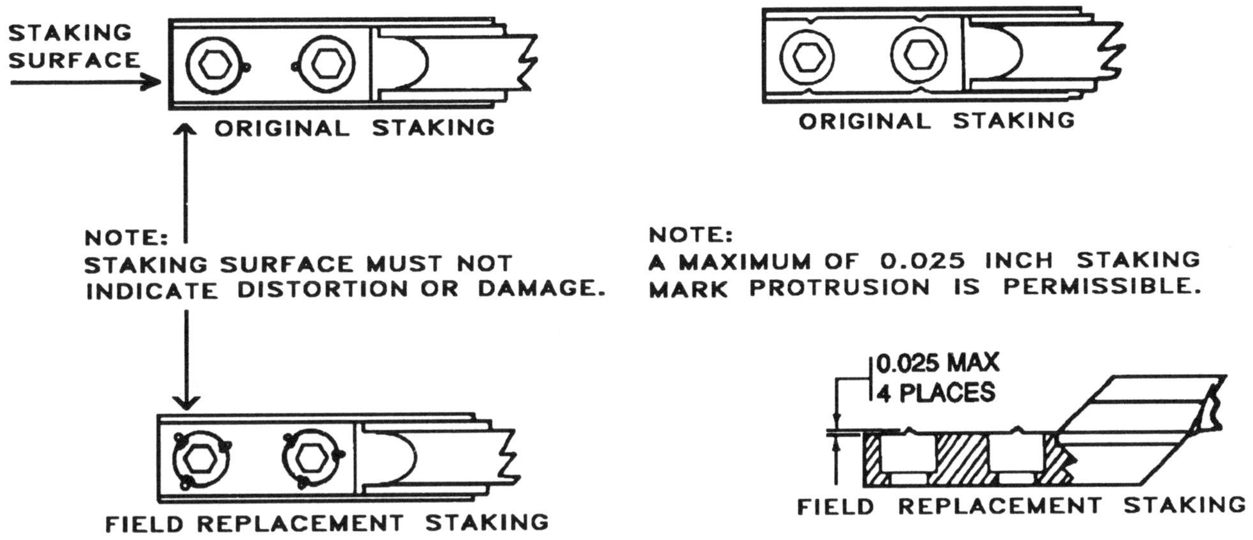

NOTE

Staking Surface must not indicate distortion or damage.
A maximum of 0.025 inch staking mark is permissible.

LOCATION	ITEM	ACTION	REMARKS
		Repair by replacing screws and torquing carrier and key screws and restaking. Using the socket head screw wrench attachment and an inch/pound torque wrench, torque the carrier and key screws to 35 to 40 inch pounds.	Do not reuse old screws. New screws must be used at assembly. Use a tight-fitting 1/8" wrench.

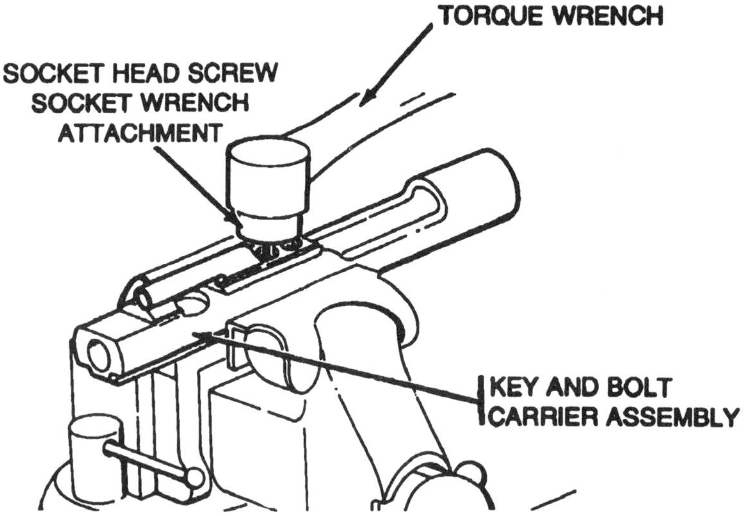

LOCATION	ITEM	ACTION	REMARKS
		Use vise jaw caps, vise, solid center punch, and hand hammer to stake the two carrier and key screws in three places.	Field staking method will be used by field units.

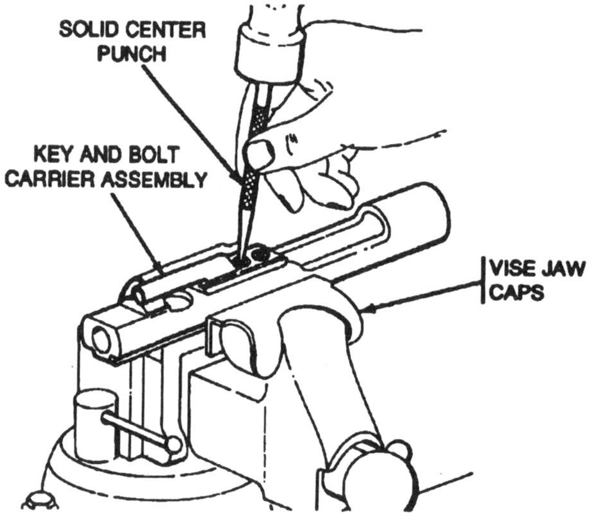

LOCATION	ITEM	ACTION	REMARKS

CAUTION

Extreme care must be exercised during the following procedure to assure that the striking force is not directed to the attaching screws and that the tube portion is not enlarged or flared beyond original requirements. Such enlargement would permit loss of gas pressure when the key and gas tube come together during functioning.

b. Key

Inspect for burrs, breaks, or bends.

Repair small dents and/or distortions using fabricated key tool (E-4, app E) as follows:

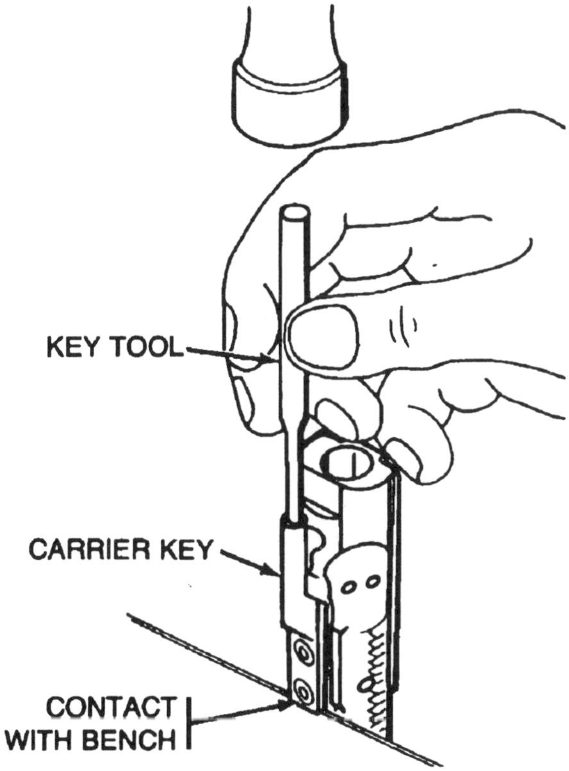

Place the key and bolt carrier assembly in a vertical position, supported so that contact is made with the rear surface of the key.

Insert the small end of the key tool (E-4), app E) into the tube portion of the key.

Strike the large end of the key tool (lightly with a 3- ounce, soft-grass hammer.

Repeat striking (gently) until the carrier key is reformed to original configuration.

c. Bolt carrier assembly

Inspect for burrs, cracks, and wear.

LOCATION	ITEM	ACTION	REMARKS
REASSEMBLY			
Key and Bolt Carrier Assembly	a. Bolt carrier key and bolt carrier	Install and position bolt carrier key onto bolt carrier.	
	b. Carrier and key screws	Install the two carrier and key screws.	Always use new screws.
		Torque and stake.	See page 3-25 and below.

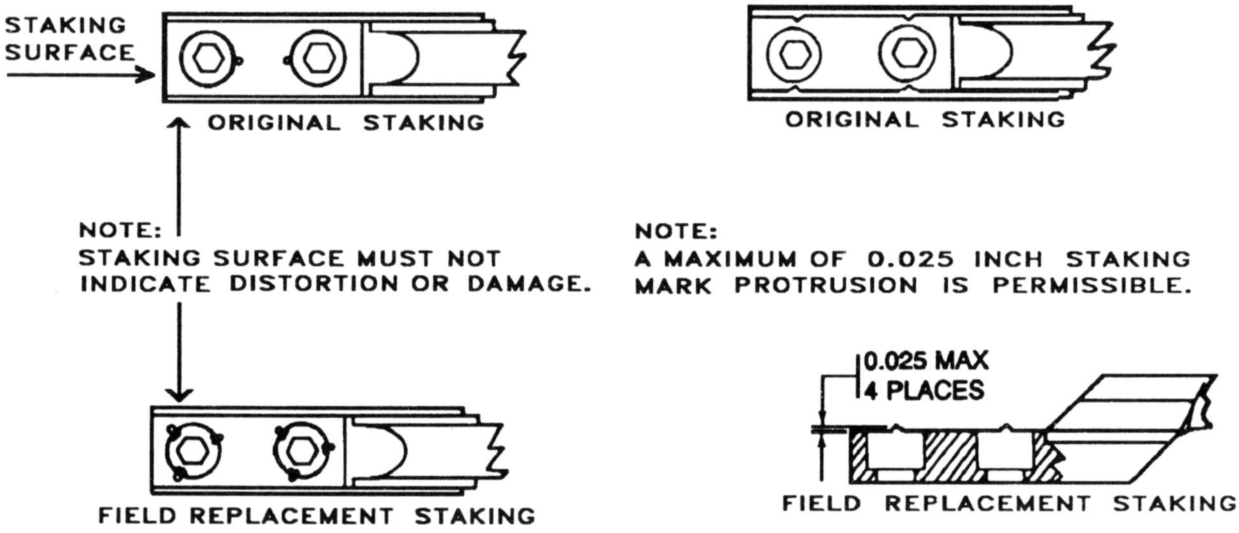

CAUTION

BLANKS MUST BE USED IF A BFA IS ATTACHED.

NOTE

If the bolt carrier key is replaced, it may be necessary to create a seal between the bolt carrier and key by firing three through eight rounds. Manual operation of the rifle may be required.

3-12. UPPER RECEIVER AND BARREL ASSEMBLY (INTERMEDIATE).

This task covers:

a. Disassembly
b. Inspection/Cleaning
c. Repair
d. Reassembly
e. Test

INITIAL SETUP

Tools

(MC) Small Arms Repairman Tool Kit
NSN 5180=00=357-7770-SL-3-00607A
Tool and Gage Set, Infantry weapons
NSN 4933-00-056-7106/SL-3-06229A
(ARMY) Small arms Repairman Tool Kit
SC 5180-95-CL-A07 (app B)
Field Maintenance Basic Less Power Small Arms
Shop set SC 4933-95-CL-A11 (19204)

Materials/Parts

Molybdenum disulfide grease (item 16, app D)
Carbon removing compound (P-C-111) (item 5, app D)
Abrasive cloth (item 10, app D)
Solid film lubricant (item 18, app D)
Technical dichloromethane (item 12, app D)
Sealing compound (item 23, app D)
Dry cleaning solvent (item 13, app D)
Gloves (item 15, app D)
Brush, cleaning, small (item 3, APP D)
Target (item 25, app D)

References

FM 23-9
TM 05538C-10/1

General Safety Instructions

To avoid injury to your eyes use care when removing and installing spring-loaded parts. When using solid film lubricant or dichloromethane, be sure the area is well ventilated. When using P-C-111, avoid skin, wash thoroughly with running water, Using a good lanolin base cream after exposure to the compound is helpful. Using gloves and protective equipment is required.

LOCATION	ITEM	ACTION	REMARKS

DISASSEMBLY

WARNING

To avoid injury to your eye, use care when removing and installing spring-loaded parts.

When using solid film lubricant or dichloromethane, be sure the area is well ventilated.

When using P-C-111, avoid skin contact. If P-C-111 comes in contact with the skin, wash thoroughly with running water. Using a good lanolin base cream after exposure to compound is helpful. Using gloves and protective equipment is required.

NOTE

Refer to TM 05538C-10/1 for "buddy system" procedure on removing handguards.

LOCATION	ITEM	ACTION	REMARKS
Upper Receiver and Barrel Assembly	a. Handguards	Remove.	
	b. Spring pin (64)	Remove. Using ballpen hammer and 5/64 inch-diameter drive pin punch, drive spring pin out of front sight assembly.	

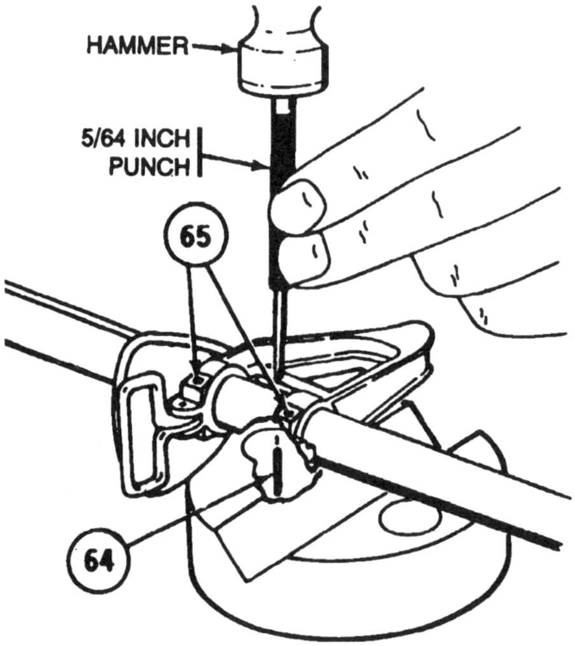

LOCATION	ITEM	ACTION	REMARKS
	c. Gas tube (66)	Remove. Slide gas tube back into receiver to clear front sight assembly. Then lift slightly, pull forward, and remove.	Do not disassemble front sight pins (65). If only one pin is missing or loose, replace it. If both pins are loose or missing, replace barrel assembly.
	d. Compensator (67)	Remove. Using barrel	

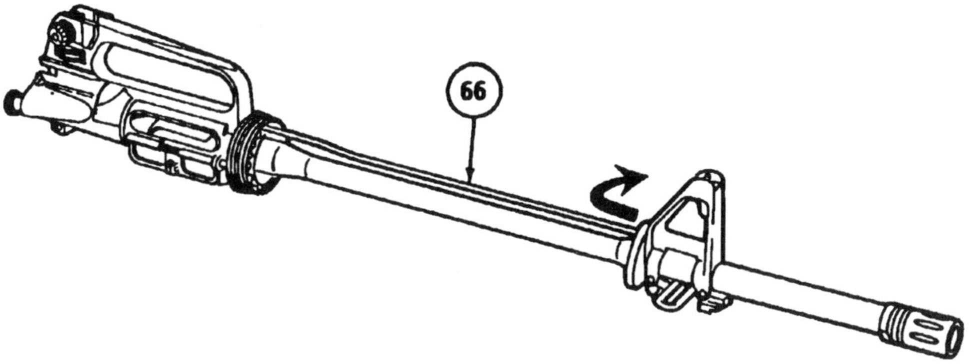

remover fixture, place upper receiver and barrel assembly in vise.

Using combination wrench and 1/2 inch-drive handle, remove compensator.

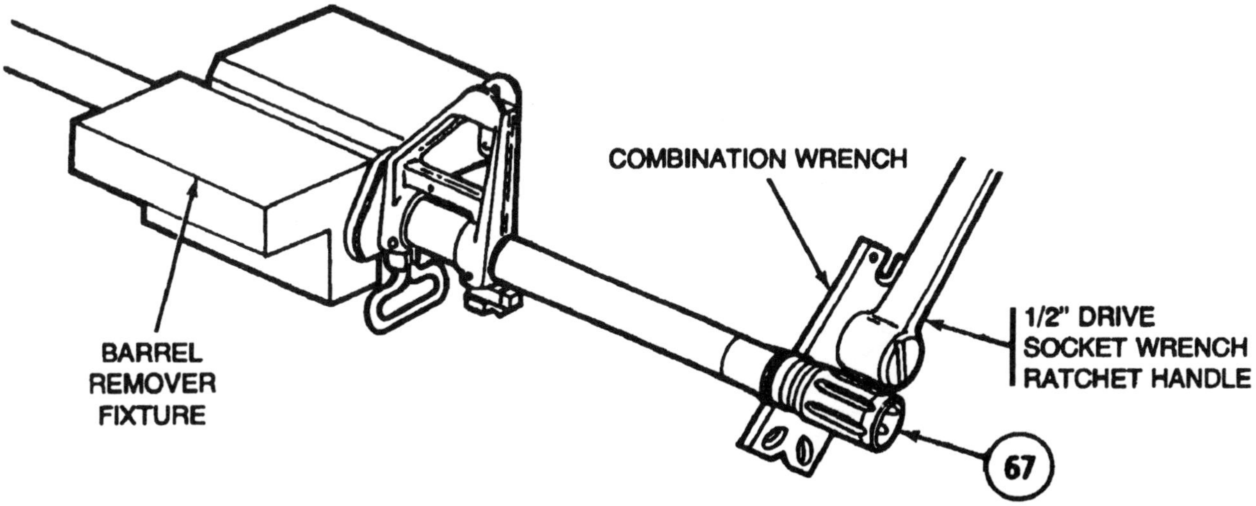

LOCATION	ITEM	ACTION	REMARKS
	e. Peel washer (68)	Remove.	Do not lose or bend thin sections of peel washer.

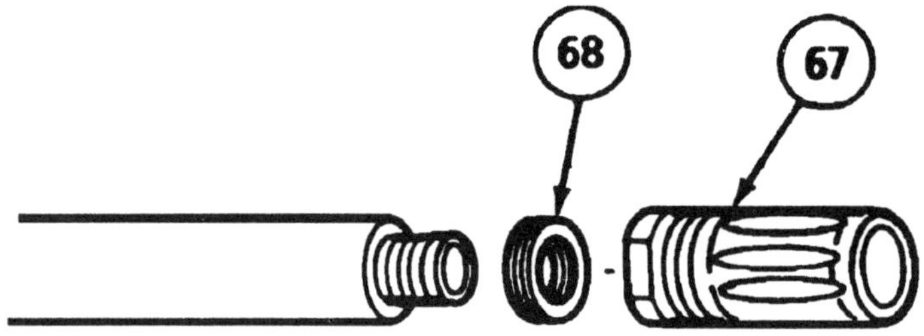

LOCATION	ITEM	ACTION	REMARKS
		Remove upper receiver and barrel assembly from barrel remover fixture.	
	f. Barrel nut assembly (69)	Place upper receiver and barrel assembly into barrel remover fixture and clamp into vise. Using socket wrench handle and combination wrench, loosen barrel nut assembly (69). Refer to page 3-27 for disassembly of barrel nut assembly.	Be sure all three drive pins on combination wrench are fully engaged with barrel nut assembly. Wrench must be pushed toward upper receiver to compress the slip ring spring.

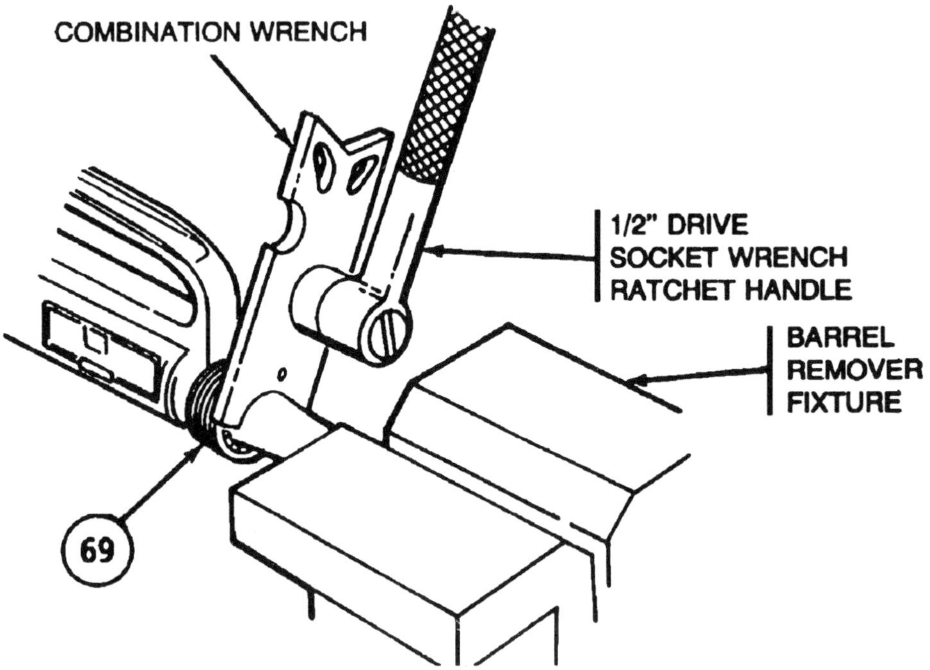

LOCATION	ITEM	ACTION	REMARKS
	g. Upper receiver assembly (70)	Separate from barrel assembly (71).	
	h. Rifle barrel assembly (71).	Remove rifle barrel assembly from remover fixture.	

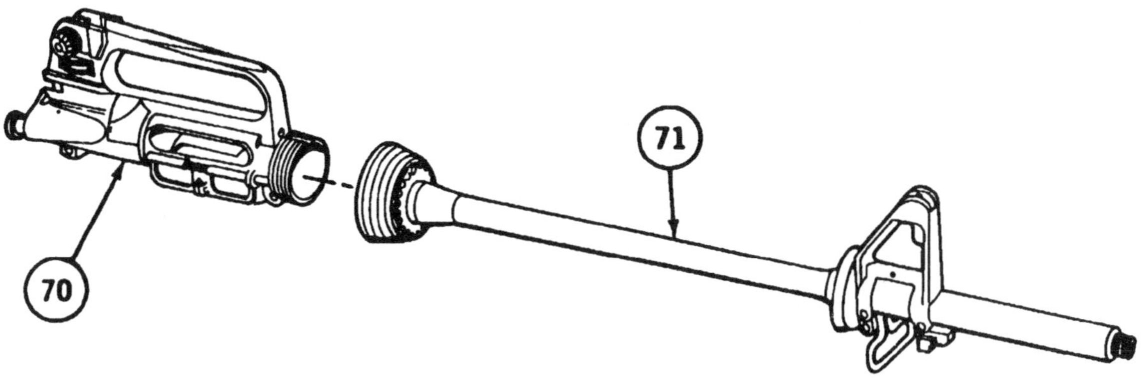

LOCATION	ITEM	ACTION	REMARKS
Barrel Nut Assembly	a. Retaining ring (72)	Remove using retaining ring pliers.	
	b. Slip ring spring (73) and handguards slip ring (74).	Remove.	
	c. Barrel nut (75)	Do not remove barrel; nut (75) from the rifle barrel assembly.	

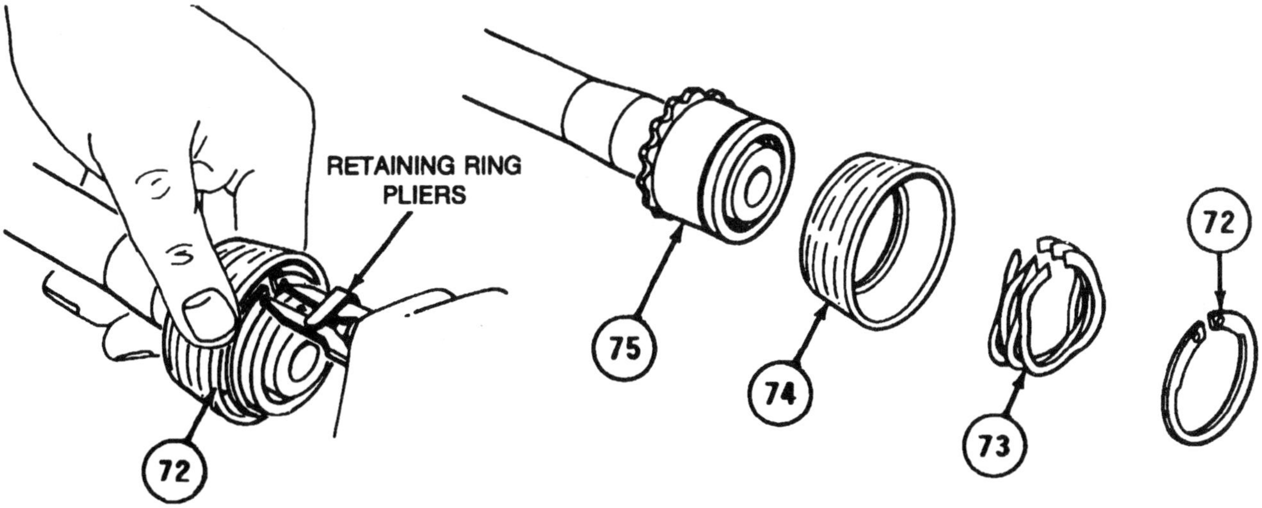

LOCATION	ITEM	ACTION	REMARKS
INSPECTION/CLEANING			
Upper Receiver and Barrel Assembly	a. Gas tube	Inspect for cracks.	
		Replace if defective.	
		Use P-C-111, carbon removing compound (item 5, app D), to remove carbon deposits from interior and exterior of gas tube.	If a large amount of carbon is found and cannot be removed, replace the gas tube.

NOTE

A small cleaning brush (item 3, app D) may be used to clean interior of front sight assembly where gas tube is secured.

LOCATION	ITEM	ACTION	REMARKS
b. Bore		Inspect for burrs, cracks, rust, bulges, and pits.	Pits no wider than a land or groove and no longer than 3/8 inch are allowed in the bore. Lands that appear dark blue due to coating of gilding metal from projectiles are allowable.
		Replace rifle barrel assembly if defective	Definitely ringed bores or bores ringed sufficiently to bulge the outside surface of the barrel are cause for rejection.
	c. Chamber	Inspect chamber using reflector tool and flashlight.	Pits 1/8 inch in length are cause for rejection.
		Replace rifle barrel assembly if defective.	

LOCATION	ITEM	ACTION	REMARKS

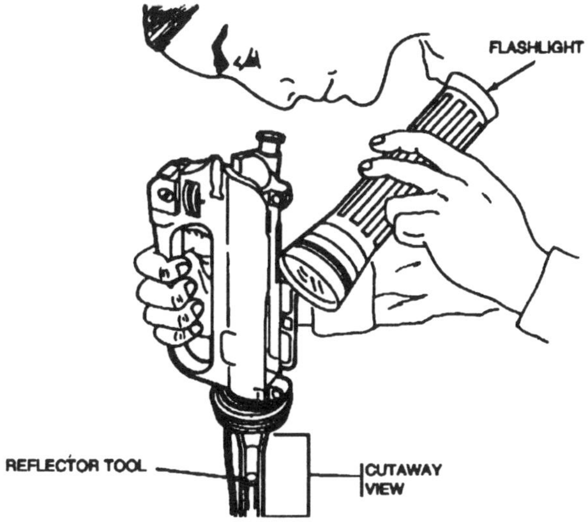

NOTE

Chamber may be inspected with or without upper receiver assembled to the barrel assembly.

d. Upper receiver

Inspect for cracks, corrosion, mutilation, wear, or damage.

Small dents or gouges that do not affect functioning will not be cause for rejection. If receiver contains cracks or holes, the receiver will be replaced.

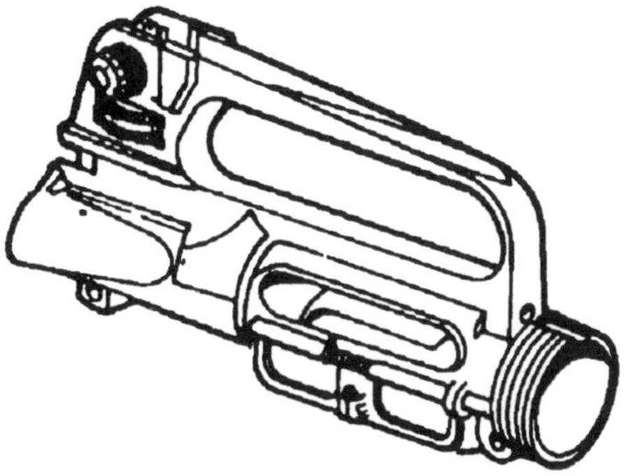

SHINY SURFACES (REPARABLE)

Inspect springs for breaks, deformation, and rust.

Repair corroded surfaces as follows:

Sand corroded area with abrasive cloth (item 10, app D) and make sure all corrosion has been removed.

Wash area with technical dichloromethane (item 12, app D) to remove all dirt, grease, and foreign material.

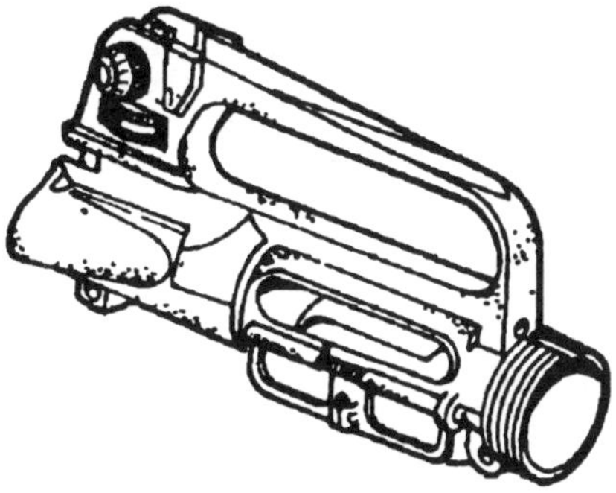

CORRODED (REPARABLE)

LOCATION	ITEM	ACTION	REMARKS

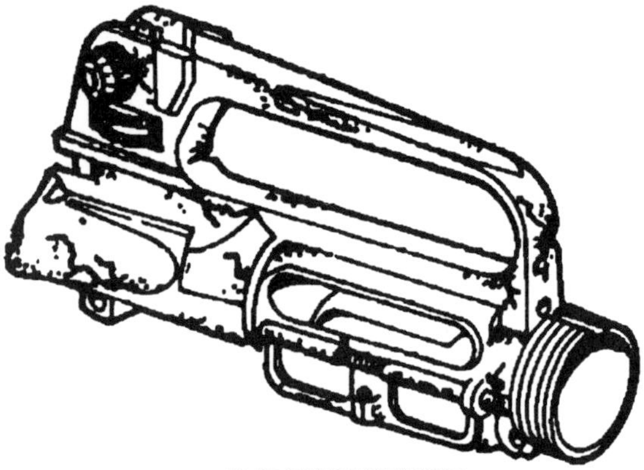

Apply sealing compound (item 23, app D), mixed in accordance with manufacturer's directions, to areas to be filled.

Spread sealing compound as smoothly as possible into defective area using a putty knife or similar tool.

NOTE

Do not feather edges.

Place a sheet of polyethylene, cut to size, over filled area. Rub by hand or smooth using small roller.

After curing, remove polyethylene sheet in accordance with instructions by the manufacturer.

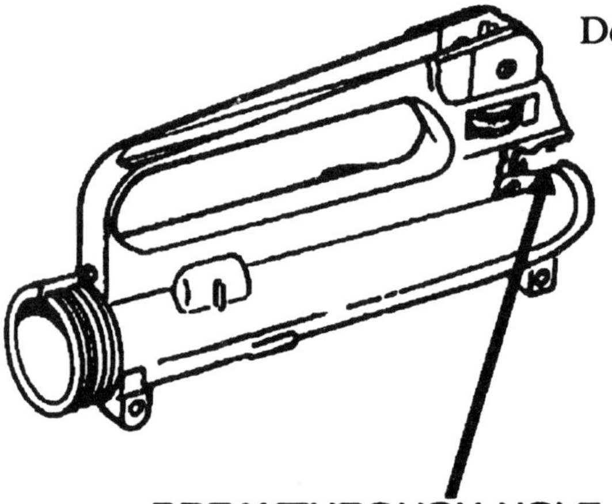

WARNING

When using solid film lubricant or dichloromethane, be sure the area is well ventilated.

CAUTION

Solid film lubricant (item 18, app D) is to be used only as an exterior surface protective finish and touch up. If solid film lubricant comes in contact with recoiling parts or functional surfaces of the rifle, remove immediately by washing with technical dichloromethane (item 12, app D).

Wash area with technical dichloromethane (item 12, app D) (methylenechloride) to remove all dirt, grease, and foreign material.

LOCATION	ITEM	ACTION	REMARKS
		Roughen area to be refinished with abrasive and clean surface again. Do not touch the area with fingers.	
		Repair shiny surface.	Spray a coat of solid film lubricant (item 18, app D) in accordance with instructions supplied by the manufacturer. Dry 24 hours before handling.
	e. All parts	Inspect for damage and wear. Replace all defective parts.	
REPAIR			
Upper Receiver and Barrel-Assembly	a. All authorized items	Replace if unserviceable	
	b. Front sight guards	Place front sight base (76) in a vise.	Use copper or brass caps (jaw inserts) on vise to prevent damage to sight base during clamping.
		Remove front sight post, plunger, and spring.	(See paragraph 2-16). Remove spring before heating. (Heat will damage spring.) The sight post and plunger may be reused unless damaged.
		Heat sight guard (77) and bend with pliers (78).	The sight guard (77) should be put back as nearly as possible to the original position.

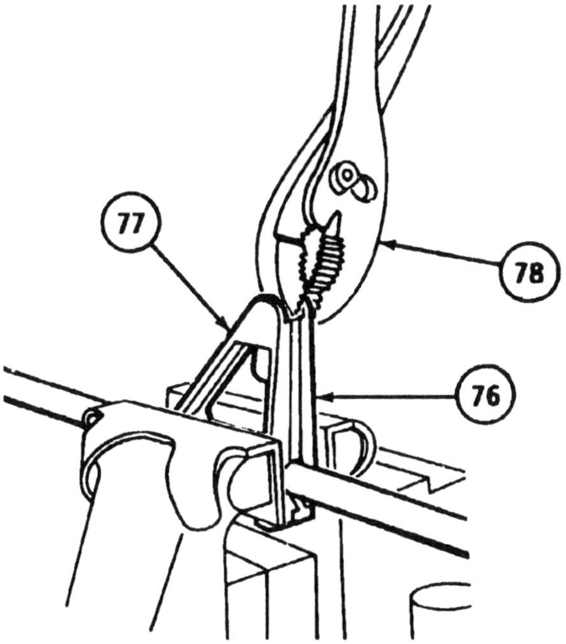

LOCATION	ITEM	ACTION	REMARKS

WARNING

Dry cleaning solvent is flammable and toxic and should be used in a well-ventilated area. The use of rubber gloves is necessary to protect skin when washing rifle parts.

		Roughen surface with abrasive cloth (item 10, app D) and clean with dry cleaning solvent (item 13, app D). Always wear rubber gloves (item 15, app D) when using dry cleaning solvent.	Allow front sight housing to air cool.

CAUTION

Do not allow solid film lubricant to flow into front sight post threaded well.

		Apply solid film lubricant (item 18, app D) to cover the damaged finish.	

REASSEMBLY

Barrel Nut Assembly and Rifle Barrel Assembly	a. Barrel nut (79)	Position barrel nut (79) on barrel.	Slide barrel nut to the rear of barrel as far as possible.
	b. Handguard slip ring (80)	Slide handguard slip ring over barrel nut	
	c. Slip ring spring (81)	Press in from both sides and insert slip ring spring into handguard slip ring.	

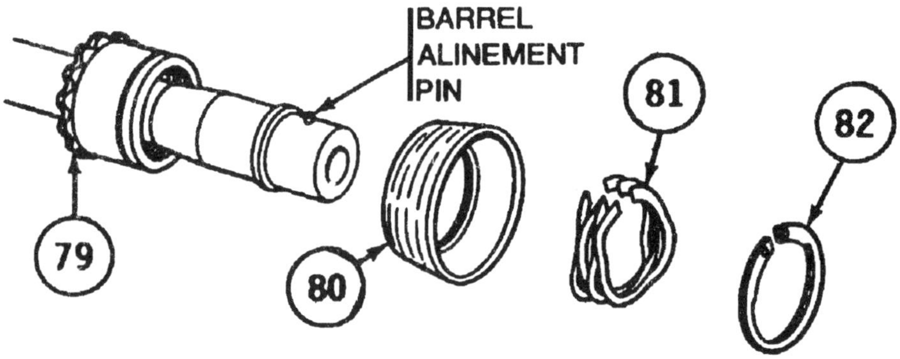

LOCATION	ITEM	ACTION	REMARKS
	d. Retaining ring (82)	Install against slip ring spring using retaining ring pliers. Snap retaining ring to barrel nut.	

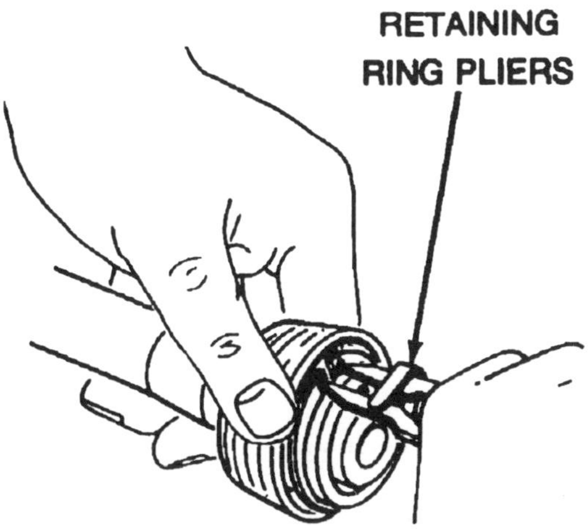

NOTE

After cleaning , apply molybdenum disulfide grease (item 16, app D) to threads of barrel nut assembly before installation.

LOCATION	ITEM	ACTION	REMARKS
Upper Receiver and Barrel Assembly	a. Rifle barrel assembly (83)	Position rifle barrel with alignment pin up. The alignment pin must not show any signs of looseness. Using barrel remover fixture, clamp barrel in vise.	

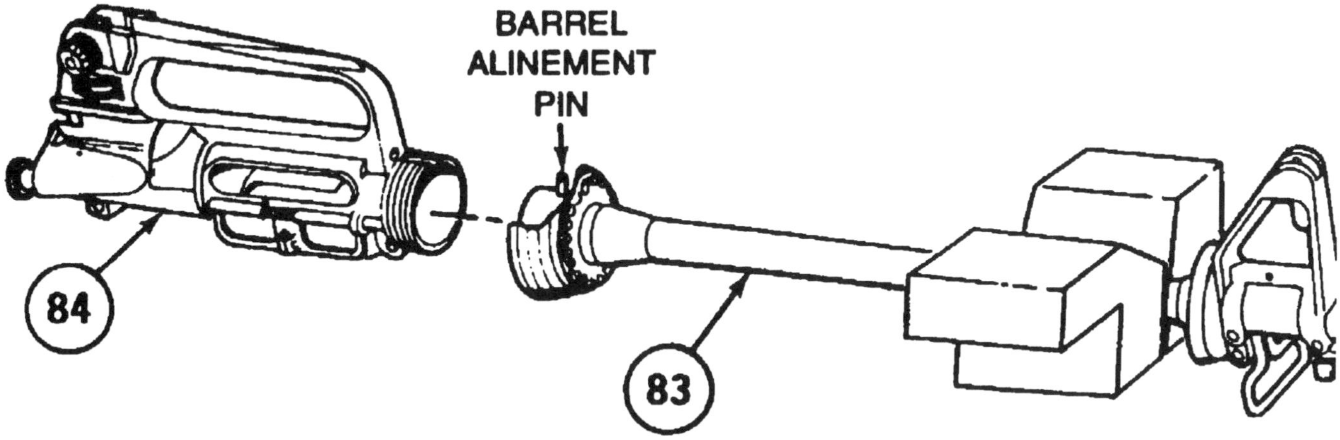

LOCATION	ITEM	ACTION	REMARKS
b. Upper receiver assembly (84).		Align upper receiver assembly using barrel alignment pin and the slot in upper receiver assembly. Install over end of barrel	The slot should fit the alignment pin perfectly with vertical or no rotational play present. Note the play in a new barrel and new upper receiver and use this as a guide.

NOTE

Wipe upper receiver thread clean and ensure there are no burrs. Apply molybdenum disulfide grease (item 16, app D) to the threads prior to installation.

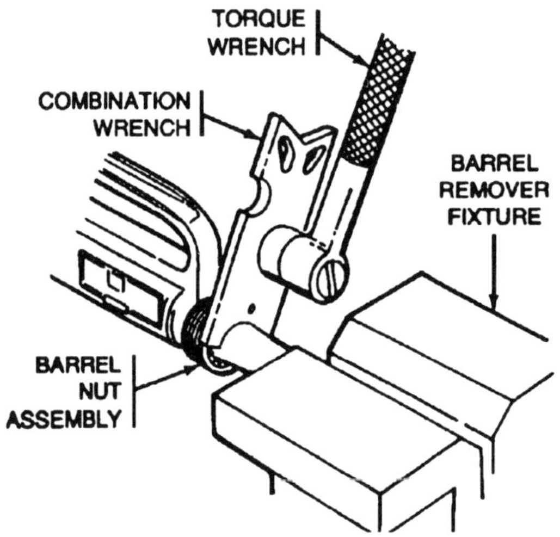

Engage threads of barrel nut assembly with upper receiver assembly.

Using combination wrench and torque wrench, torque barrel nut assembly to 31-35ft-lb. Torque is measured when both wrenches are used together.

LOCATION	ITEM	ACTION	REMARKS
		Make certain all three drive pins on combination wrench are engaged with barrel nut assembly. Loosen and repeat torque operation. Then loosen the barrel nut again.	Two time torquing (three times total) procedures provide for a better thread fit and prevent barrel nuts from becoming loose.
			Do not use the torque wrench for loosening.
		Front sight post must be installed. Loosen the vise and align the bore on a distant vertical target. Center the target in the bore from 12 o'clock through 6 o'clock. The front sight post should be on line and vertical with the target. Tighten vise. Adjust the rear sight windage until a proper sight picture is obtained on the vertical target. The rear sight aperture will be approximately in the center of the rear sight base if the barrel is properly aligned in the receiver.	If barrel (usually new) is not properly aligned in the receiver (usually an old part), excessive windage will be present and the receiver will require replacement to obtain the proper fit between the alignment pin and slot.

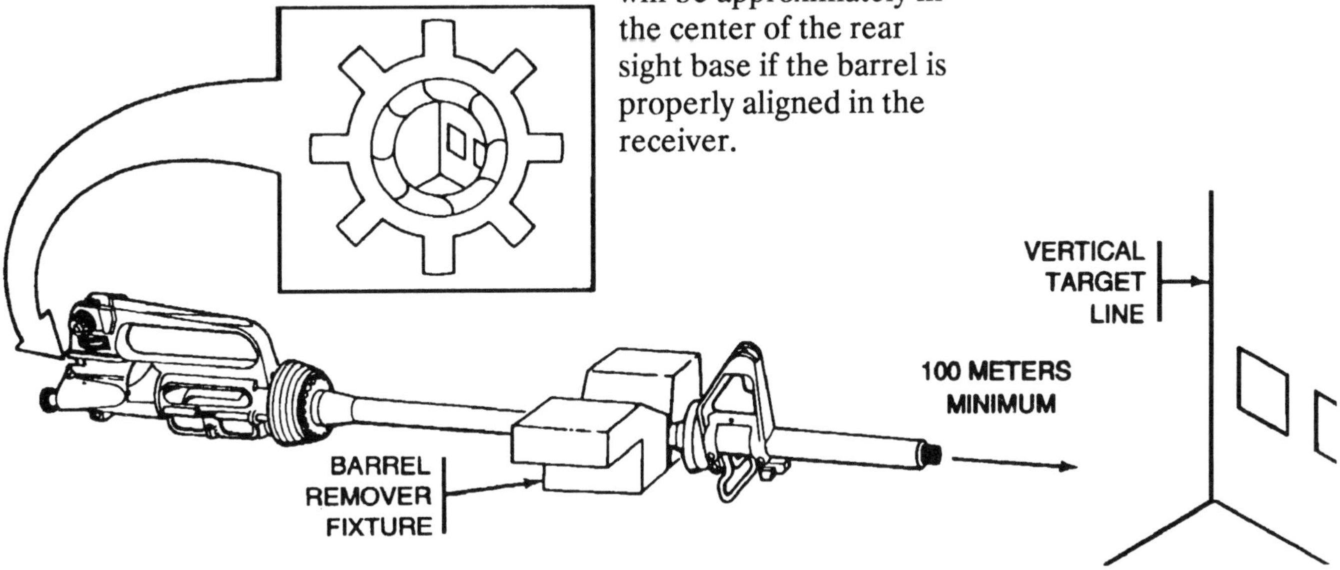

LOCATION	ITEM	ACTION	REMARKS
		The barrel may be tightened beyond 35 ft-lb to align the barrel serrations for proper gas tube clearance. Never loosen the barrel nut to align for gas tube clearance.	Do not attempt to hold the upper receiver with a pry bar; however, if the barrel turns in the holding fixture, a pry bar may be used through the front sight base to help prevent the barrel from turning in the holding fixture. Use care not to distort or bend front sight or retaining pins. Use "buddy system" to hold pry bar.
		Check alignment of barrel nut assembly with upper receiver assembly.	The front eight inches of a gas tube may be used as an alignment tool (see illustration). This is inserted into the bolt carrier key and then inserted into the rear of the receiver. If the parts of the barrel nut assembly are properly aligned, the tool will pass freely and lay top dead center along the top of the barrel. A # 15 twist drill (.180 inch) may also be used as an alignment tool.

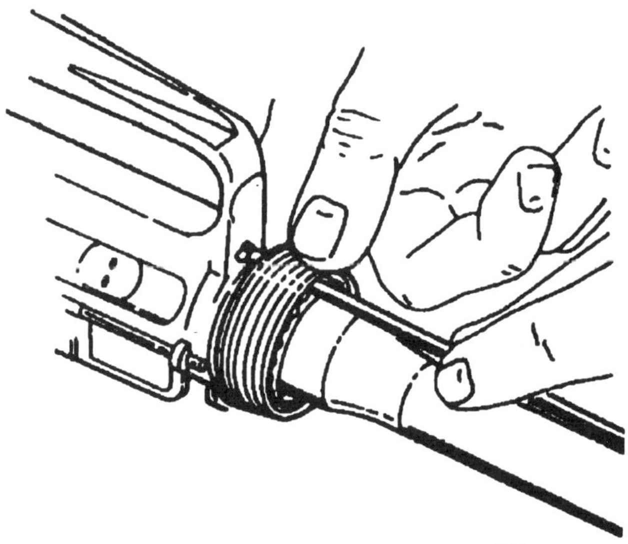

		If necessary, tighten nut to next hole to allow proper alignment. Remove upper receiver and barrel assembly from barrel remover fixture.	

LOCATION	ITEM	ACTION	REMARKS
	c. Peel washer (85) and compensator (86)	Install on barrel.	Peel washer (7) may be heated with a match to remove thin sections. Always place thin sections to rear.

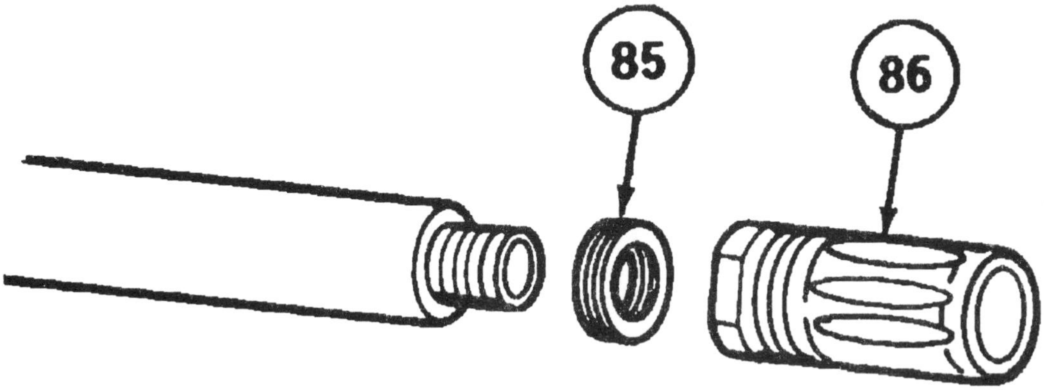

		Torque to 15-20 ft-lb using combination wrench and 1/2" drive torque wrench. Torque is measured when both wrenches are used together.	The third or middle slot must be straight up at proper torque level. Thin sections of peel washer may be removed or added as required. Save unused sections.
		Check for Top Dead Center (TDC) of middle or third slot.	Adjust thickness of peel washer as required.

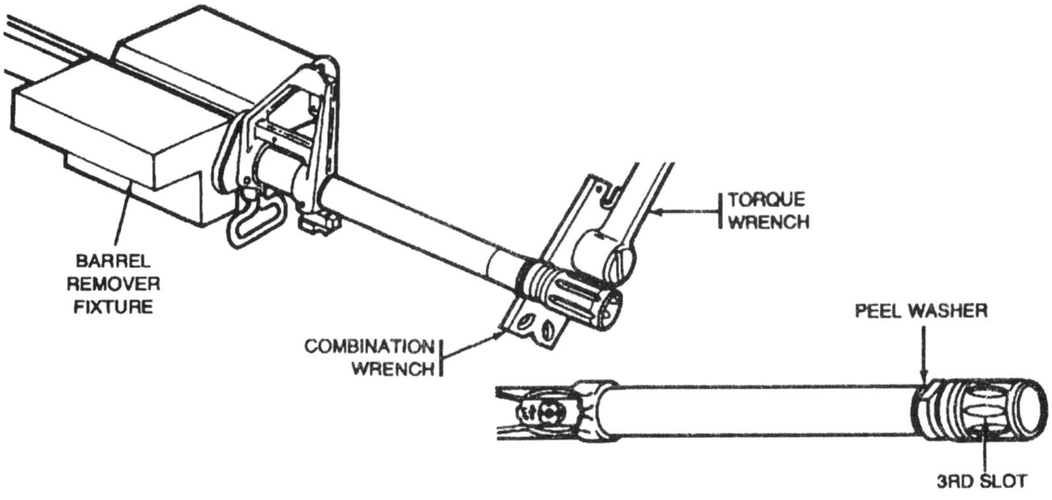

LOCATION	ITEM	ACTION	REMARKS
	d. Gas tube (87).	Install.	Slide gas tube (87) through the barrel nut assembly and then slide forward inserting gas tube into hole in the front sight assembly.

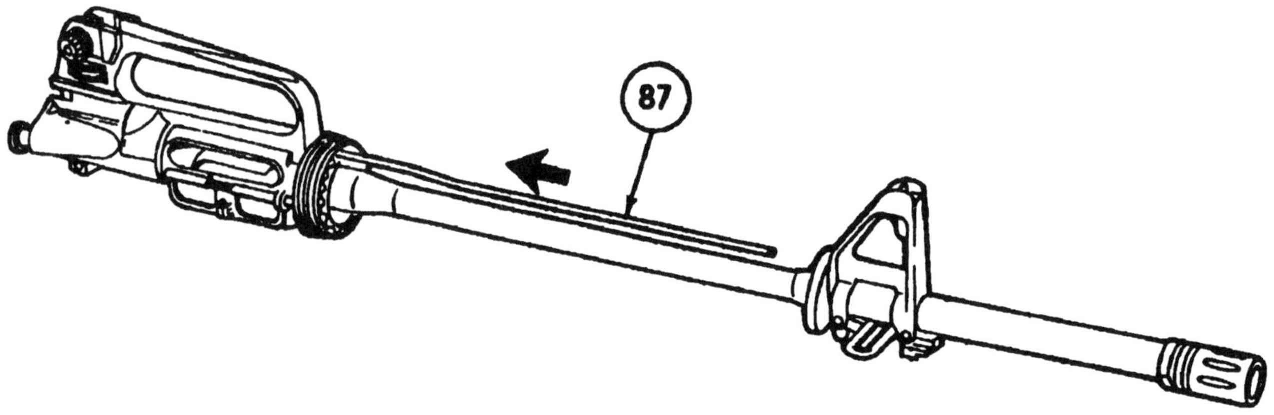

	e. Spring pin(88)	Install. Align the holes in gas tube and sight. Using ball peen hammer and 5/64-inch diameter drive pin punch, drive spring pin into front sight assembly to secure gas tube.	

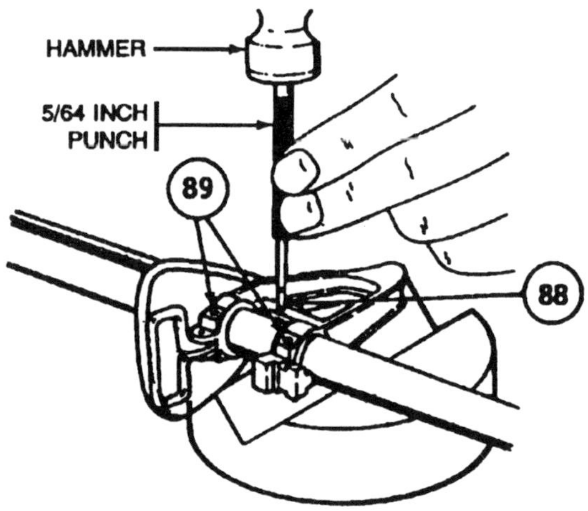

	f. Front sight pins (89)	Replace.	Replace only if one falls out. If both fall out, replace barrel assembly.

LOCATION	ITEM	ACTION	REMARKS
	g. Handguards	Install.	

TEST

Upper receiver and barrel assembly

NOTE

1. The following information pertains to the use of breech bore and other gages:

   a. All M16A2 barrels and chambers are chromed.
   b. Barrel erosion gage P/N 8448496 (normally used on M16A1 fully- chromed barrels) can be used to gage M16A2 barrels. A second reject mark (for M16A2 barrels) must be applied 5mm to the rear of the original mark.

2. The bore straightness gage, P/N 8448202, is required for use on all barrels. The gage must pass through the barrel without being forced.

LOCATION	ITEM	ACTION	REMARKS
	a. Barrel	From chrome barrel, use barrel erosion gage 8448496 and install bolt carrier and key assembly with bolt assembly and firing pin removed. Hold rifle vertical with receiver up. Insert gage into rear of key and bolt carrier assembly. The reject line must be read at the rear edge of the key and bolt carrier assembly.	If the reject mark passes beyond the rear surface of the bolt carrier assembly, the barrel is unserviceable and shall be replaced.

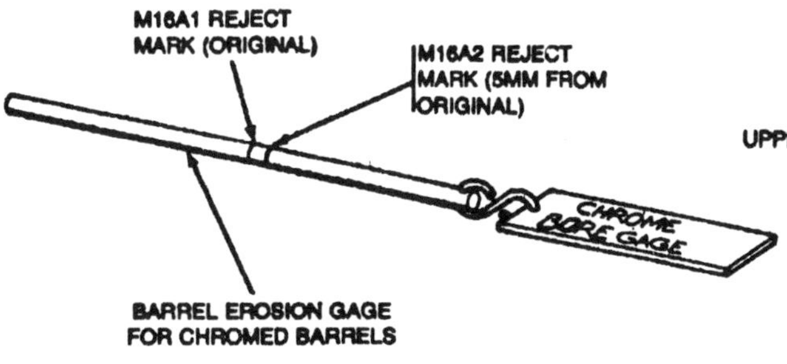

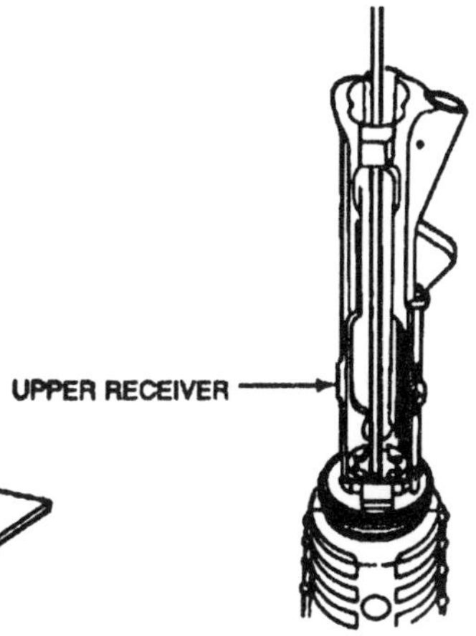

LOCATION	ITEM	ACTION	REMARKS
	b. Bore	Check straightness using straightness gage 8448202. Put gage in barrel. Tilt barrel and allow gage to fall through. Catch gage as it falls through.	Gage must pass freely through barrel. If the gage does not pass through the barrel, clean the bore with a new bore brush and repeat the test. If the barrel is defective, it must be replaced.

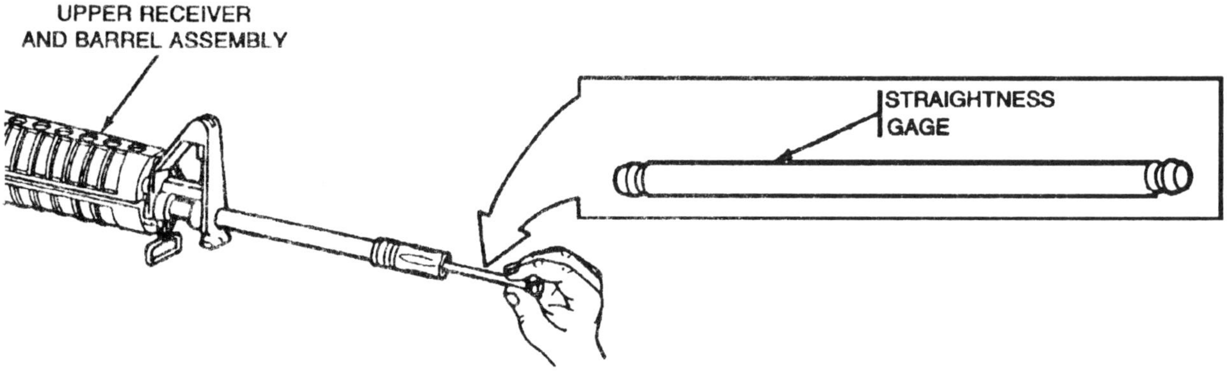

	c. Chamber	Assemble charging handle assembly, bolt assembly, and bolt carrier into upper receiver. Insert headspace gage 7799734 in chamber.	

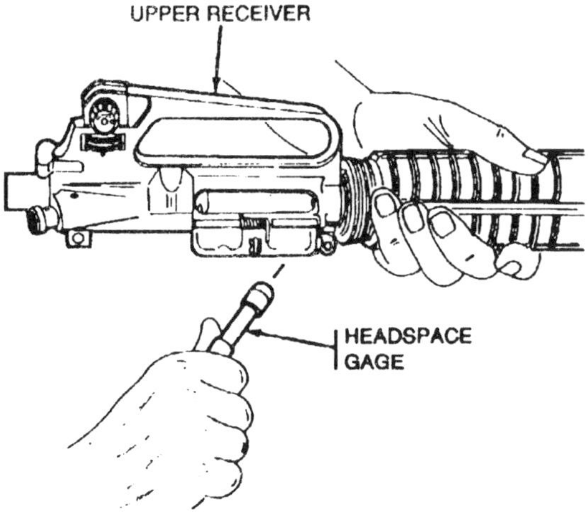

LOCATION	ITEM	ACTION	REMARKS
		Check headspace by pressing bolt carrier and bolt assembly and charging handle forward using light finger pressure.	Bolt should not rotate to locked position. Bolt carrier and bolt assembly must protrude from rear of receiver for proper headspace. If bolt carrier is flush with or indented to rear surface, this indicates excessive headspace. If excessive headspace, first replace old bolt assembly with an unused bolt assembly and then recheck. If headspace is not corrected, replace barrel assembly; then recheck with the original bolt to determine if the bolt is still good or if the bolt should be replaced also.

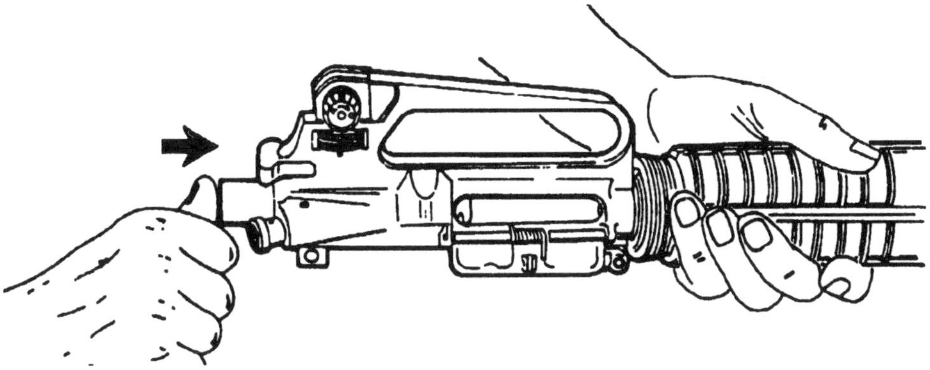

		Remove bolt carrier and bolt assembly and charging handle and headspace gage.	

NOTE

Weapons which have been rebarreled must be function-fired with nine rounds of ball ammunition. After rebarreling, the weapon must be targeted with three rounds of ball ammunition at a 25- meter range using target item 25, app D. Refer to TM 05538C-10/1 and FM 23-9.

3-13. UPPER RECEIVER ASSEMBLY AND REAR SIGHT ASSEMBLY (INTERMEDIATE).

This task covers:

a. Disassembly
b. Inspection
c. Repair
d. Lubrication
e. Reassembly

INITIAL SETUP

Tools

(MC) Small Arms Repairman Tool Kit
NSN 5180-00-357-7770/SL-3-00607A
(ARMY) Small Arms Repairman Tool Kit
SC 5180-95-CL-A07 (app B)
Field Maintenance Basic Less Power Small Arms
Shop Set SC 4933-95-CL-A11 (19204)
Permanent magnet NSN 5340-01-054-0124

Materials/Parts

Solid film lubricant (item 18, app D)
Cleaner, lubricant and preservative (CLP) (item 6, app D)

General Safety Instructions

To avoid injury to your eyes use care when removing and installing spring-loaded parts.

When using solid film lubricant or dichloromethane, be sure the area is well ventilated.

LOCATION	ITEM	ACTION	REMARKS

DISASSEMBLY

CAUTION

Be sure to catch small parts

LOCATION	ITEM	ACTION	REMARKS
Upper Receiver Assembly and Rear Sight Assembly	a. Spring pin (90)	Remove using 1/16-inch punch and hammer	Use magnet to keep from losing small parts (90, 92 and 93).
	b. Rear sight windage knob (91) helical spring (92), and bearing ball (93).	Remove.	

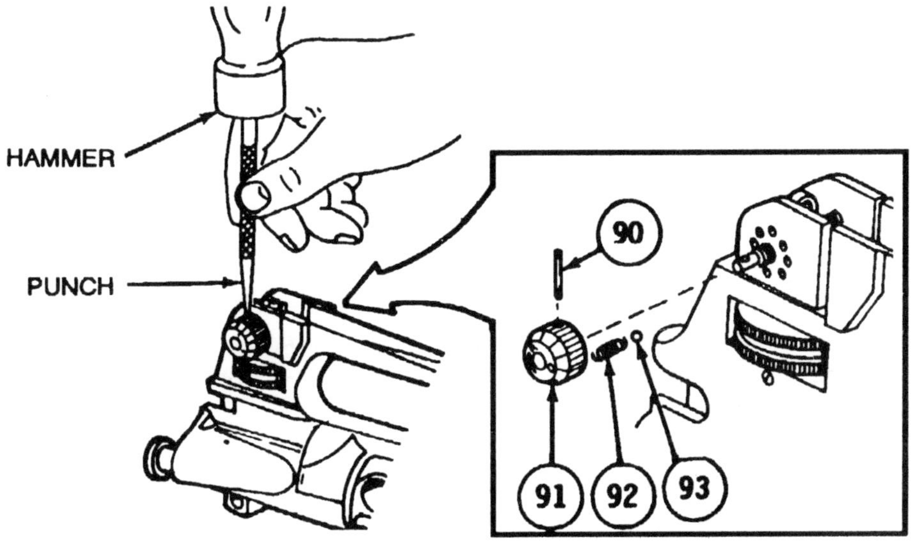

LOCATION	ITEM	ACTION	REMARKS
	c. Windage screw (96).	Remove using flat-bladed screwdriver.	
	d. Sight aperture (95) and flat spring (96).	Remove.	

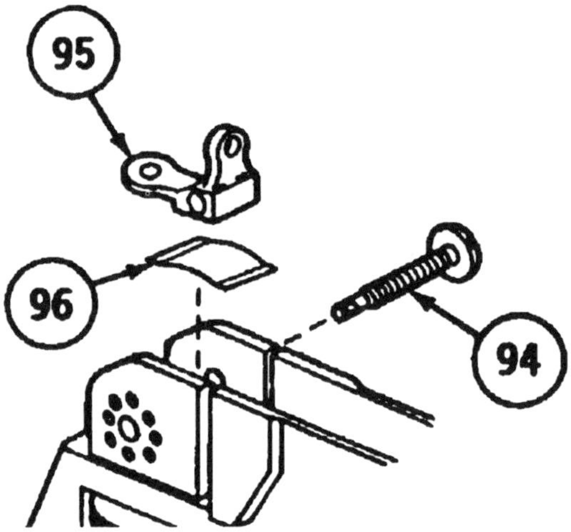

LOCATION	ITEM	ACTION	REMARKS
	e. Spring pin (97) and helical spring (98).	Drive out with 3/32 inch punch.	Catch spring when punch is withdrawn.
	f. Rear sight base (99) bearing ball (100) and helical spring (101).	Rotate elevation index (102) until sight base clears the upper receiver.	Catch bearing ball and helical spring as base clears. Use magnet.
	g. Elevation index (102) bearing ball (103) and helical spring (104).	Push elevation index out with thumb using slight rotation motion.	Catch bearing ball and helical spring as base clears. Use magnet.
	h. Index screw (105) and elevation knob (106).	Use 1/16 inch allen wrench to remove screw. Separate elevation index (102) from elevation knob by hand.	Elevation index should easily separate from base with screw removed.
	i. Spring pin (107)	Remove using 3/32-inch drive pin punch and hand hammer.	

LOCATION	ITEM	ACTION	REMARKS
	j. Forward assist assembly (108), helical spring (109), and cartridge receiver 9110).	Remove. If further disassembly is required, see page 3- 45.	

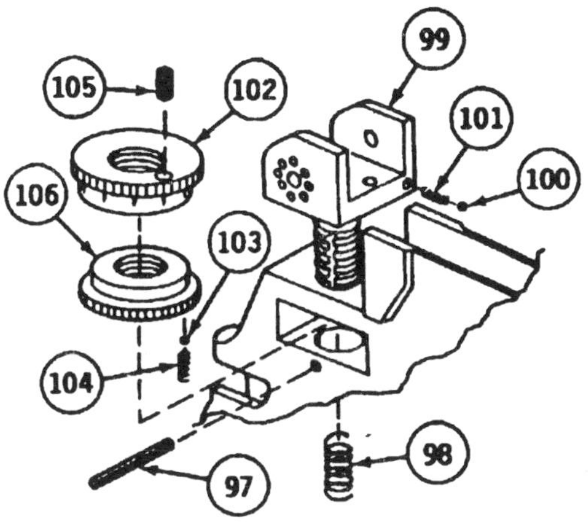

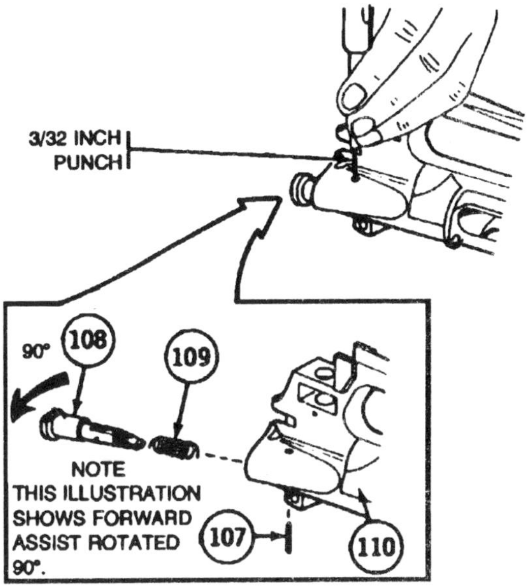

INSPECTION

LOCATION	ITEM	ACTION	REMARKS
Upper Receiver assembly and Rear Sight Assembly	a. Rear sight parts	Check for serviceability. Replace if defective.	Inside of apertures should be round and distinct.
	b. Rear sight helical springs (111) bearing balls (112), and helical (elevation) spring (113).	Check for serviceability. Replace if defective.	Make a visual inspection. Look for broken, bent, or missing springs and bearing balls. Bearing balls should be smooth and round.

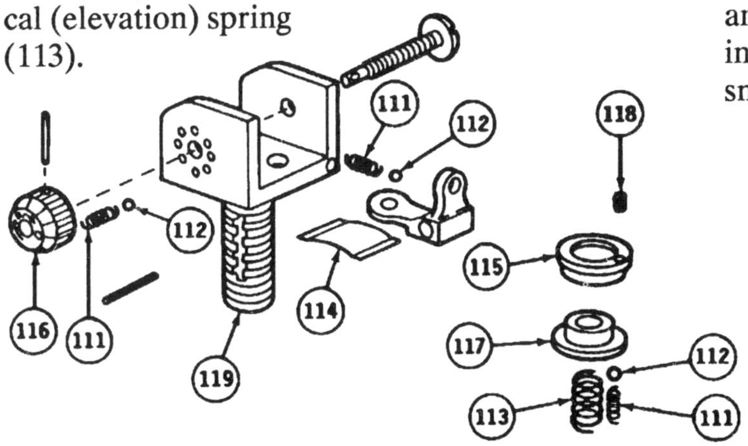

LOCATION	ITEM	ACTION	REMARKS
	c. Upper receiver	Check for cracks, corrosion, and mutilation.	Clear drain hole with a piece of wire.
		Repair or replaces if defective.	Refer to page 3-27.
	d. Flat spring (114).	Spring shall retain the sight firmly in either position.	If sight is not firm, replace spring.
	e. Elevation index (115) and windage knobs (116).	Rotate and test for ease of functioning and legibility of markings.	Underside of elevation windage knobs should be checked for cracks. Detente indexing surfaces should be well formed.
	f. Elevation knob zero (117).	Rotate elevation knob counter clockwise until the rear sight is all the way down. If a whole click is not felt as the sight stops, the sight has bottomed-out and will not pivot freely. position elevation knob back slightly to its last whole click so the rear sight base is under tension of the bearing ball and helical spring (items 111 and 112). Now, rotate the elevation knob clockwise three clicks. The 300 meter mark should align with the mark on the receiver.	If the 300 meter mark is not aligned with the mark on receiver, slip the range scale in the following manner. Position the 300 meter mark on the receiver. Insert a 1/16" Allen wrench through the access hole of the rear sight base and into the index screw (item 18 page 3-50). Loosen the index screw three turns and leave the wrench in place. Rotate the lower portion of elevation knob clockwise three clicks. Tighten index screw and remove Allen wrench. Check for proper setting as described in the ACTION column.

LOCATION	ITEM	ACTION	REMARKS
	g. Index screw (118)	Check for serviceability	Thread should not be damaged and hex recess should not be stripped.
	h. Rear sight base (119)	Check for serviceability.	Clear drain holes for each of the four springs with a piece of wire. Threaded portion of rear sight base and elevation knob should be well formed.

REPAIR

Upper Receiver Assembly and Rear Sight Assembly	a. Rear sight guards	Remove rear sight components and place carrying handle (120) in a vise (121).	Tighten vise (121) to firmly hold upper receiver (122).
		Using two eight-inch adjustable wrenches, gradually bend guard (123) to straighten.	When bending the guards (123), gradually bend beyond the straight point as the guard will partially return when bending pressure is stopped.
		After straightening, use a flat file to remove any nicks, kinks, or burrs that remain on the inside of guards (123).	
		Apply solid firm lubricant (item 18), app D) to brightened area for final protective coating.	

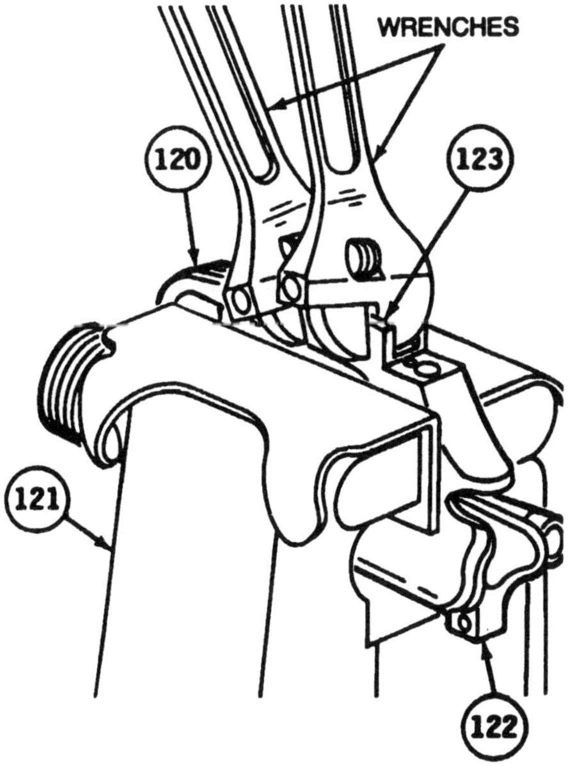

LOCATION	ITEM	ACTION	REMARKS
		Replace rear sight components and check that sight functions properly.	If sight functions check out, return upper receiver to service.

LUBRICATION

LOCATION	ITEM	ACTION	REMARKS
Upper Receiver Assembly and Rear Sight Assembly		Lubricate	Apply CLP (item 6, app D) to springs and bearing balls (three each) and threaded screw portions before installation. Lubricate springs and bearing balls through their respective drain holes.

REASSEMBLY

LOCATION	ITEM	ACTION	REMARKS
Upper Receiver Assembly and Rear Sight Assembly	a. Helical spring (124) and forward assist assembly (125)	Install upper cartridge receiver (126).	Apply CLP (item 6, app D) to helical spring, plunger assembly, pawl detent, and spring pin.
	b. Spring pin (127)	Install using 3/32-inch drive pin punch and hand hammer.	

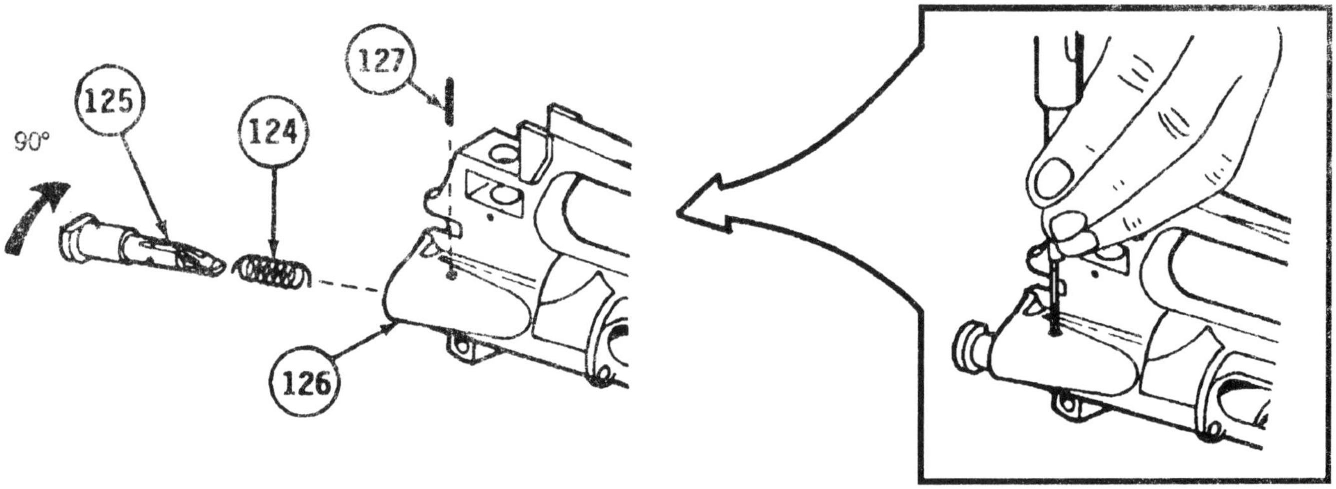

LOCATION	ITEM	ACTION	REMARKS
	c. Elevation knob (128) elevation index (129) and index screw (130).	Assemble using 1/16-inch allen wrench.	Do not overtighten index screw as scale will require adjustment.
	d. Bearing ball (131) and helical spring (132)	Install with needle-nose pliers or tweezers. Slide in elevation knob assembly.	Depress bearing ball with a punch inserted through access hole as elevation knob is pushed in from side. Center elevation knob in upper receiver.

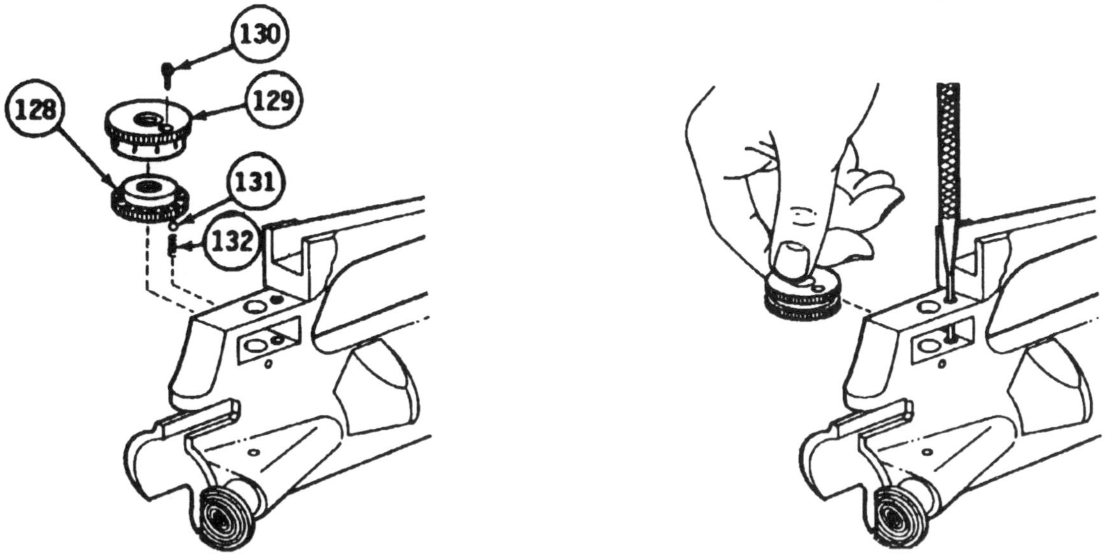

NOTE

All springs are identical when new. Once disassembled from the rifle, their free length may vary due to different amounts of compression when installed. If the length of springs varies, use longest spring as # 134, the next longest as # 141, and the shortest as # 132.

WARNING

To avoid injury to your eyes, use care when removing and installing spring-loaded parts.

LOCATION	ITEM	ACTION	REMARKS
	e. Rear sight base (133), helical spring (134), bearing ball (135), helical spring (136), and spring pin (137).	Insert threaded portion of rear sight base into receiver and rotate elevation knob assembly until threads engage. Insert helical spring (134) and bearing ball (135) in their hole as base is lowered into receiver as elevation knob is further rotated.	Rotate elevation knob until sight base is all the way down. Then come up 22 clicks before installing spring pin. Check spring action of helical spring (134) on upper receiver.
		Insert helical spring (136) through underside of receiver. Install spring pin (137) while helical spring is held compressed.	As spring pin is installed, spring must be held compressed with a small tip screwdriver. Pin must pass over spring, not through its coils. Rotate elevation knob until rear sight base is all the way down.

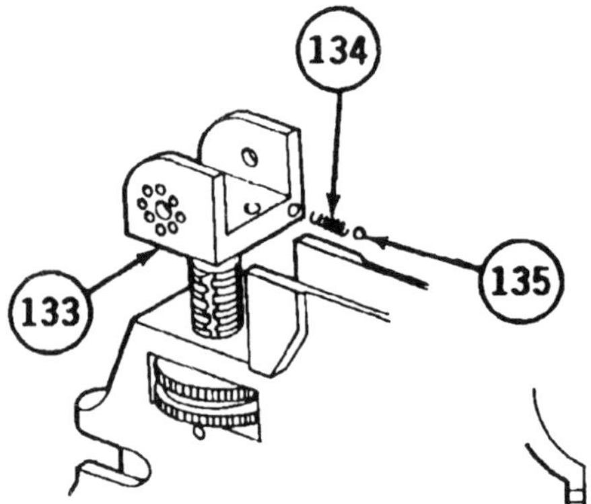

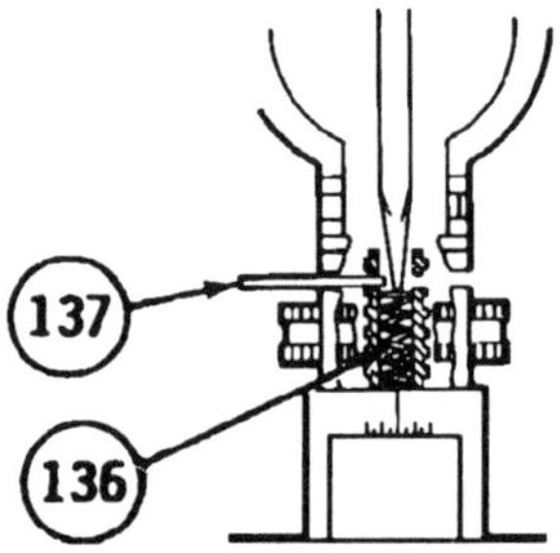

LOCATION	ITEM	ACTION	REMARKS
	f. Flat spring (138), sight aperture (139), and windage screw (140).	Install spring and aperture in rear sight base. Install screw with screwdriver.	
	g. Helical spring (141), bearing ball detent (142), windage knob (143), an spring pin (144).	Insert spring and bearing ball detent in windage knob. position windage knob assembly on shaft of windage screw. Install pin.	Tilt receiver toward windage knob during positioning to prevent loss of bearing ball.

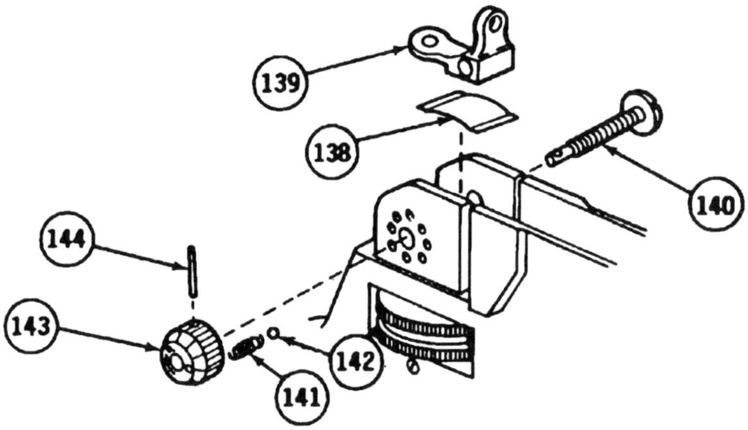

NOTE: Refer to upper receiver & rear sight assembly **INSPECTION**, item f., to check elevation knob zero.

3-14. FORWARD ASSIST ASSEMBLY (INTERMEDIATE).

This task covers:

a. Disassembly
b. Inspection
c. Repair
d. Reassembly

INITIAL SETUP

Tools

(MC) Small Arms Repairman Tool Kit
NSN 5180-00-357-7770/SL-3-00607A
(ARMY) Small Arms Repairman Tool Kit
SC 5180-95-CL-A07 (app B)
Field Maintenance Basic Less Power Small Arms
Shop Set SC 4933-95-CL-A11 (19204)

Materials/Parts

CLeaner, lubricant and preservative (CLP) (item 6, app D)

General Safety Instructions

To avoid injury to your eyes use care when removing and installing spring-loaded parts.

LOCATION	ITEM	ACTION	REMARKS
DISASSEMBLY			
Forward Assist Assembly	a. Spring pin (1450.	Remove using 1/16-inch drive pin punch and hard hammer.	
	b. Forward assist pawl (146), pawl detent (147), helical spring (148), and plunger assembly (149)	Remove.	

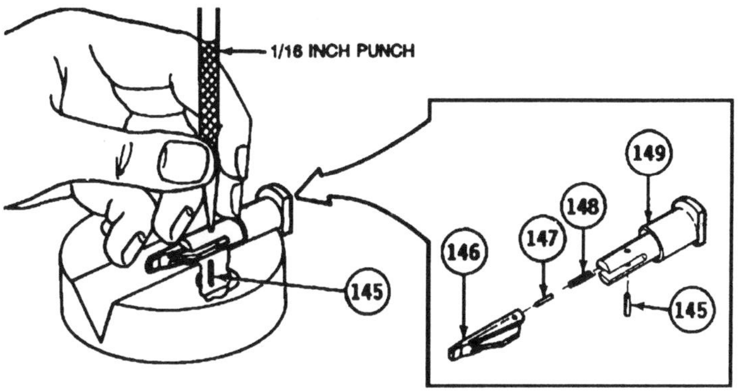

LOCATION	ITEM	ACTION	REMARKS
INSPECTION			
Forward Assist Assembly	a. Forward assist pawl	Inspect for burrs, chips, and cracks.	Minor burrs may may be removed using fine files or stones, as required. Replace if defective.
	b. Pawl detent	Inspect for burrs and cracks.	Minor burrs may be removed using fine files or stones, as required. Replace if defective.
	c. Helical spring	Inspect for kinks, breaks, and wear.	Replace if defective.
	d. Plunger assembly	Inspect for wear, burrs, chips, and breaks.	Minor burrs may be removed using fine files or stones, as required. Replace if defective.
REPAIR			
Forward Assist Assembly	a. Forward assist pawl	Using fine files or stones, as required, smooth burrs but do not deform forward assist pawl.	
	b. Pawl detent	Using fine files or stones, as required, smooth burrs but do not deform pawl detent.	
	c. Plunger assembly	Using fine files or stones, as required, smooth burrs but do not deform plunger assembly.	

LOCATION	ITEM	ACTION	REMARKS
REASSEMBLY			

WARNING

To avoid injury to your eyes, use care when removing and installing spring-loaded parts.

LOCATION	ITEM	ACTION	REMARKS
Forward Assist Assembly		Lubricate.	Apply CLP (item 6, app D) to forward assist pawl, pawl detent, and helical spring before installation.
	a. Helical spring (148), plunger assembly (149), pawl detent (147), and forward assist pawl (146)	Install.	
	b. Spring pin (1450).	Install using 1/16-inch drive pin punch and hand hammer. Pin must be flush or slightly below flush after reassembly.	

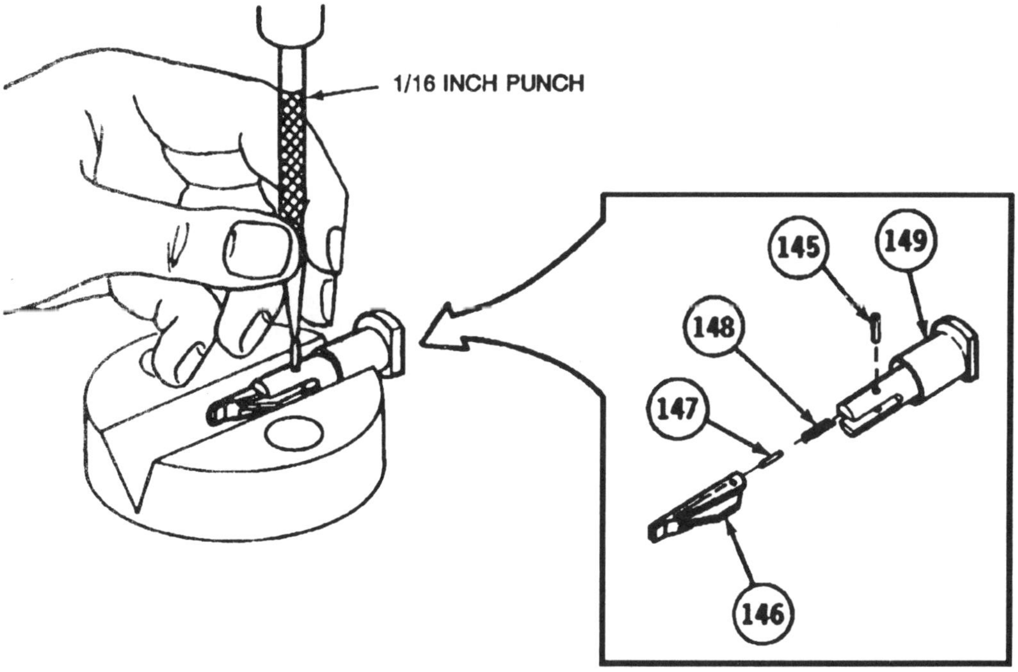

3-15. LOWER RECEIVER AND BUTTSTOCK ASSEMBLY (INTERMEDIATE).

This task covers:
a. Disassembly
b. Inspection
c. Repair
d. Test
e. Reassembly

INITIAL SETUP

Tools
(MC) Small Arms Repairman Tool Kit
NSN 5180-00-357-7770/SL-3-00607A
Tool and Gage Set, Infantry Weapons, M16A2
NSN 4933-00-056-7106/PN 8426685/SL-3-06229A
(ARMY) Small Arms Repairman Tool Kit
SC 5280-95-CL-A07 (app B)
Field Maintenance Basic Less Power Small Arms
Shop Set SC 4933-95-CL-A11 (19204)
Pivot pin removing tool (E-3, app E)
Lower receiver gage (E-5, app E)
Modified old trigger "slave" pin (E-7, app E)

Materials/Parts
Solid film lubricant (item 18, app D)
Technical dichloromethane (item 12, app D)
Cleaner, lubricant and preservative (CLP) (item 6, app D)

References
TM 9-1005-301-30

General Safety Instructions
To avoid injury t your eyes use care when removing and installing spring-loaded parts.
When using solid film lubricant or dichloromethane, be sure the area is well ventilated.

LOCATION	ITEM	ACTION	REMARKS
DISASSEMBLY			
Lower receiver and Buttstock Assembly	a. Machine screw (150), and lock washer (151).	Using screwdriver, reach inside rifle grip and remove screw and lock washer.	

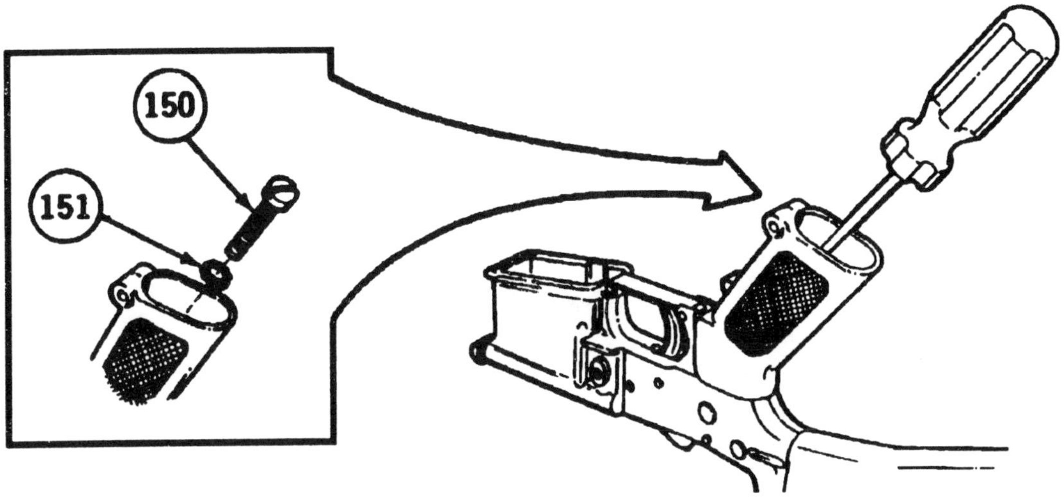

LOCATION	ITEM	ACTION	REMARKS
	b. Rifle grip (152), helical spring (153), and safety detent (154).	Carefully remove rifle grip and catch helical spring and safety detent to prevent loss.	

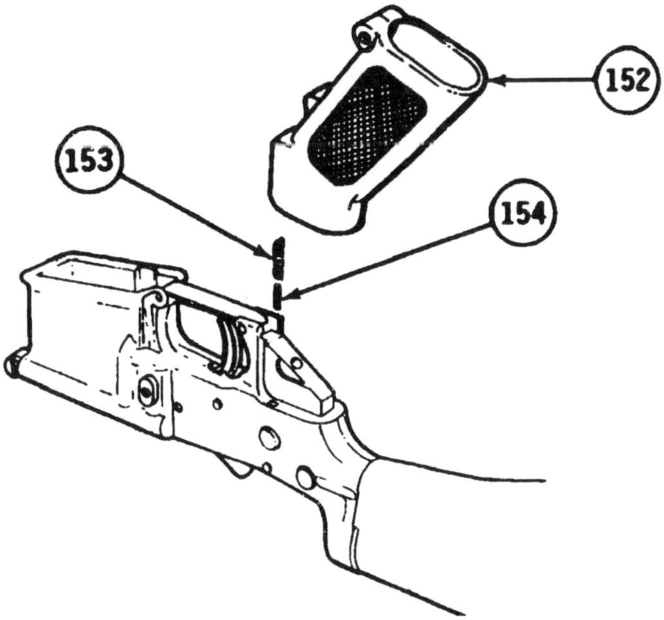

LOCATION	ITEM	ACTION	REMARKS
	c. Self-locking screw (155)	Remove.	

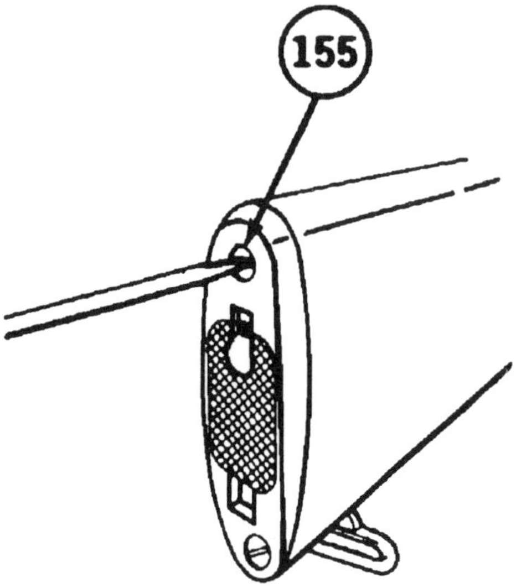

LOCATION	ITEM	ACTION	REMARKS
	d. Buttstock assembly (156), stepped spacer (157), helical spring (158), takedown pin detent (159), and takedown pin (160)	Remove stock carefully and use magnet to hold small parts. Catch helical spring, detent, and takedown pin to prevent loss.	

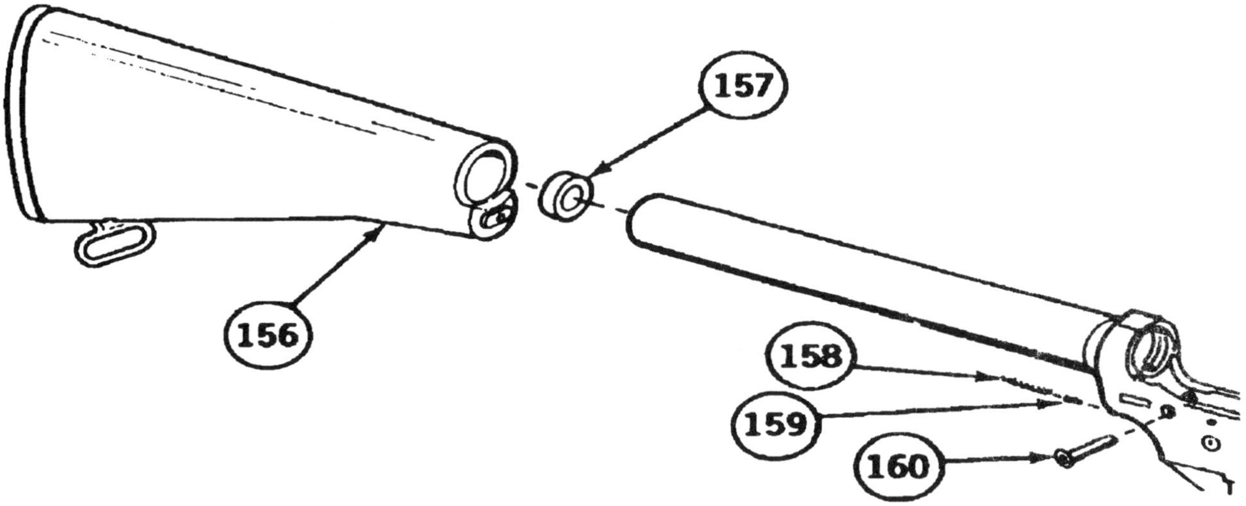

LOCATION	ITEM	ACTION	REMARKS
	e. Pivot pin (161)	Insert fabricated tool (E-3, app E) to compress detent. Turn pin a quarter turn. Remove tool and pin.	

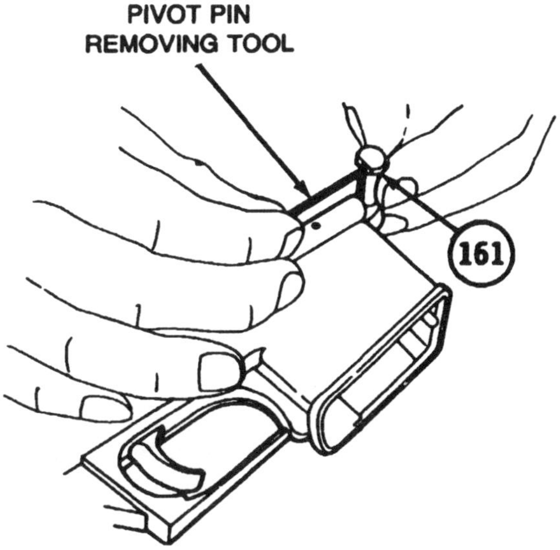

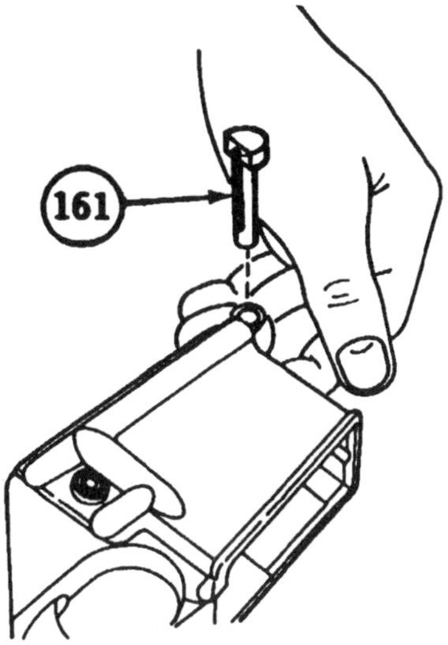

LOCATION	ITEM	ACTION	REMARKS
	f. Takedown pin detent (162) and helical spring (163).	Be sure to hold cupped hand in front of detent and helical spring to prevent loss of detent and spring as pivot pin is removed.	

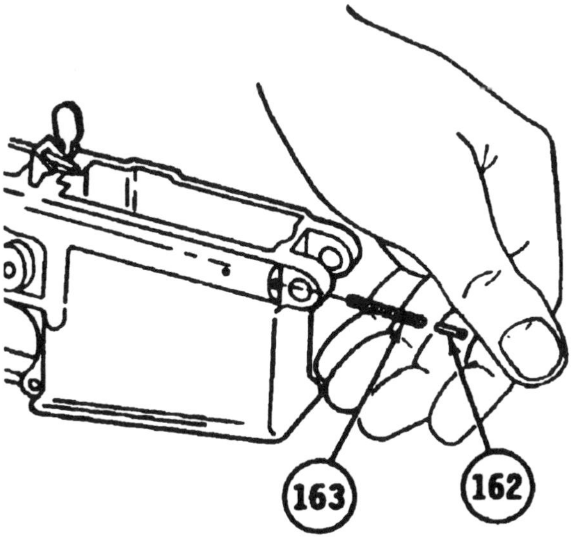

LOCATION	ITEM	ACTION	REMARKS
	g. Buffer assembly (164) and action spring (165).	Press buffer assembly in. Using screwdriver, depress buffer retainer and release buffer and action spring.	

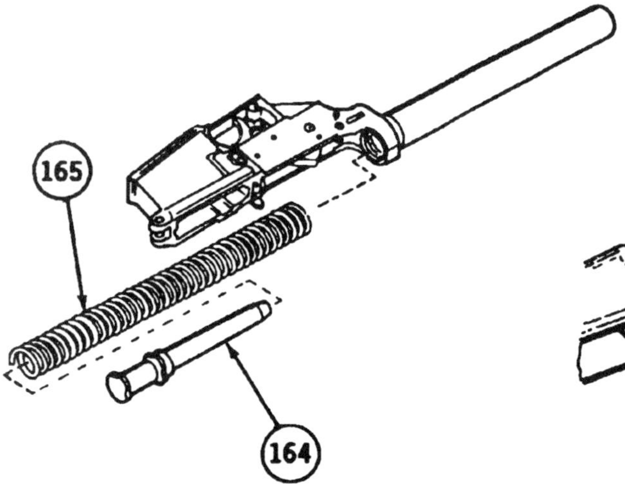

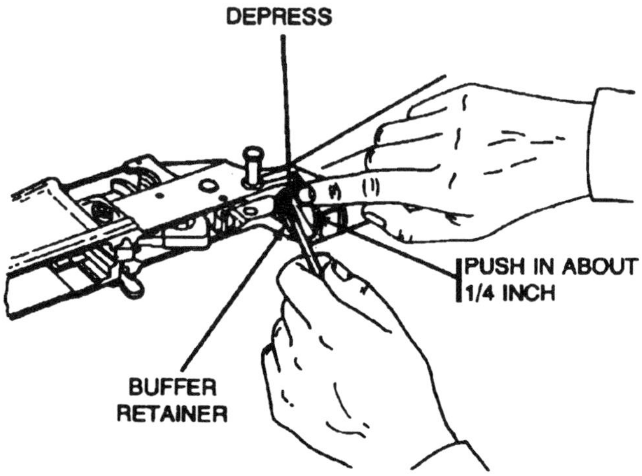

LOCATION	ITEM	ACTION	REMARKS
	h. Spring pin (166)	Remove using 3/32-inch drive pin punch and hand hammer.	
	i. Bolt catch (167), bolt catch plunger (168), and helical spring (169).	Remove.	

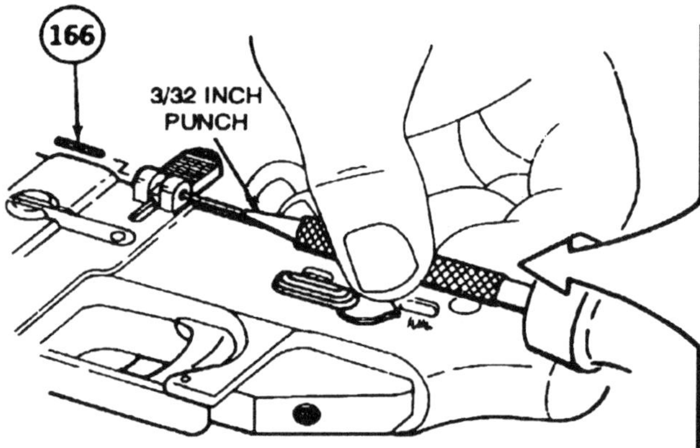

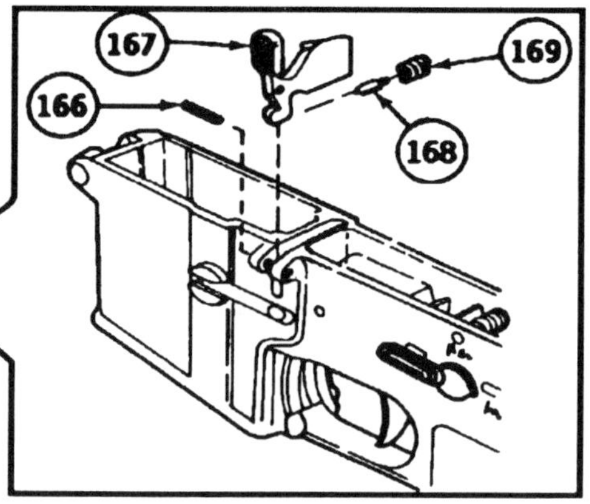

LOCATION	ITEM	ACTION	REMARKS
	j. Magazine catch (170).	Remove. Using drive pin punch, press in on magazine button (171) and turn magazine catch counterclockwise to unscrew.	
	k. Magazine button (171) and helical spring (172).	Remove.	

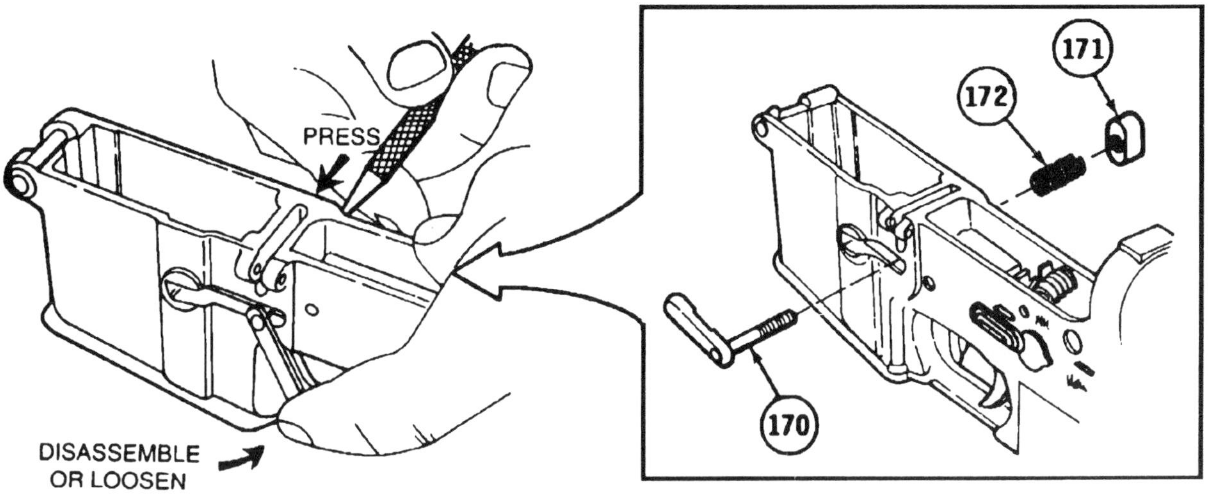

LOCATION	ITEM	ACTION	REMARKS
	l. Automatic sear pin (173).	Remove. Using rounded tip drive pin punch, push automatic sear pin out of receiver.	To remove sear, safety selector lever must be positioned to burst (if installed).
	m. Sear (174) and selector lever (175).	Remove.	

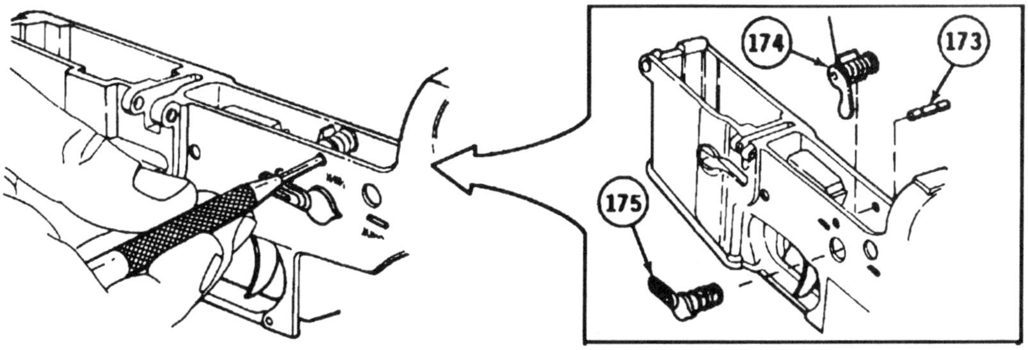

LOCATION	ITEM	ACTION	REMARKS
	n. Hammer pin (176)	Remove. Using drive pin punch, push pin from receiver.	To remove (hammer should be forward), place safety selector lever (if installed) in SEMI position.
	o. Hammer assembly (177).	Remove. If further disassembly is required see paragraph 3-17	Hammer pin should offer resistance as it is removed. See page 3-14, step 16.

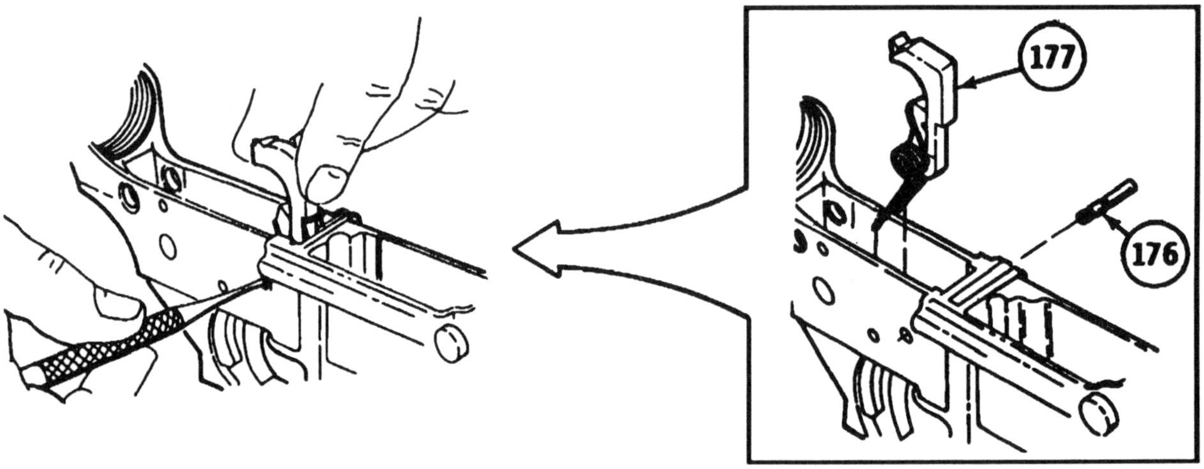

LOCATION	ITEM	ACTION	REMARKS
	p. Trigger pin (178).	Remove. Using "slave" pin (E-7, app E) and drive pin punch, push out left side of receiver.	"Slave" pin will allow removal of these parts as a unit.
	q. Semiautomatic disconnector (179), burst disconnector (180), trigger assembly (181), and lower receiver and extension assembly (182).	Remove. If further disassembly is required, see paragraph 3-18.	

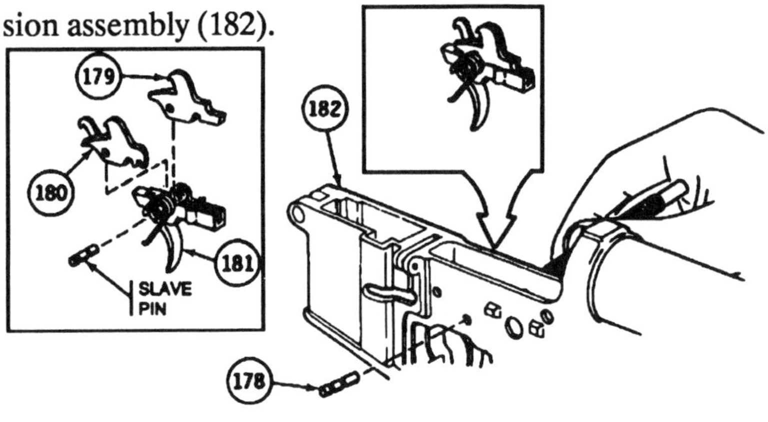

LOCATION	ITEM	ACTION	REMARKS
INSPECTION			
Lower Receiver and Buttstock Assembly	a. All parts	Inspect for cracks, corrosion, and mutilation which would affect functioning.	Small dents and gouges will not be cause for rejection.
	b. All parts	Inspect for damage	
	c. Buffer assembly	The buffer assembly must not be cracked between hole and end of housing.	New buffers do not have hole in housing and are not likely to crack.

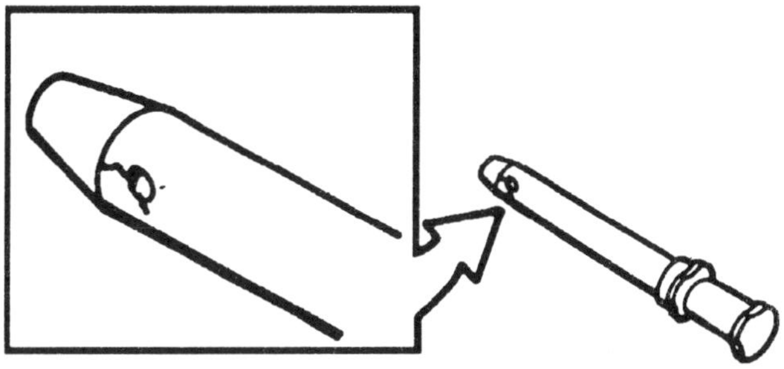

	d. Helical spring	The free length of the helical spring must be between 11 3/4 minimum and 13 1/2 maximum inches.	

NOTE

M16A2 Buttstocks, PN9349121, with unauthorized markings, may be used during Direct Support repair under the following conditions:

a. Buttstocks with unauthorized markings that have been stamped into the surface of the buttstock will not be used.

b. Unauthorized markings that have been scratched, etched, carved, etc, are acceptable if the marks do not extend into the fiber of the buttstock. Cutting into the fiber of the buttstock may weaken it.

c. These marks may be at any location on the buttstock. Unauthorized markings are not desirable, however, they will be allowed during repair due to the cost of the buttstock.

LOCATION	ITEM	ACTION	REMARKS
	e. Stock assembly	Inspect for breaks and separation of material which could prevent proper functioning of weapon.	Cracks or breaks in critical areas will be repaired or rejected. For stock repair, see TM 9-1005-301-30.
		Inspect for dents, cracks, and chips.	Cracks in other than critical areas, not exceeding three inches in length and 1/16 inch in width, may be repaired. Buttstock shall be free of rough surfaces, sharp edges, chips, or cracks, except as follows: Under the following conditions, hairline cracks (no chipped away material allowed) originating from the buttplate end of the buttstock are acceptable without repair. a. One hairline crack, not to exceed 1" in length per side of buttstock. b. Two additional hairline cracks up to .22" in length, per side of buttstock.

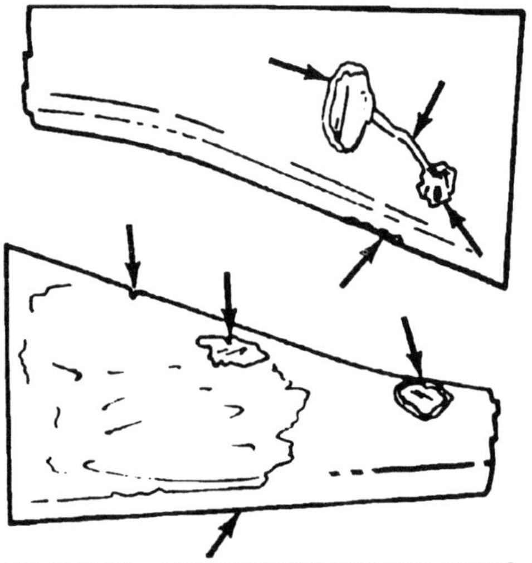

BUTTSTOCK - REPARABLE DAMAGED AREAS

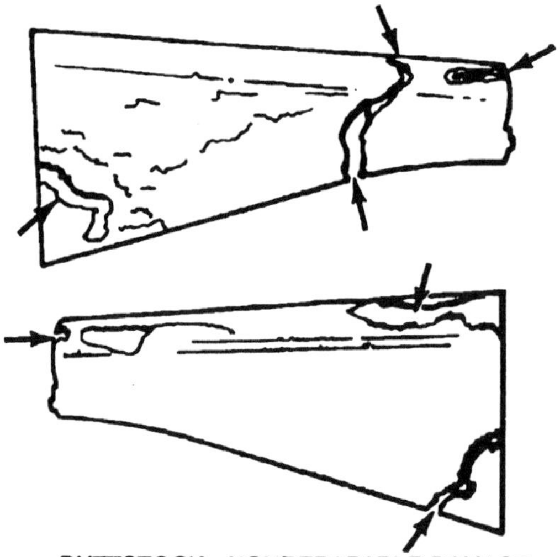

BUTTSTOCK - NONREPARABLE DAMAGE

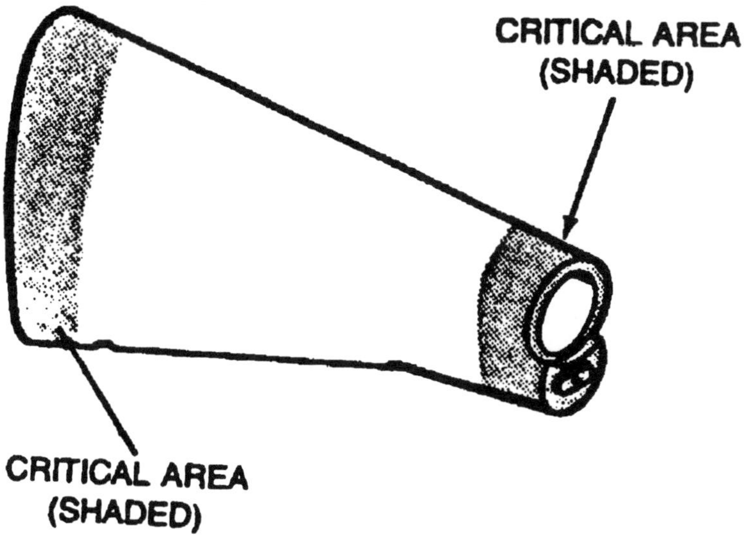

c. A total of three cracks per side of the buttstock, originating from the buttplate end, are allowable without repair. Buttstocks with cracks originating from the buttplate end of the buttstock; but not meeting above criteria, may be repaired if the cracks are not longer than 2 1/2" in length and if width of unfilled crack is not greater than .125". No more than two cracks may be filled on each side of the buttstock. In addition to these repaired cracks, two hairline cracks up to .22" in length are allowed per side of the buttstock

Cracks in the moldmark (seam) area at the top of buttstock, originating from the buttplate end, will be included in the above criteria.

Cracks in the front end of the buttstock are not acceptable. Buttstocks with cracks in this area must be replaced.

WARNING

When using solid lubricant (item 18, app D) or dichloromethane (item 12, app D), be sure the area is well ventilated.

Apply solid film lubricant (item 18, app D) to shiny surfaces.

LOCATION	ITEM	ACTION	REMARKS
	f. Lower receiver and buttstock assembly	Inspect for corrosion in the lower receiver lobes of the pivot area or hinge pin area.	
		If extensive corrosion appears in these areas, the receiver will not be repaired and rifle will be turned in for replacement.	Refer to paragraph 3-12 for repair for repair of corroded surfaces.

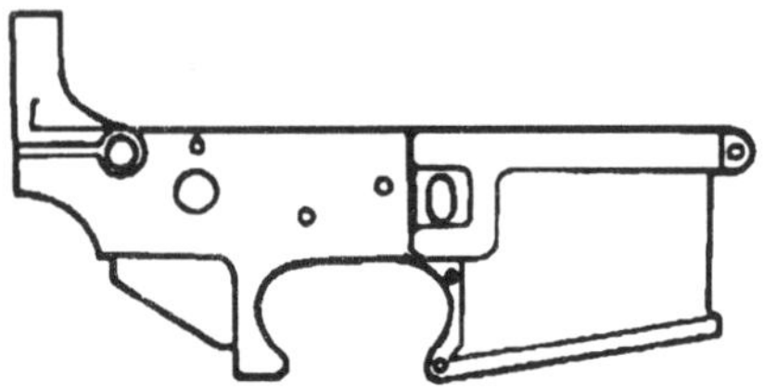

SHINY SURFACES
(REPARABLE)

SHINY SURFACES
(REPARABLE)

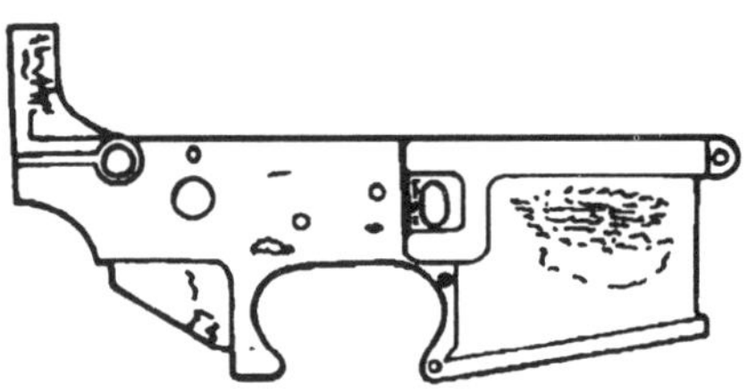

CORRODED AND NO HOLES
(REPARABLE)

CORRODED
(REPARABLE)

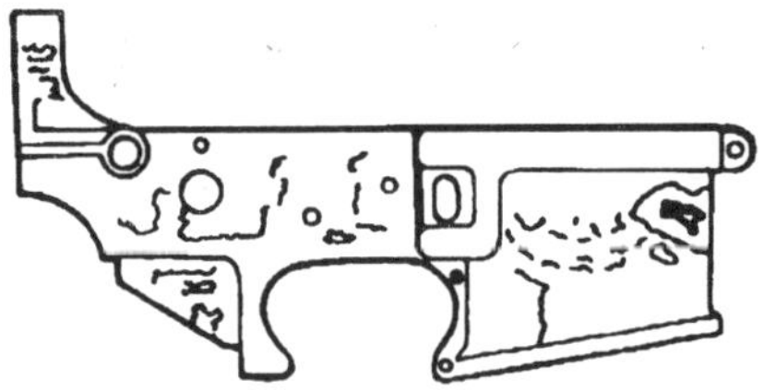

CORRODED WITH HOLE
(NONREPARABLE)

CORRODED LOBES - WEAKENING
PIVOT PIN AREA
(NONREPARABLE)

LOCATION	ITEM	ACTION	REMARKS

SHINY SURFACES
(REPARABLE)

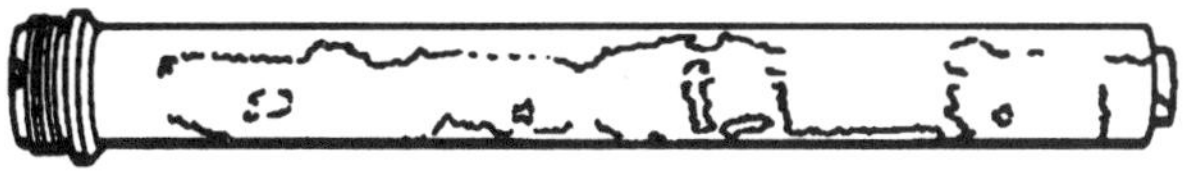

CORRODED
(REPARABLE)

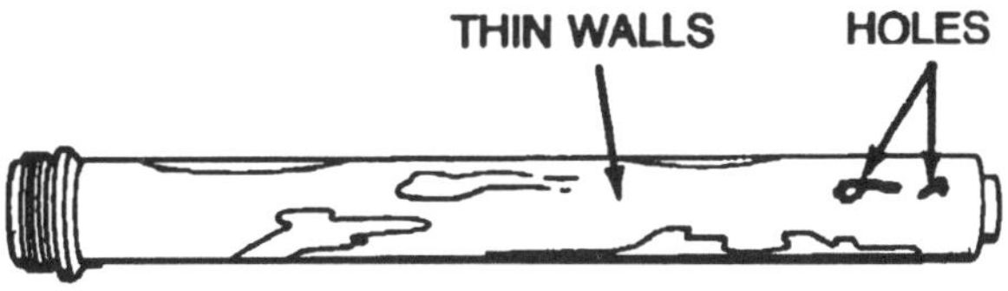

HOLES AND THIN WALLS

REPAIR

LOCATION	ITEM	ACTION	REMARKS
Lower Receiver and Buttstock Assembly	All parts	Repair or replace if defective.	For stock repair, see TM 9-1005-301-30.

TEST

LOCATION	ITEM	ACTION	REMARKS
Weapon	Lower receiver and buttstock assembly	(MC ONLY) Test lower receiver pivot pin lug clearance using fabricated lower receiver go-no go gage (E-5, app E).	Do not force gage to fit between pivot pin lugs.

If lower receiver go-no go gage E-5, app E) enters far enough to pass or cover the entire pivot hole, the rifle is unserviceable and will be turned in for replacement.

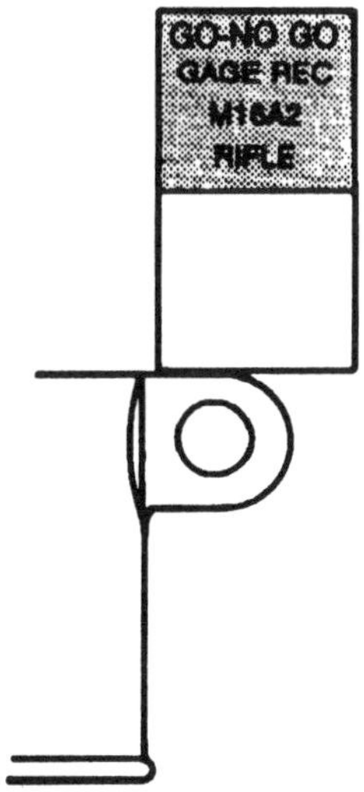

SERVICEABLE

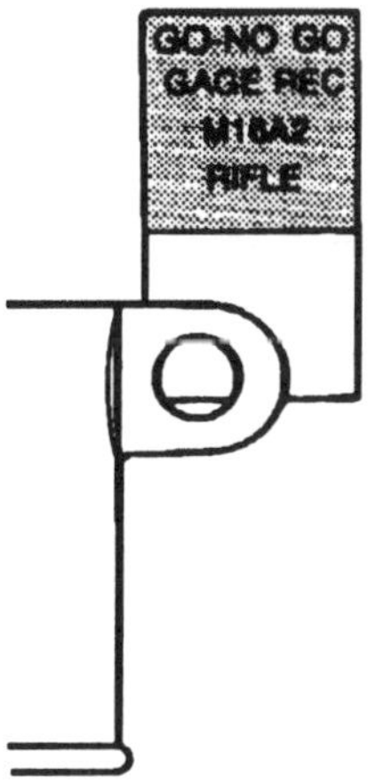

SERVICEABLE

If lower receiver go-no go gage (E-5, appE) does not enter or enters but does not pass or cover the entire pivot pin hole, receiver is still service.

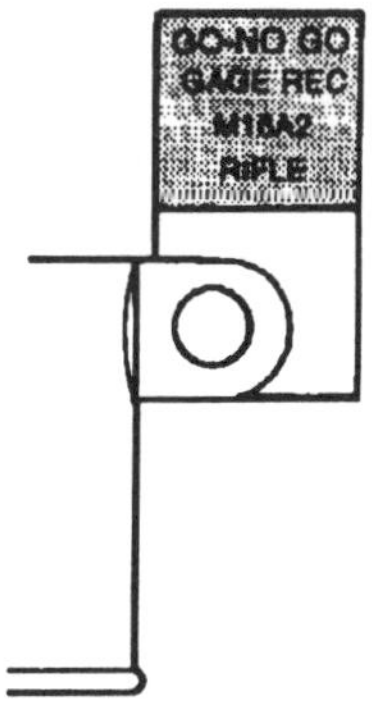

UNSERVICEABLE

LOCATION	ITEM	ACTION	REMARKS
		(ARMY ONLY) Delete this test. Test two hammer pin holes and two trigger pin holes using no-go plug gage 12006472. This test may be conducted by disassembly of the lower receiver (paragraph 3-15) or by pushing the pin far enough to disengage the end of the pin from the side of the receiver which is being tested.	Visually inspect the lower receiver before beginning this test. It is not necessary to disassemble the lower receiver for the sole purpose of this visual inspection. If broken or damaged parts are found, disassemble and repair as authorized.
		If the lower receiver is not disassembled and the no-go plug gage enters any hole to first shoulder (A) the lower receiver must be disassembled and all four holes must be tested again.	
		Gently insert the no-go plug gage and rotate it 180 degrees. If the no-go plug gage passes through any one of the four pin holes, the rifle is unserviceable and will be turned in for replacement. The gage must extend through the wall thickness to be unserviceable.	

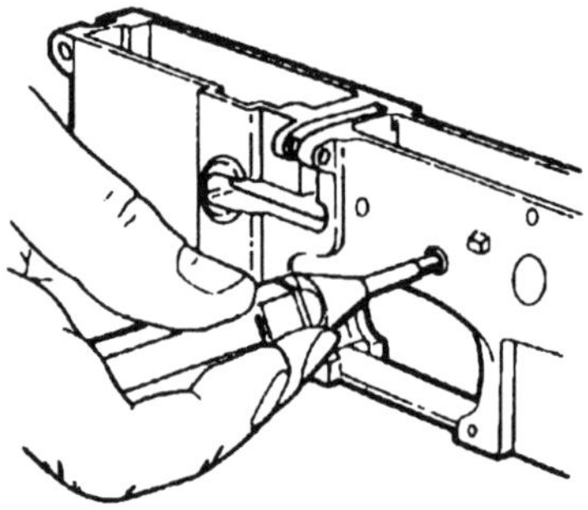

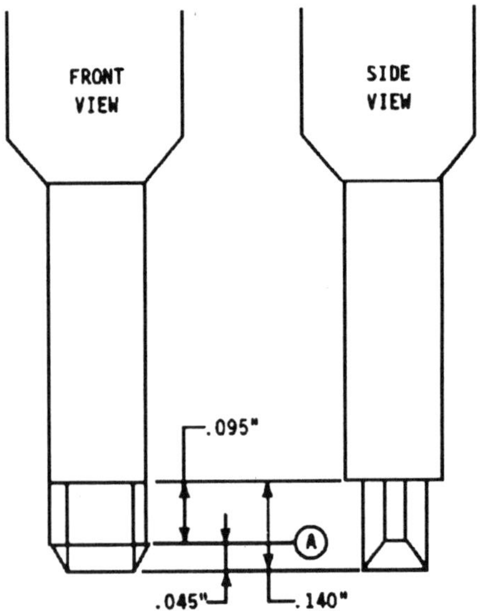

LOCATION	ITEM	ACTION	REMARKS

REASSEMBLY

WARNING

When using solid film lubricant (item 18, app D) or technical dichloromethane (item 12, app D), be sure the area is well ventilated.

NOTE

Before reassembling parts, clean them with technical dichloromethane (item 12, app D),

LOCATION	ITEM	ACTION	REMARKS
Lower Receiver and Buttstock Assembly	a. Lower receiver and extension assembly (183), trigger assembly (184), semiautomatic disconnector (185), and burst disconnector (186).	Install.	Assemble as a unit using "slave" pin. Install in receiver using trigger pin to push out slave pin.
	b. Trigger pin (187)	Install using drive pin punch. Push in until flush.	

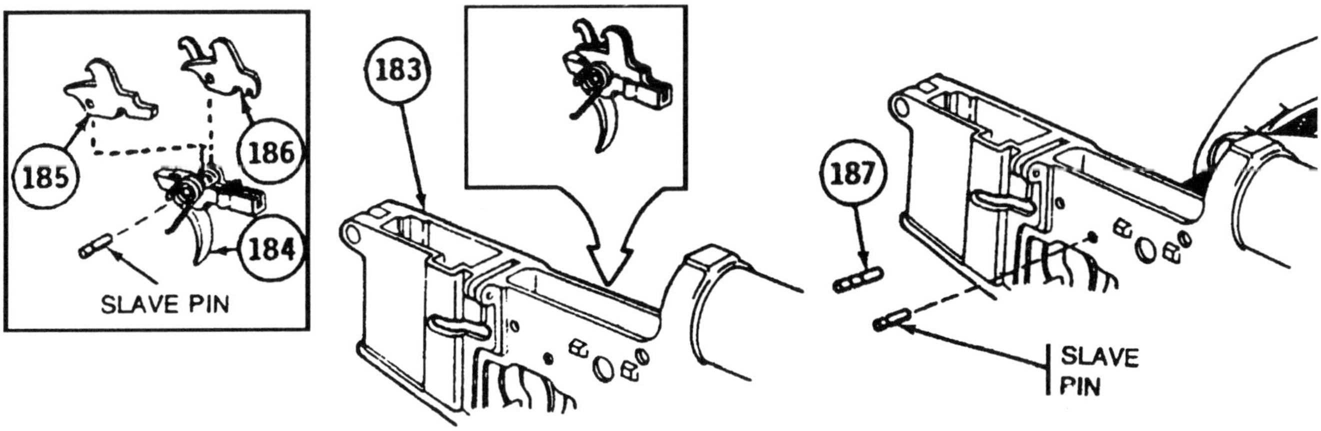

LOCATION	ITEM	ACTION	REMARKS
	c. Hammer assembly (188).	Install.	
	d. Hammer pin (189)	Install using drive pin punch. Push in until flush.	Ends of hammer spring to be installed to rear of hammer pin (189), resting in the annular groove on upper surface of trigger pin.

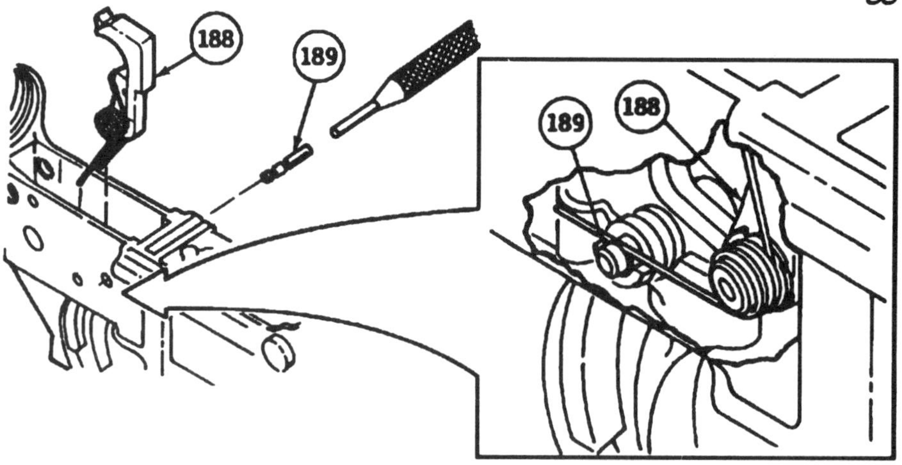

NOTE

Hammer should be cocked prior to installing the selector lever.

LOCATION	ITEM	ACTION	REMARKS
	e. Selector lever (190) and sear (191).	Install.	Selector, if installed, must be positioned to burst. Long leg of spring must rest on top of selector.
	f. Automatic sear pin (192).	Install automatic sear pin into receiver using drive pin punch. Push flush.	

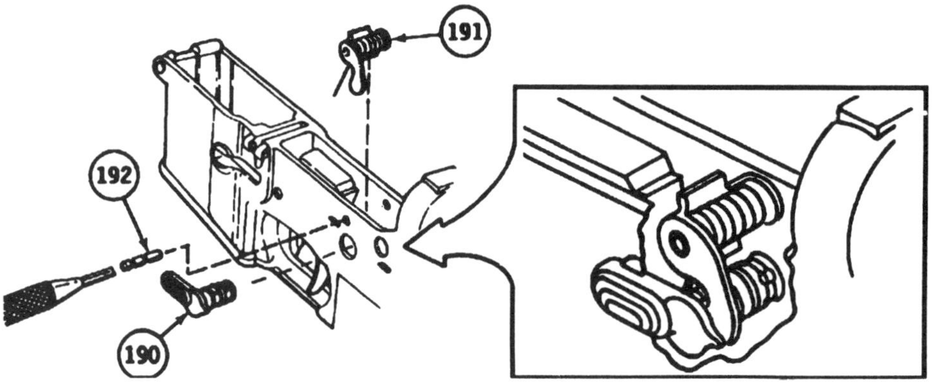

LOCATION	ITEM	ACTION	REMARKS
	g. Helical spring (193)	Install.	
	h. Magazine button (194)	Install.	
	i. Magazine catch (195)	Install. Using drive pin punch, push in and turn magazine catch (195) clockwise until end of catch is flush with magazine button head.	Pin punch should be larger than hole in magazine button.

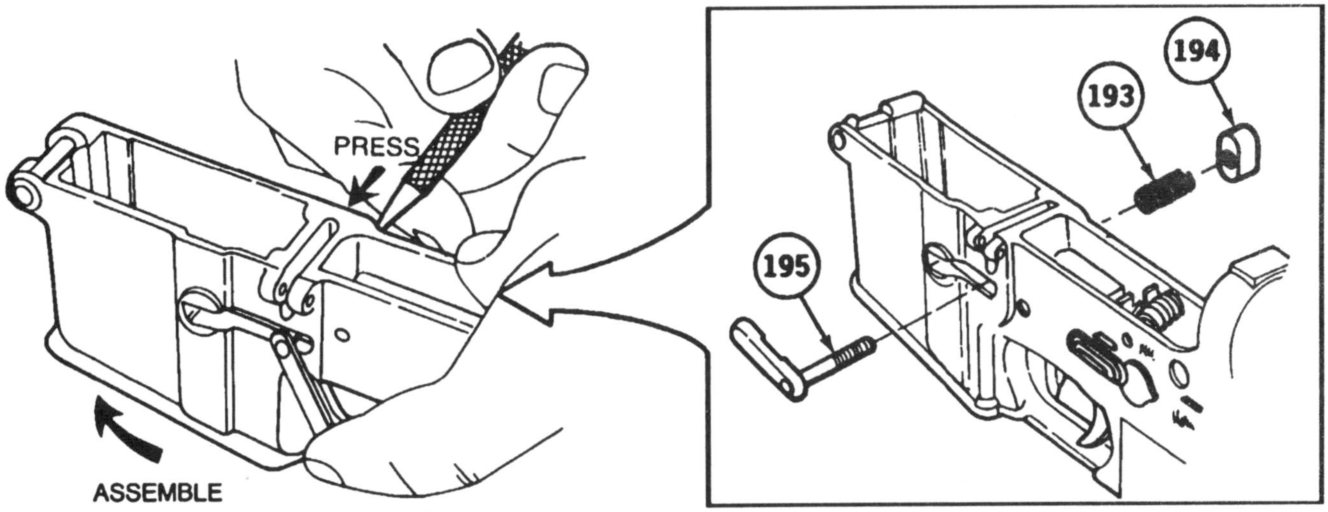

LOCATION	ITEM	ACTION	REMARKS
	j. Helical spring (196), bolt catch plunger (197), and bolt catch (198).	Install.	
	k. Spring pin (199)	Install using 3/32-inch drive pin punch and hand hammer.	

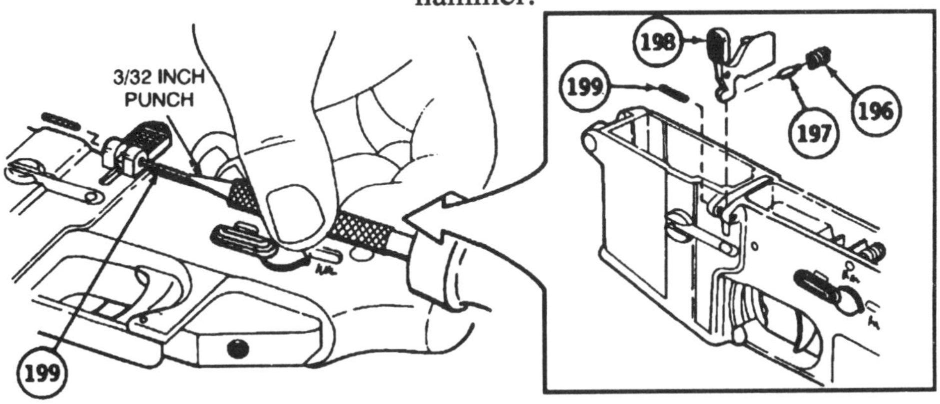

LOCATION	ITEM	ACTION	REMARKS
	l. Action spring (200) and buffer assembly (201).	Press in until retainer snaps up.	

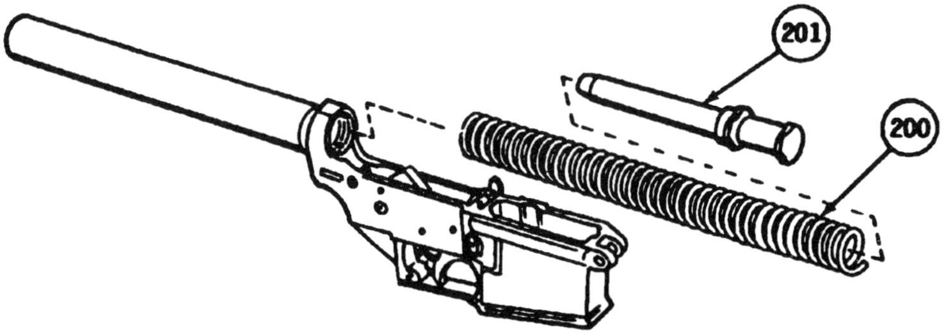

LOCATION	ITEM	ACTION	REMARKS
	m. Helical spring (202) takedown pin detent (203) and pivot pin (204)	Install pivot pin installation tool (E-6, app E). Insert spring and detent. Compress detent in recess and rotate tool.	Be sure detent is in groove of pivot pin.

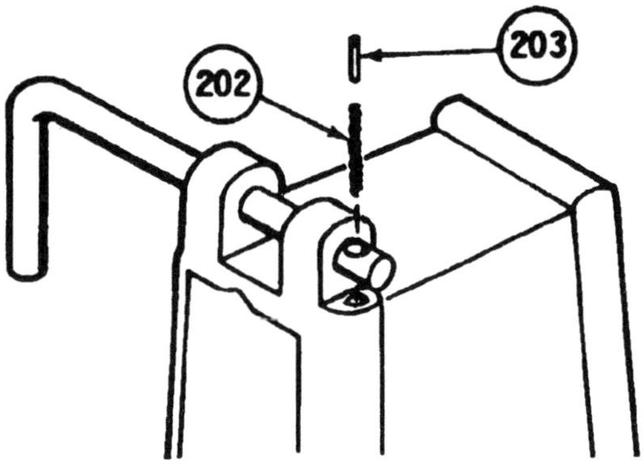

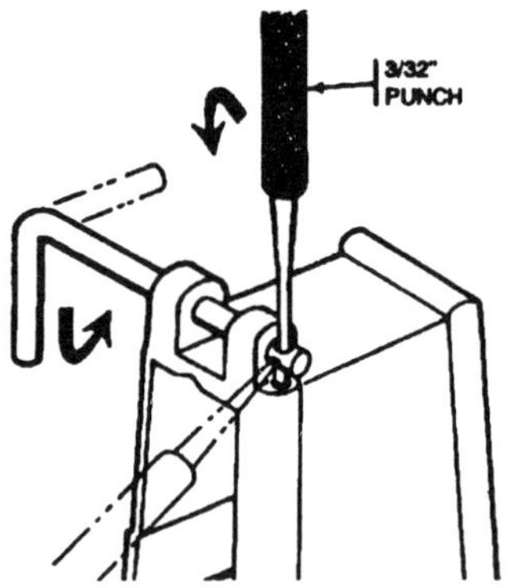

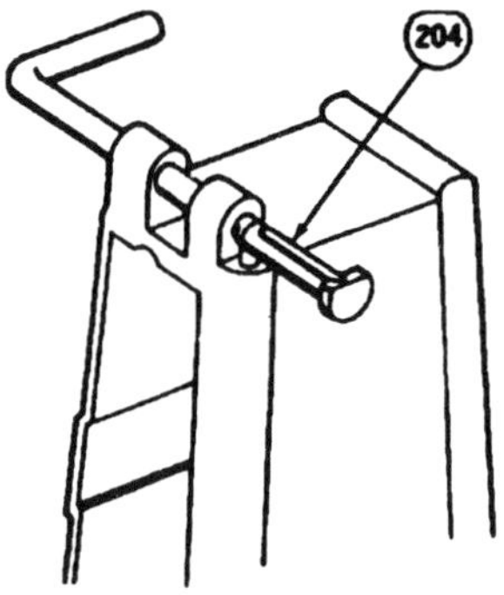

PUSH OUT TOOL USING PIVOT PIN.

LOCATION	ITEM	ACTION	REMARKS

NOTE

Replace the self-locking screw (210) with a new one.

LOCATION	ITEM	ACTION	REMARKS
	n. Takedown pin (205) takedown pin detent (206), helical spring (207), stepped spacer (208), buttstock assembly (209), and self-locking screw (210)	Install takedown pin with groove to the rear. Install detent and spring from the rear. Carefully compress the spring with stock and secure the stock in place with the self-locking screw.	

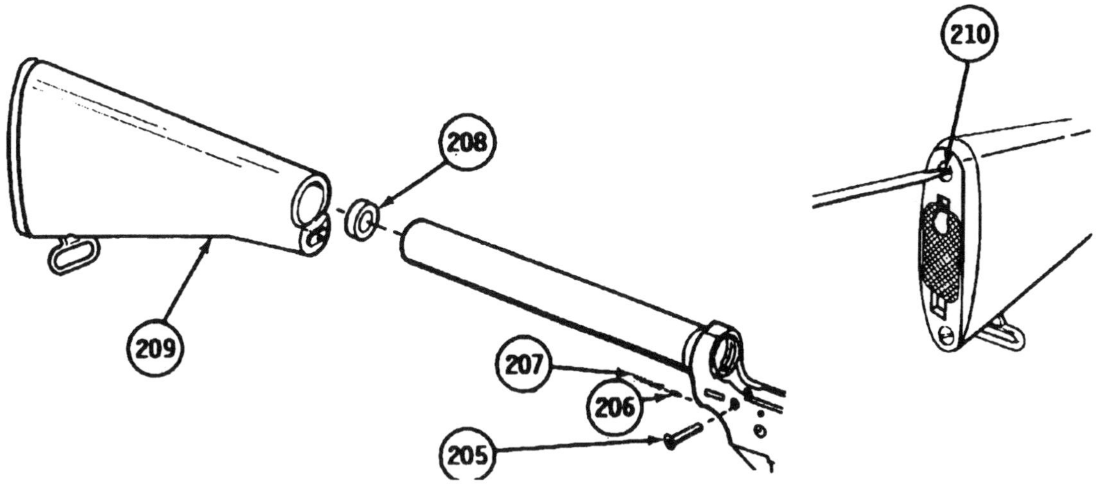

LOCATION	ITEM	ACTION	REMARKS
	o. Safety detent (211) helical spring (212), rifle grip (213), lock washer (214), and machine screw (215)	Install detent, pointed toward selector, and spring from the bottom. Carefully compress the spring with the rifle grip and secure the grip in place with the lock washer and screw.	

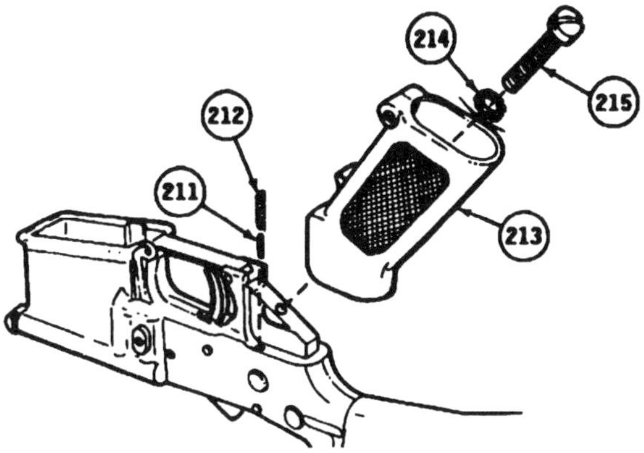

3-16. BUTTSTOCK ASSEMBLY (INTERMEDIATE).

This task covers:
- a. Inspection
- b. Repair

INITIAL SETUP

References
TM 9-1005-301-30

LOCATION	ITEM	ACTION	REMARKS
INSPECTION			
Buttstock Assembly	Buttstock	Inspect.	See paragraph 3-15.
REPAIR			
Buttstock Assembly	Buttstock	Repair	See Tm 9-1005-301-30.

3-17. HAMMER ASSEMBLY (INTERMEDIATE).

This task covers:
- a. Disassembly
- b. Inspection
- c. Reassembly

DISASSEMBLY

LOCATION	ITEM	ACTION	REMARKS
Hammer Assembly	Hammer spring (216), cam clutch spring (217), burst cam (218), and hammer assembly (219)		

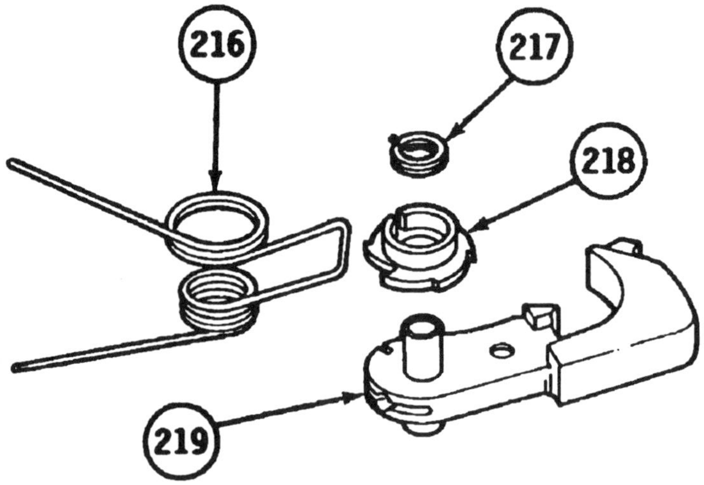

LOCATION	ITEM	ACTION	REMARKS
INSPECTION			
Hammer Assembly	a. Hammer spring	Inspect for deformities, breaks, and bends.	Pay special attention to large coil. Replace if defective.
	b. Cam clutch spring	Inspect for deformities, breaks, and bends.	
	c. Burst cam	Inspect for deformities, breaks, and bends.	
	d. Firing hammer	Inspect for chips and breaks.	Hammer pin should "click" home under strong finger pressure
		Install hammer pin into hole in hammer to check spring retention of the hammer pin.	Replace if defective.
REASSEMBLY			
Hammer Assembly	Hammer assembly (219), burst cam (218), cam clutch spring (217), and hammer spring (216)	Assemble in sequence.	Cam clutch spring should be assembled with bend to the inside and the large loop of the hammer spring (216) over the burst cam (218).

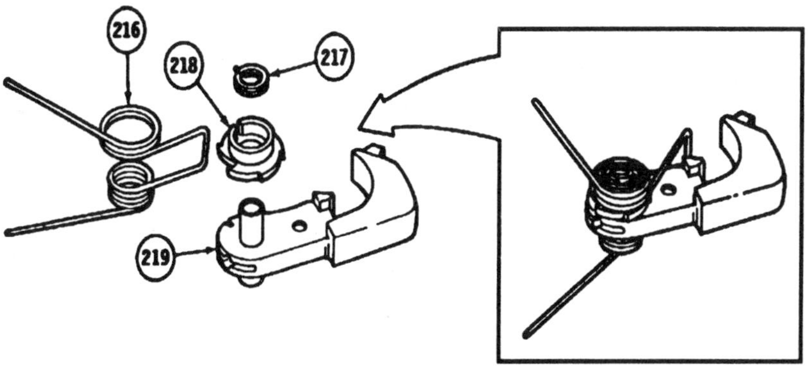

3-18. TRIGGER ASSEMBLY (INTERMEDIATE).

This task covers:
- a. Disassembly
- b. Inspection
- c. Reassembly

INITIAL SETUP

Tools

(MC) Small Arms Repairman Tool Kit
NSN 5180-00-357-7770/SL-3-00607A
(ARMY) Small Arms Repairman Tool Kit
SC 5180-95-CL-A (app B)
Field Maintenance Basic Less Power Small Arms Shop Set SC 4933-95- CL-A11
(19204)

General Safety Instructions

To avoid injury to your eyes use care when removing and installing spring-loaded parts.

LOCATION	ITEM	ACTION	REMARKS
DISASSEMBLY			
Trigger Assembly	Trigger spring (220), helical springs (221), and trigger (222).	Remove.	

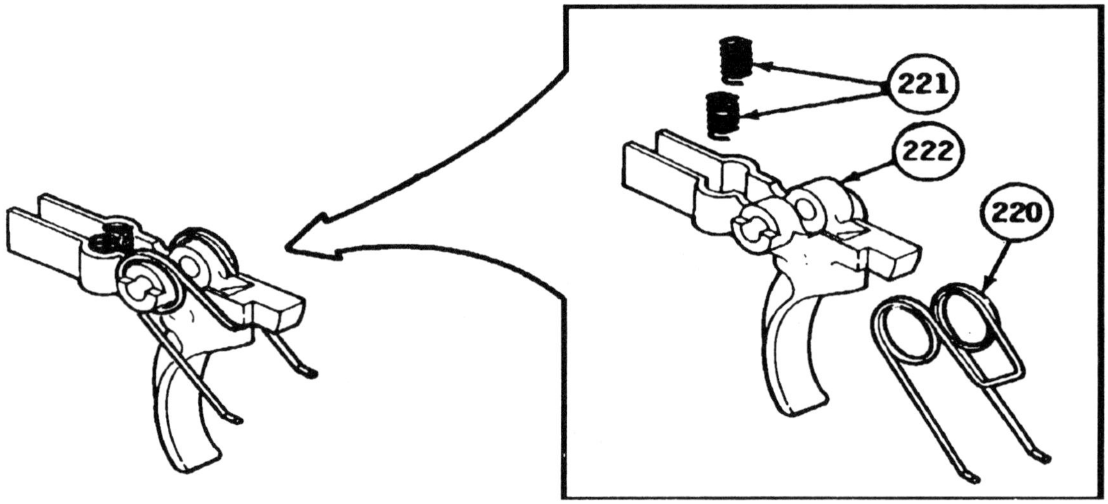

LOCATION	ITEM	ACTION	REMARKS
INSPECTION			
Trigger Assembly	a. Trigger spring	Inspect for kinks, deformities, and weakness. Replace if defective.	
	b. Helical springs	Inspect for deformities, bends, breaks, and weakness. Replace if defective.	
	c. Trigger	Inspect for chips and cracks. Replace if defective.	
REASSEMBLY			
Trigger Assembly	a. Trigger (222) and helical springs (221)	Install helical springs in trigger.	Large end of springs should snap into trigger recesses.
	b. Trigger spring (220).	Install.	

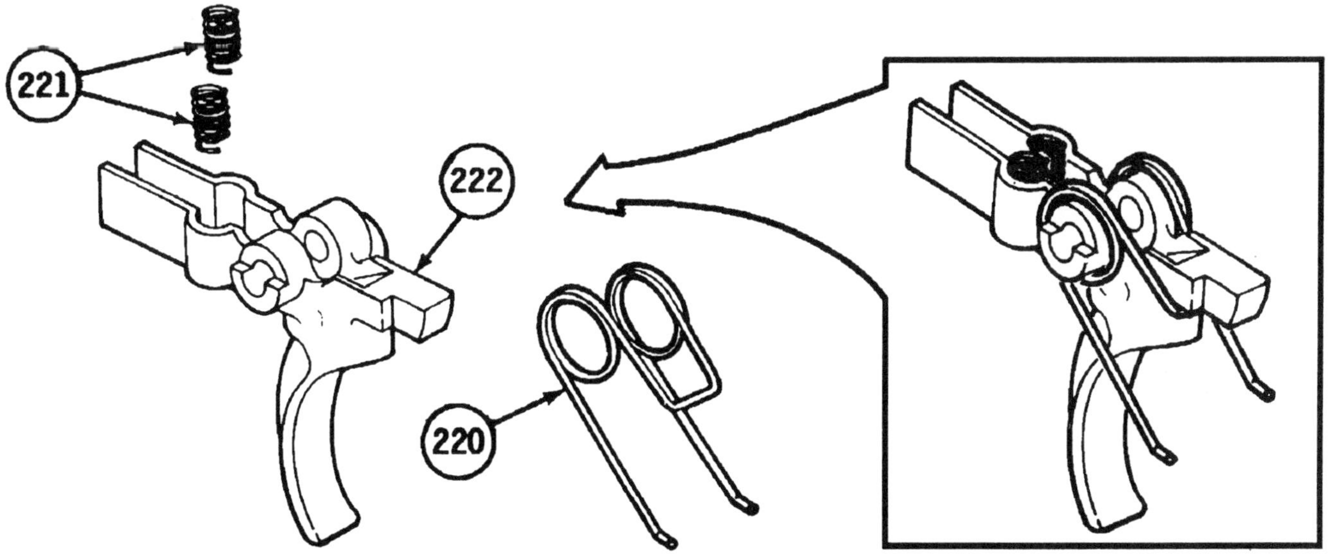

3-19. LOWER RECEIVER AND RECEIVER EXTENSION ASSEMBLY (INTERMEDIATE).

This task covers:

a. Disassembly
b. Inspection
c. Repair/Modify
d. Test
e. Reassembly

INITIAL SETUP

Tools

(MC) Small Arms Repairman Tool Kit
NSN 5180-00-357-7770/SL-3-00607A
Tool and Gage Set, infantory weapons, M16A2
NSN 4933-00-056-7106/SL-3-06229A
(ARMY) Small Arms Repairman Tool Kit
SC 5180-95-CL-A (app B)
Field Maintenance Basic Less Power Small
Arms Shop Set SC 4933-95-CL-A11 (19204)

Materials/Parts

Abrasive cloth (item 10, app D)
Molybdenum disulfide grease (item 16, app D)
Solid film lubricant (item 18, app D)

General Safety Instructions

To avoid injury to your eyes use care when removing and installing spring-loaded parts.

LOCATION	ITEM	ACTION	REMARKS
DISASSEMBLY			
Lower Receiver and Receiver Extension Assembly	a. Spring pin (223)	Remove using 1/8-inch drive pin punch and hand hammer.	
	b. Trigger guard (224)	Remove.	

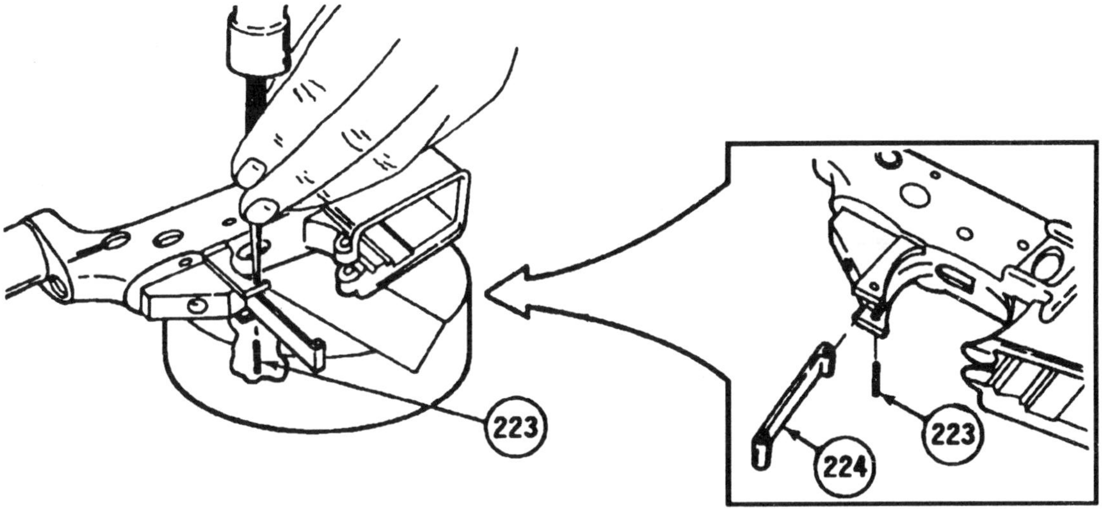

	c. Lower receiver extension (225)	Remove using vise, vise jaw caps, combination wrench, and socket wrench handle. Clamp lower receiver in vise and tighten on solid portion just tight enough to hold.	

NOTE

Use wooden vise jaws in place of brass vise jaw caps.

LOCATION	ITEM	ACTION	REMARKS
	d. Buffer retainer (226) and helical spring (227)	Remove.	As lower receiver extension is removed, catch buffer retainer and spring.
	e. Lower receiver (228)		Lower receiver is a serial number controlled item.

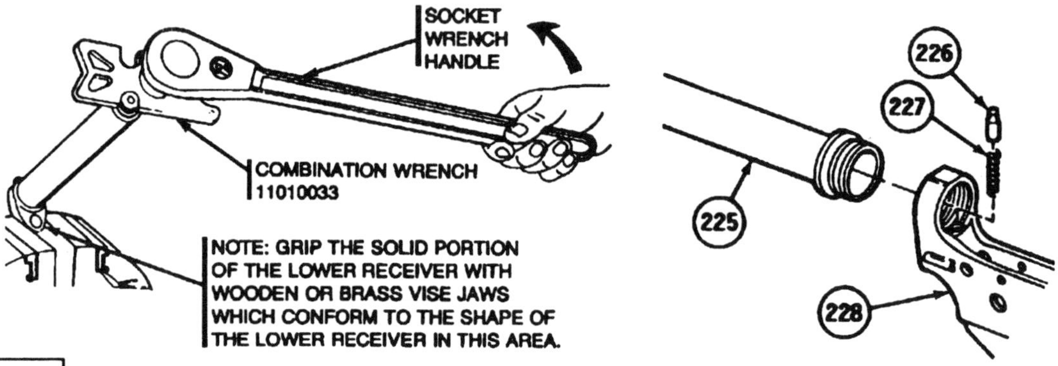

INSPECTION

LOCATION	ITEM	ACTION	REMARKS
Lower Receiver and Receiver Extension Assembly	a. Lower receiver extension (225)	Inspect for corrosion, dents, and wear. Repair or replace if defective.	See paragraph 3-15.
	b. Buffer retainer (226)	Inspect for wear and replace if defective.	
	c. Helical spring (227)	Inspect for deformities and breaks.	
	d. Lower receiver (228)	Inspect.	See paragraph 3-15
	e. Trigger guard (224)	Inspect for deformities and check plunger and spring.	Replace if defective.

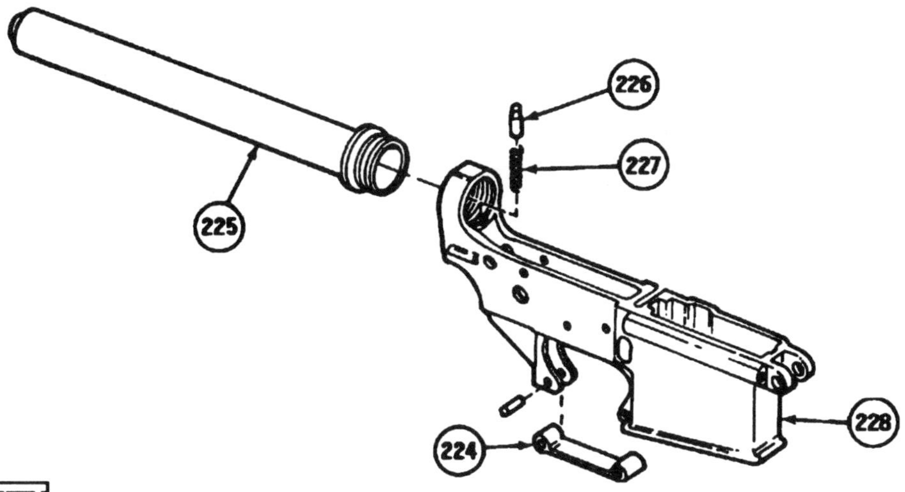

REPAIR/MODIFY

LOCATION	ITEM	ACTION	REMARKS
Lower Receiver and Receiver Extension Assembly	a. Lower receiver extension	Repair. Using abrasive cloth (item 10 app D), remove light corrosion and use solid film lubricant (item 18, app D) to retouch.	
	b. Lower receiver	Inspect for damage, wear, and corrosion.	See paragraph 3-15.
		Repair or replace weapon.	
		Modify (when required) using 1/16 twist drill and portable electric drill per drawing.	This procedure will only be applied to rifles whose pivot pin, detent, or spring cannot be removed in any other manner.

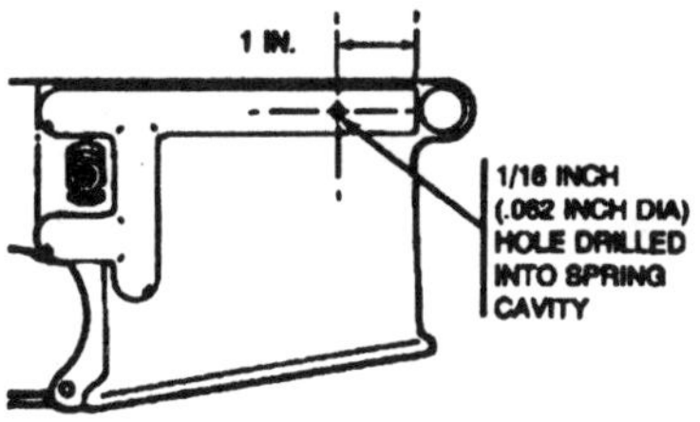

CAUTION

EXERCISE EXTREME CARE WHEN DRILLING HOLE THAT PENETRATION IS NOT MADE IN INNER WALL OF SPRING CAVITY.

LOCATION	ITEM	ACTION	REMARKS
TEST			
Lower Receiver and Receiver Extension Assembly	a. Trigger pin holes and hammer pin holes	Test.	See paragraph 3-15.
	b. Lower receiver pivot pin area spacing.	Test.	See paragraph 3-15.
REASSEMBLY			
Lower Receiver and Receiver Extension Assembly		Lubricate threads of lower receiver and receiver extension assembly with molybdebum disulfide grease (item 16, app D) before reassembly.	
	a. Helical spring (227), lower receiver (228), and buffer retainer (226)	Install.	
	b. Lower receiver extension (225)	Install while depressing buffer retainer.	

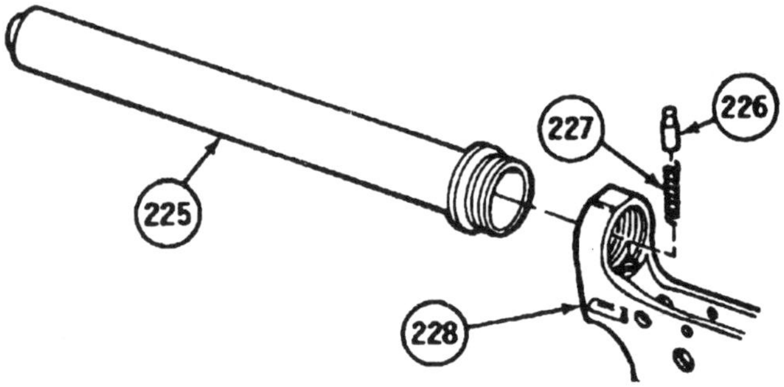

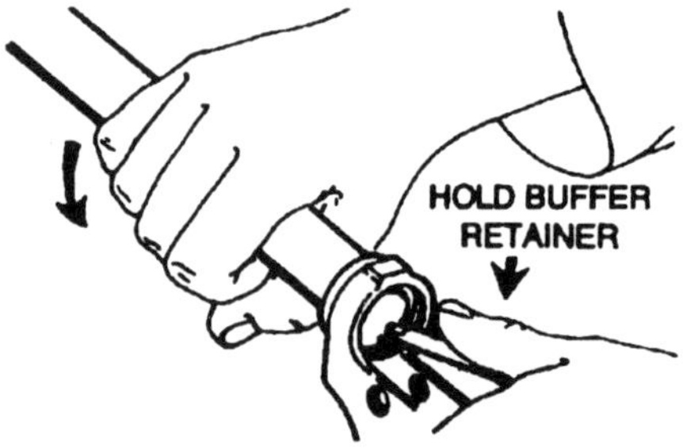

LOCATION	ITEM	ACTION	REMARKS
		Torque using vise, vise jaw caps, combination wrench 11010033, and torque wrench, clamping solid portion of lower receiver torque to 35 - 39 ft-lb.	Use wooden vise jaws in vise in place of brass vise jaw caps, if available.

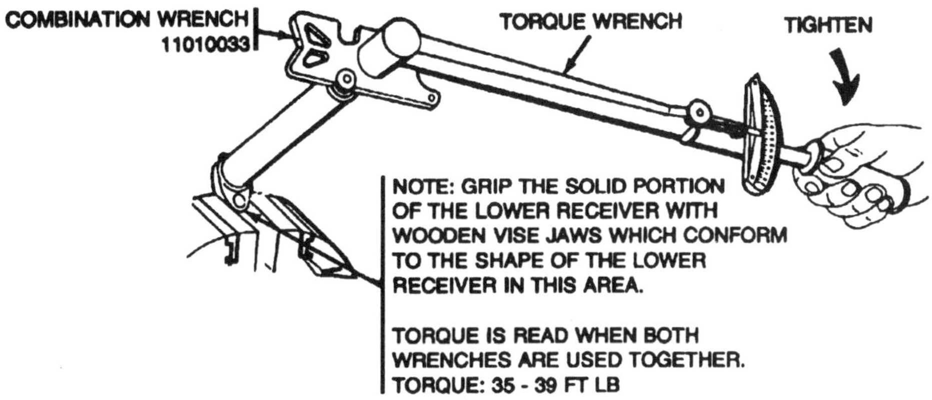

LOCATION	ITEM	ACTION	REMARKS
	c. Trigger guard (224)	Install.	
	d. Spring pin (229)	Install using 1/8-inch drive pin punch and hand hammer.	

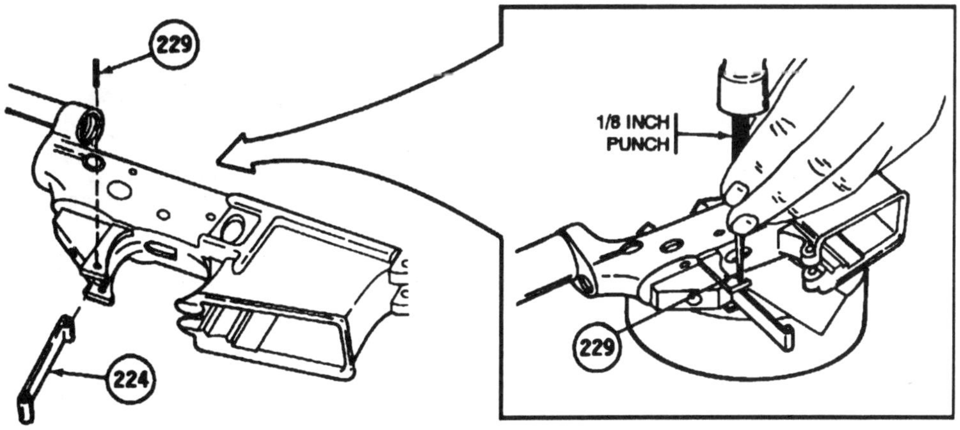

3-20. MAJOR COMPONENTS OF M16A2 RIFLE.

This task covers:

a. Reassembly
b. Test

INITIAL SETUP

Tools

(MC) Small Arms Repairman Tool Kit
NSN 5180-00-357-770/SL-3-00607A
Tool and Gage Set, infantry weapon, M16A2
NSN 4944-00-056-7106/SL-3-06229A
(ARMY) Small Arms Repairman Tool Kit
SC 5180-95-CL-A (app B)

References

TM 05538C-10/1

General Safety Instructions

To avoid injury to your eyes, use care when removing and installing spring-loaded parts.

Live ammunition should not be near the work area.

LOCATION	ITEM	ACTION	REMARKS
REASSEMBLY			
Weapon	Lower receiver assembly (230), upper receiver and barrel assembly (231), charging handle (232), bolt carrier assembly (233), small arms sling (234, and cartridge magazine (235).	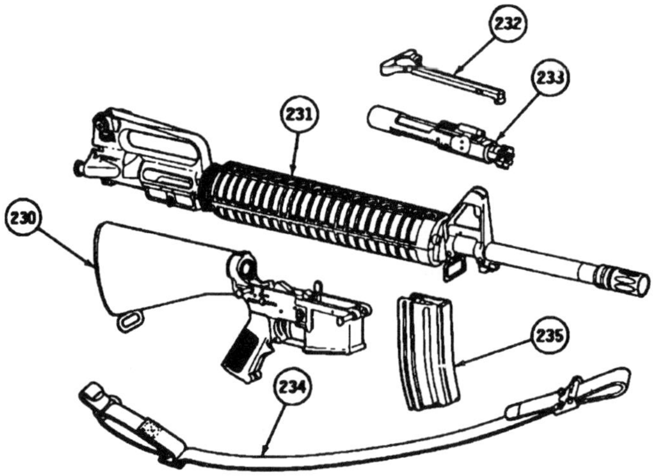 Install.	Refer to TM 05538C-10/1

LOCATION	ITEM	ACTION	REMARKS
TEST			
Weapon	Trigger	Test trigger pull. Using trigger pull measuring fixture 7274758, add weights until hammer trips. Determine weight applied.	Place weapon in SEMI position and hold weapon in vertical position.
			Hammer should not trip until 5.5 pounds have been applied, and it must trip prior to applying 9.5 pounds.
			If rifle fails trigger pull test or excessive creep is present, replace trigger and/or hammer. Always gage trigger and hammer pin holes with no go plug gage 2006472 before replacing parts.

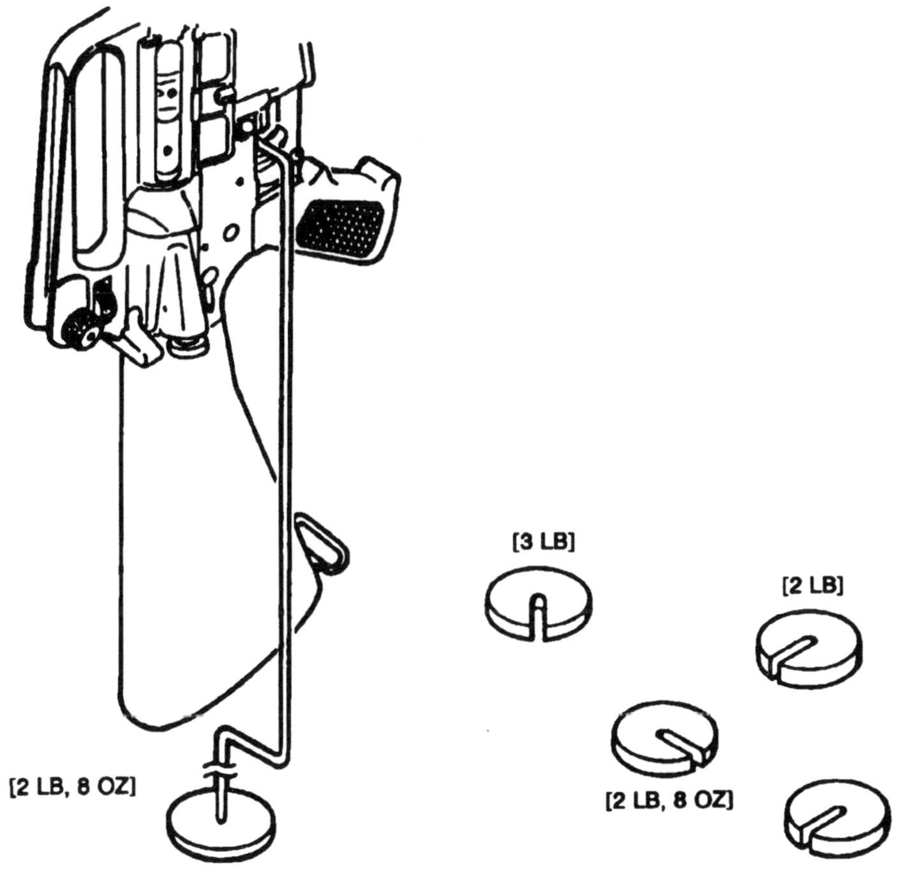

3-21. M16A2 RIFLE FINAL INSPECTION FOR INTERMEDIATE SUPPORT UNITS.

This task covers:
- a. Final inspection
- b. Test
- c. Functional theory of three-round burst control

INITIAL SETUP

Tools

Tool and Gage Set, infantry weapon, M16A2
NSN 4933-00-056-7106/SL-3-06229A

References

TM 05538C-10/1

General Safety Instructions

Live ammunition should not be near the work area.

LOCATION	ITEM	ACTION	REMARKS
FINAL INSPECTION			
Weapon	a. General appearance	Weapon should look almost new.	All metal surfaces are to have a dull, rust- or corrosion-resistant finish with no burrs or deep scratches.
		Visually inspect for serviceability	Barrels must be straight, clean, free of rust, powder fouling, and free of bulges and rings. Fine pitting is allowable.

LOCATION	ITEM	ACTION	REMARKS
		Visually inspect for missing parts, serial numbers, steel parts, spring pins, and screws.	All parts must be attached, and all modifications must be applied. Serial numbers must be legible and steel parts must be rust free. Spring pins must be secure and screws must be tight.
	b. Bolt Carrier and Gas Tube	Functionally inspect key and bolt carrier assembly and gas tube alignment using the following procedures:	Refer to TM 05538C-10/1.
		Step 1. Disengage the takedown pin and open the receiver.	Refer to TAM 05538C-10/1.
		Step 2. Remove bolt carrier assembly.	Refer to ATM 05538C-10/1.
		Step 3. Remove bolt assembly from bolt carrier assembly.	Refer to TM 05538C-10/1.
		Step 4. Insert key and bolt carrier assembly into upper receiver and barrel assembly.	The bolt assembly must not be installed while performing test.
		Step 5. Slide bolt carrier and key forward to detect binding between key and bolt carrier assembly and gas tube by feel.	Badly bent gas tube could cause damage to both the bolt key and bolt carrier assembly or the gas tube. A slightly bent gas tube will cause unnecessary wear of the carrier and key assembly and gas tube.

LOCATION	ITEM	ACTION	REMARKS
		Step 6. Correct slight binding by removing weapon handguards and by slightly bending gas tube in the handguard area while repeating step 5 above until no binding is detected. Badly bent gas tubes will be replaced.	
		Step 7. Remove key and bolt carrier assembly from upper receiver and barrel assembly.	
		Step 8. Reassemble bolt assembly into key and bolt carrier assembly.	Refer to TM 05538C-10/1.
		Step 9. Reinstall bolt carrier assembly into upper receiver and barrel assembly.	
	c. Assembled Rifle	Functional Inspection.	Make a functional check of the rifle while the selector lever is in SAFE, SEMI, and BURST positions. Any portion of this check may be used alone to determine the operational condition of any specific fire selection.

LOCATION	ITEM	ACTION	REMARKS
	d. Charging handle	Pull to rear. Check to assure that chamber is clear.	Leave hammer in cocked position.
	e. Selector lever	Place in SAFE position and squeeze trigger.	Hammer should not fall.

WARNING

If weapon fails the following tests, continued use of weapon could result in injury of death.

	f. Three-round burst		
		Place in BURST position. Cock weapon and squeeze trigger.	Hammer should fall.
		While holding the trigger to the rear, pull the charging handle assembly to the rear and release it three times.	Hammer should not fall. The burst disconnector should have held the hammer to the rear while the trigger was in the squeezed position.
		Squeeze the trigger.	Hammer should fall. This should be the first round of a three-round burst.

NOTE

A detailed explanation of the three-round burst control can be found in the following pages.

	g. Magazine catch button	Press magazine catch button.	Make sure if functions properly.
	h. Bolt catch	Press.	Make certain it operates smoothly and holds bolt in open position.

LOCATION	ITEM	ACTION	REMARKS
	i. Front sight and rear sight	Inspect.	Make certain they can be adjusted properly. Refer to paragraph 2-16 and paragraph 3-13.
	j. Forward assist assembly	Actuate.	It must work freely.
	k. Upper receiver and barrel assembly	Inspect.	Barrel assembly should not rotate within upper receiver assembly.
TEST			
	a. Headspace	Check headspace using headspace gage 7799734.	See paragraph 3-12.
	b. Firing pin	Check firing pin protrusion using firing pin protrusion gage 7799735.	See paragraph 3-12.
	c. Barrel	Check barrel erosion using proper barrel erosion gage.	See paragraph 3-12.
	d. Compensator	Third or middle slot should be straight up (TDC)	See paragraph 3-12.

FUNCTIONAL THEORY OF THREE-ROUND BURST CONTROL

NOTE

First become familiar with the functioning of the firing mechanism especially when in the SAFE and SEMI positions. You should also understand the role that the automatic sear plays when firing in the BURST position. Functioning of the mechanism is explained below in a step by step manner. This actually will seem to complicate something that is really very simple and happens in less than one second. The diagrams below and on the following pages do not show the associated springs for the sake of simplicity. The positioning of the burst cam is shown in detail.

Functional check of three-round burst is as follows:

Assume the weapon is fully loaded with a live round in the chamber and the selector lever on BURST:

a. Hammer is cocked.
b. Front hook of burst disconnector is in stop notch.
c. Trigger is pulled.

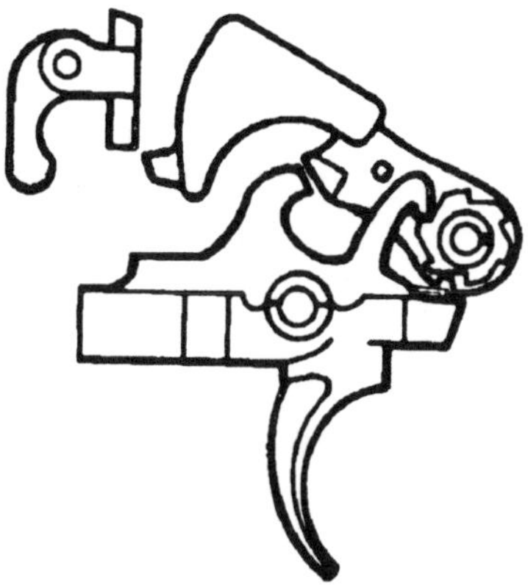

d. Trigger nose drops and hammer falls firing the FIRST ROUND.
e. Front hook of burst disconnector holds burst cam in place as hammer falls.

NOTE: Anytime the hammer falls forward, the clutch spring releases the burst cam and allows the front hook of the burst disconnector to keep it in place.

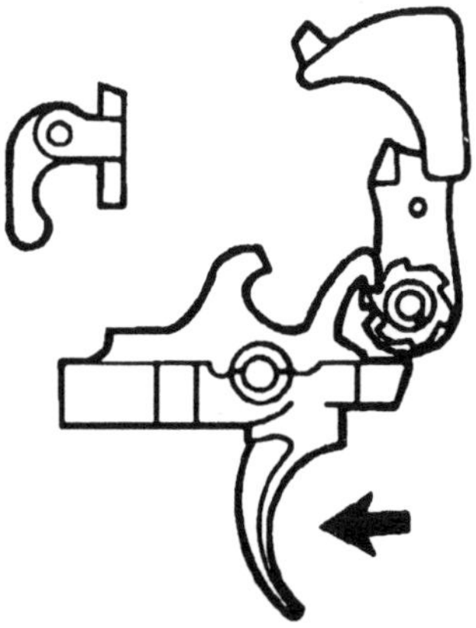

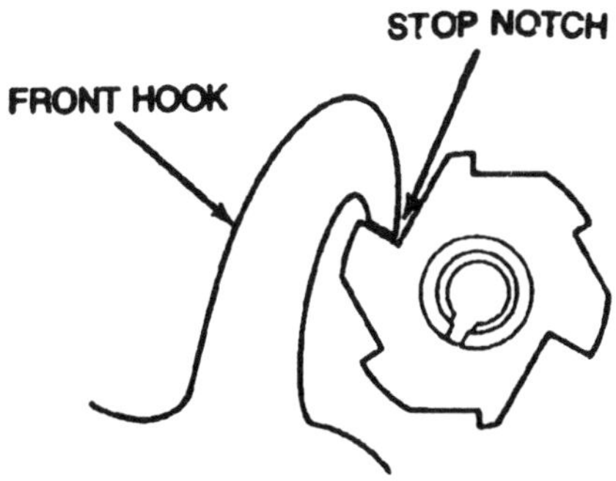

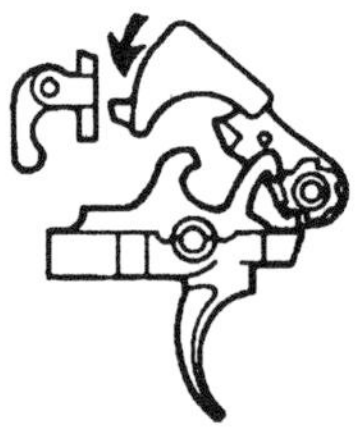

f. As the bolt carrier assembly moves to the rear, the hammer is forced to the rear.

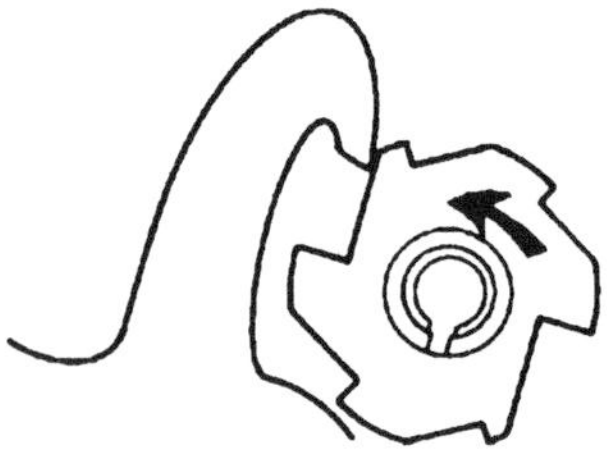

g. The clutch spring of the burst cam clutches the cam and causes it to rotate one notch as the hammer is forced back.

h. When hammer is fully to the rear, the automatic sear catches it.

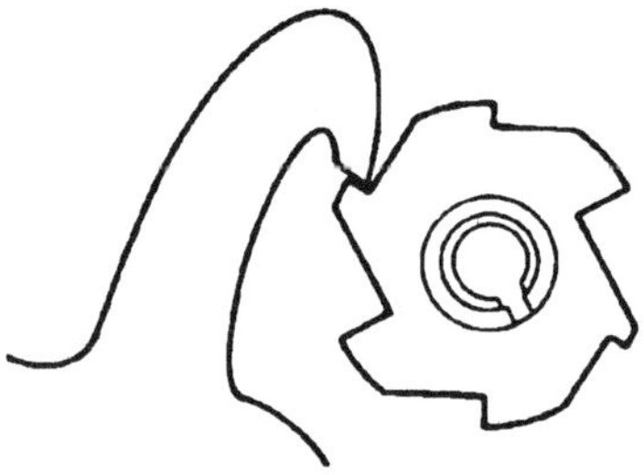

i. The front hook of the burst disconnector is now fully in the second notch.

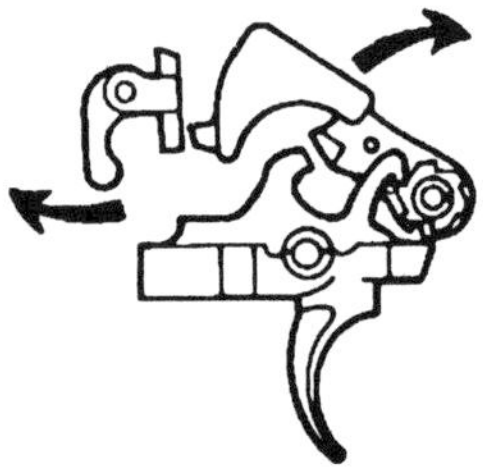

j. As the bolt carrier assembly travels forward, the automatic sear releases the hammer and the hammer falls.

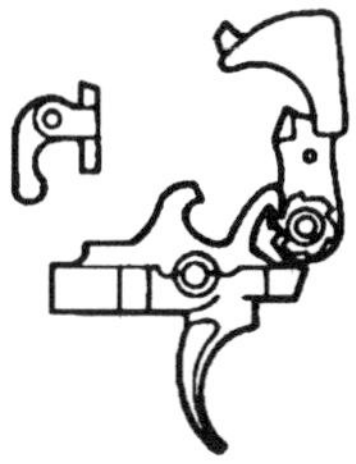

k. When the hammer falls, the SECOND ROUND is fired.

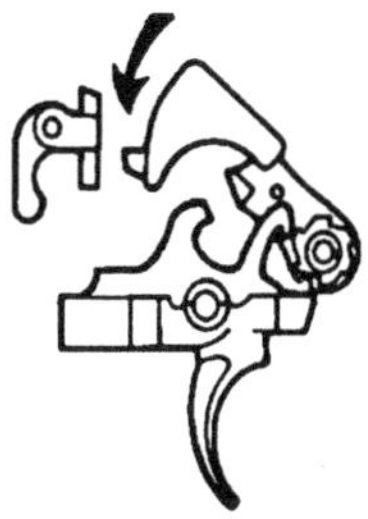

l. As the bolt carrier assembly moves to the rear, the hammer is forced back to the rear.

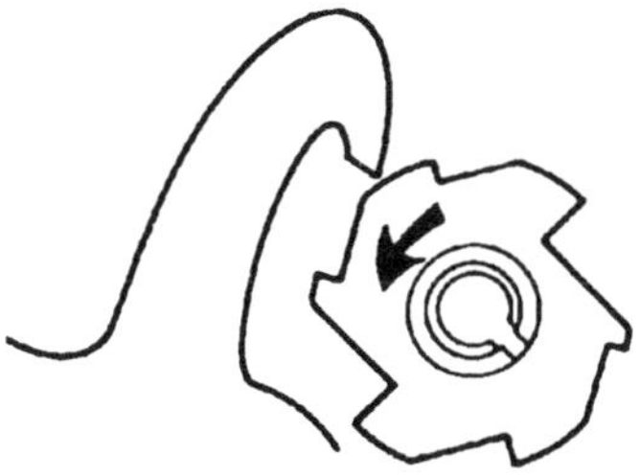

m. The clutch spring of the burst cam clutches against the cam and causes it to rotate one notch as the hammer is forced back.

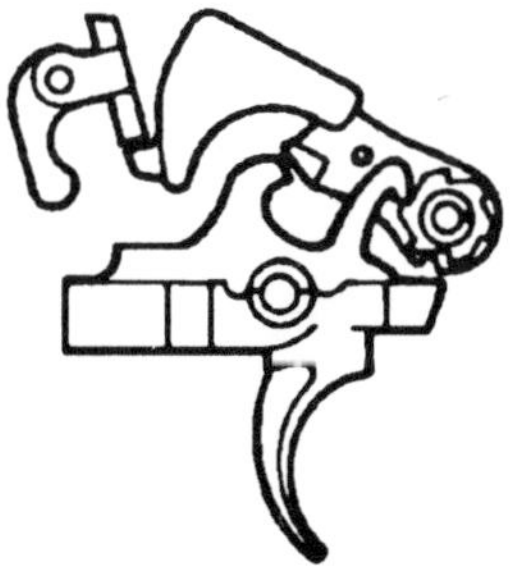

n. When the hammer is fully to the rear, the automatic sear catches it.

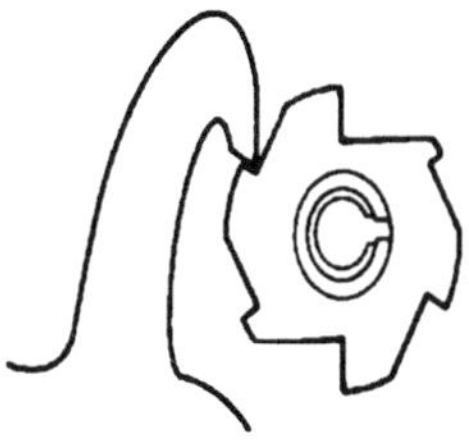

o. The front hook of the burst disconnector is now fully in the third notch.

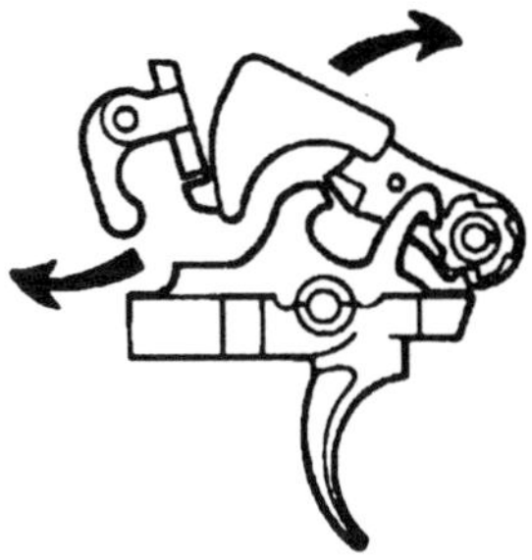

p. As the bolt carrier assembly travels forward, the automatic sear releases the hammer and the hammer falls.

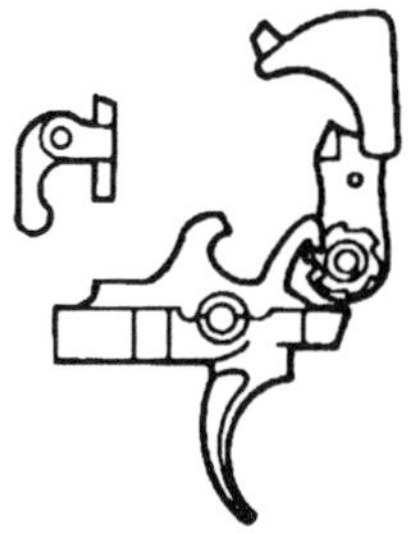

q. When the hammer falls the THIRD ROUND is fired.

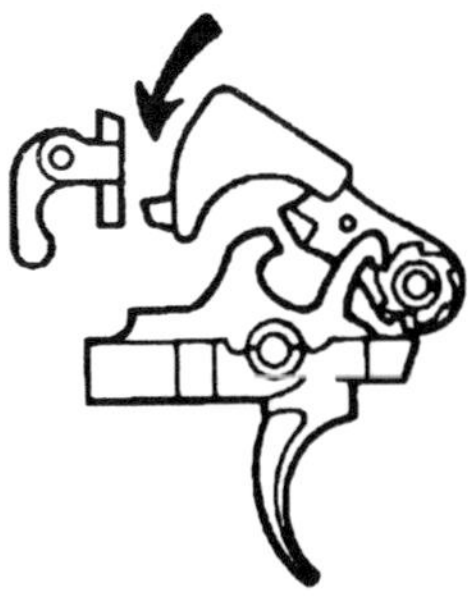

r. As the bolt carrier moves to the rear, the hammer is forced back to the rear.

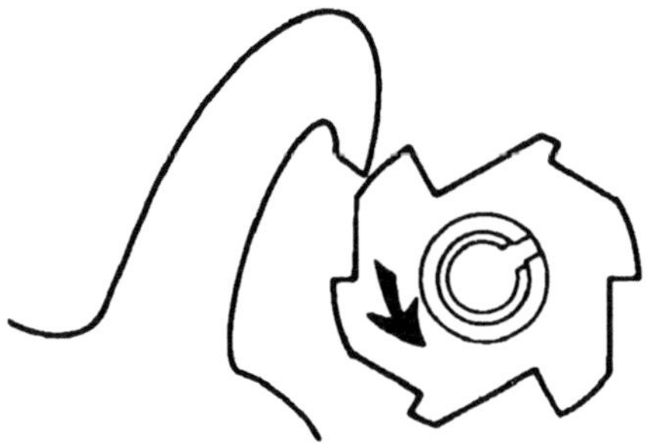

s. The clutch spring of the burst cam clutches against the cam and causes it to rotate one notch as the hammer is forced back.

t. When the hammer is fully to the rear, it is initially caught by the automatic sear. However, the front hook

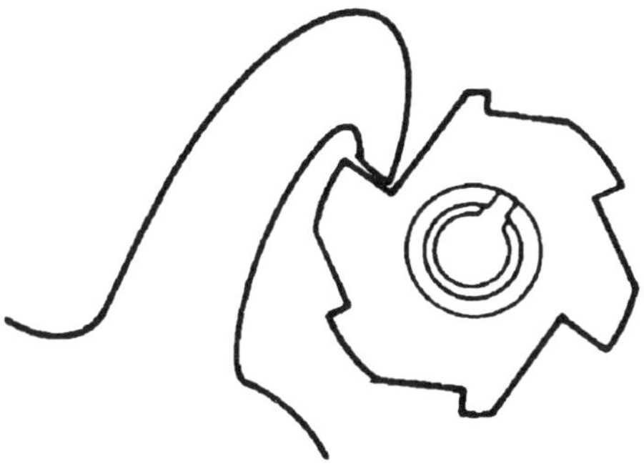

of the burst disconnector is now fully in the next stop notch which is deeper than the others.

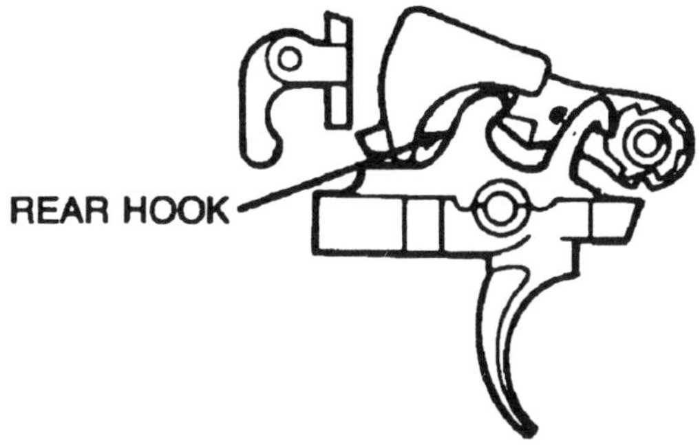

u. Because a stop notch is deeper than the others, it allows the front hook of the burst disconnector further forward than before. This allows the rear hook of the burst disconnector to latch on the rear hammer notch. This holds the hammer fully to the rear even though the trigger is still to the rear. This happens when the burst is over and the firing is stopped.

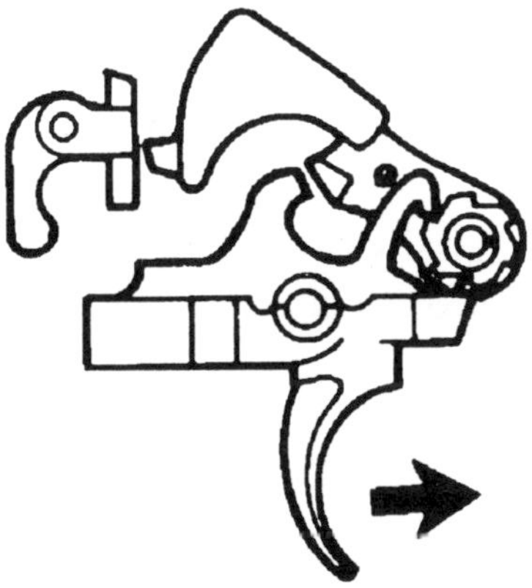

v. Once the trigger is released, the trigger nose comes up and holds the hammer back.

NOTE

Pulling the trigger to the rear and holding it back again will fire another three-round burst. This will continue until the magazine is empty. However, the trigger must be released between each burst.

3-22. M16A2 RIFLE ANNUAL ORGANIZATIONAL AND INTERMEDIATE SUPPORT LIMITED TECHNICAL INSPECTION (LTI) INSPECTION AND GAGING REQUIREMENTS.

This task covers:

a. LTI inspection
b. Gagging

INITIAL SETUP

Tools

DA Form 2407
(MC) Small Arms Repairman Tool Kit
NSN 5180-00-357-7770/SL-3-00607A
Tool and Gage set, infantry weapon, M16A2
NSN 4933-00-056-7160/SL-3-06229A
(ARMY) Small Arms Repairman Tool Kit
SC 5180-96-CL-A (app B)
Field Maintenance basic Less Power Small Arms Shop Equipment SC 4933-95-CL-A11 (19204)

References

TM 05538C-10/1
TM 4700-15/1

General Safety Instructions

To avoid injury to your eyes, use care when removing and installing spring-loaded parts.

All M16A2 rifles must have an LTI and be gaged at least once annually for safety. In addition, an LTI will be performed at the time of rifle issue and prior to annual requalification.

LOCATION	ITEM	ACTION	REMARKS
LTI INSPECTION			
Weapon	General appearance	Overall appearance should indicate a well-maintained weapon.	All visual and functional inspection requirements must be met.
	Lower receiver and buttstock assembly	Perform final inspection procedures to include functional inspection of trigger mechanism	See paragraph 3-21.
GAGING			
Weapon	a. Bolt carrier assembly	Gage firing pin protrusion using firing pin protrusion gage 7799735.	See paragraph 3-9.
		Gage firing pin hole using no go plug gage 12620101.	See paragraph 3-9.
	b. Upper receiver and barrel assembly	Inspect chamber using chamber reflector tool 8448201.	See paragraph 3-12.
	c. Upper receiver and barrel assembly	Gage barrel using proper barrel erosion gage, as applicable, and bore straightness gage 8448202.	See paragraph 3-12.
	d. Upper receiver and extension assembly	Check headspace by inserting headspace gage 7799734 in chamber.	See paragraph 3-12.
	e. Lower receiver and extension assembly	Gage pivot pin lug area clearance using fabricated lower receiver go-no go gage.	See paragraph 3-15.

LOCATION	ITEM	ACTION	REMARKS
	f. Weapon	Gage trigger pull using trigger pull measuring fixture 7274758.	See paragraph 3-20.

(ARMY ONLY)

Document	NAVMC 11003	Document all LTI's when completed.	See TM 4700-15/1.
	DA FORM 2407	Document Inspection when completed.	

Section V. PREPARATION FOR STORAGE OR SHIPMENT

3-23. GENERAL. Refer to SB 38-100.

Section VI. PREEMBARKATION INSPECTION OF MATERIAL IN UNITS SLATED FOR OVERSEAS MOVEMENT.

3.24. GENERAL. Refer to TB 9-1000-247-34.

CHAPTER 4
MAINTENANCE OF AUXILIARY EQUIPMENT

CHAPTER OVERVIEW

This chapter contains information and instructions to keep auxiliary equipment used with your weapon in good repair. The chapter contains:

I. Organizational Level Auxiliary Equipment Repair
II. Intermediate Support Level Auxiliary Equipment Repair

Section I. ORGANIZATIONAL LEVEL AUXILIARY EQUIPMENT REPAIR

4-1. GENERAL

a. The following items of auxiliary equipment are used with the M16A2 rifle:
(1) Bayonet-Knife M7
(2) Bayonet-Knife Scabbard M8A1 or M10
(3) 40-mm Grenade Launcher M203
(4) Lock Plate
(5) Top Sling Adapter
(6) Blank Firing Attachment M15A2

b. Refer to TM 9-1010-221-24&P for organizational maintenance for the Grenade Launcher M203.

c. (ARMY ONLY) Reference TM 9-6920-363-12&P for M261 (Caliber .22 Rimfire Adapter) M16, M16A1, and M16A2 Rifles.

d. (ARMY ONLY) Reference TM 9-1005-237-23&P for repair parts on bayonet-knife and scabbard.

4-2. BAYONET-KNIFE M7.

This task covers:
a. Disassembly
b. Inspection/Repair
c. Reassembly

INITIAL SETUP

General Safety Instructions
Keep tip of blade pointed away from body at all times.

LOCATION	ITEM	ACTION	REMARKS
DISASSEMBLY			
Bayonet-knife M7	a. Grip screws (1)	Remove	
	b. Lock washers (2) and grips (3 and 4)	Remove.	

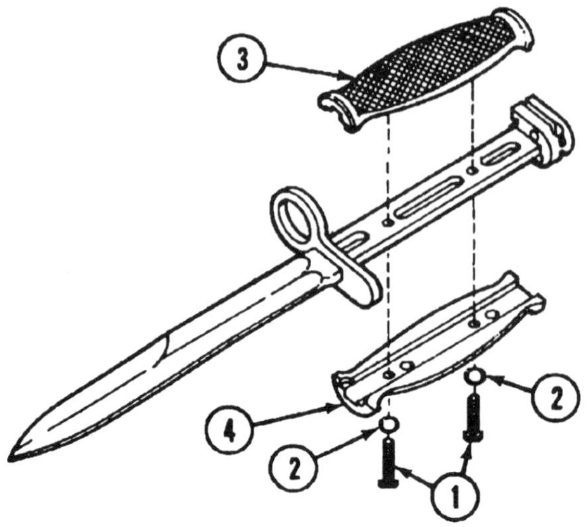

LOCATION	ITEM	ACTION	REMARKS
INSPECTION/REPAIR			
Bayonet-knife M7	a. Grip screws	Inspect threads and replace if stripped or damaged.	
	b. Grips	Inspect for cracks in both grips and for stripped threads in the left grip.	Notify intermediate maintenance if grips are cracked or if grip screws have stripped threads.
	c. Blade assembly	Inspect blade assembly for nicks, breaks or dents.	Blades with blunt points and nicks will be restored by stoning. The length of the blade (measured from the front face of the guard) must not be less than 6 1/8 inches after repointing. Notify intermediate maintenance if grinding is needed.

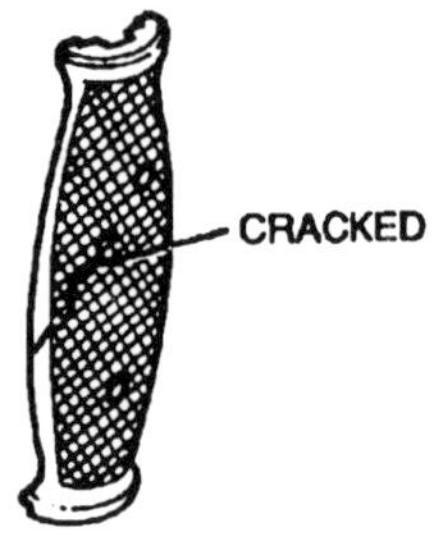

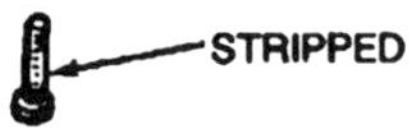

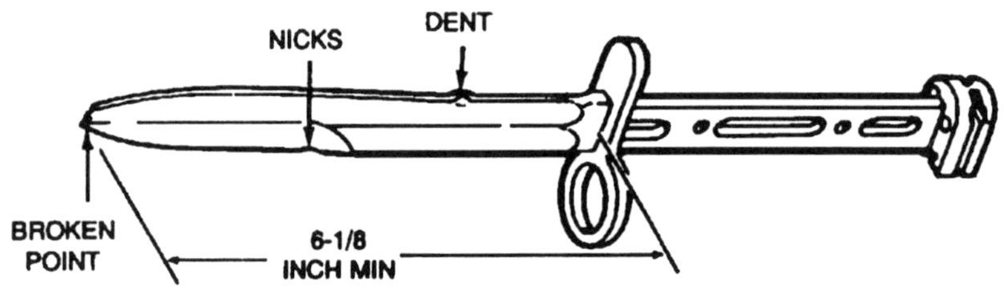

LOCATION	ITEM	ACTION	REMARKS
REASSEMBLY			
Bayonet-knife M7	Grips (3 and 4), lock washers (2), and grip screws (1).	Install grips and secure with lock washers and grip screws.	

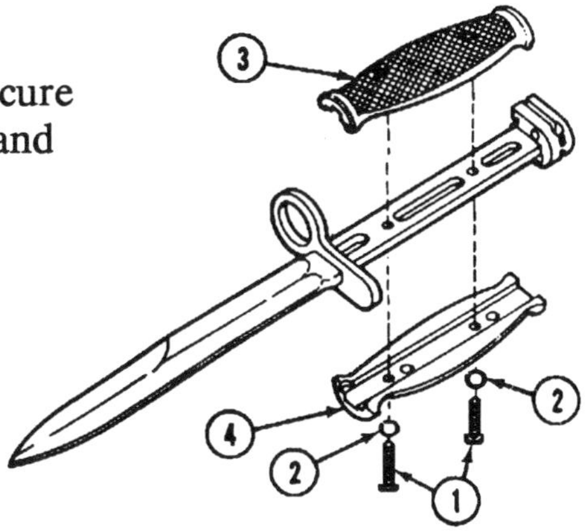

4-3. BAYONET-KNIFE SCABBARD M8A1 OR M10.

This task covers inspection/repair.

INITIAL SETUP

Materials/Parts

Olive drab enamel (item 14, app D)
Solid film lubricant (item 18, app D)

LOCATION	ITEM	ACTION	REMARKS
INSPECTION/REPAIR			
Bayonet-knife Scabbard M8A1 or M10	All parts.	Inspect metal parts. They must be dark. Worn metal area will be repaired by applying solid film lubricant (item 18, app D).	
		Inspect scabbard for chipped or exposed fabric and scratched or marred surface.	
		Repair by smoothing, as required, and paint with olive drab enamel (item 14, app D).	
		Inspect lace. Clean and/or replace damaged lace.	Scabbard is considered serviceable if lace is missing.

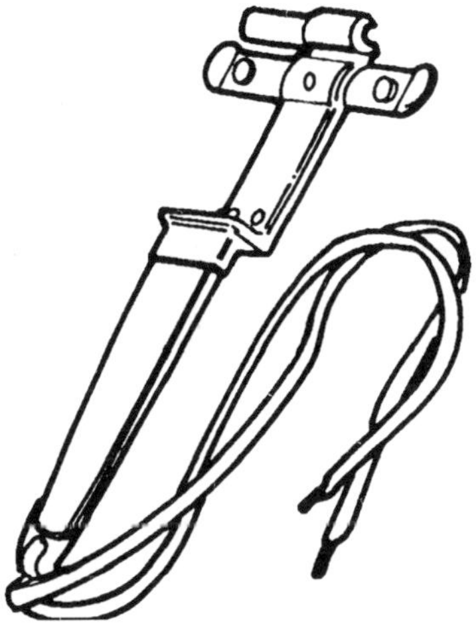

LOCATION	ITEM	ACTION	REMARKS

4-4. LOCK PLATE.

This task covers:

a. Installation
b. Removal
c.Inspection

INITIAL SETUP

Tools

(MC) Small Arms Repairman Tool Kit
NSN 5180-00-357-7770/SL 3-00607A
(ARMY) Small Arms Repairman Tool Kit
SC 5180-95-CL-A (app B)
NSN 5180-00-357-7770/SL-3-00607A

WARNING

The lock plate prevents the selector from being placed in BURST and will be installed at the discretion of the unit commander. It is recommended for use in civil disturbance (riot control).

INSTALLATION

LOCATION	ITEM	ACTION	REMARKS
Lower Receiver and Buttstock Assembly	a. Screw (5) and lock washer (6)	Using screwdriver, reach inside rifle grip and remove screw and lock washer.	

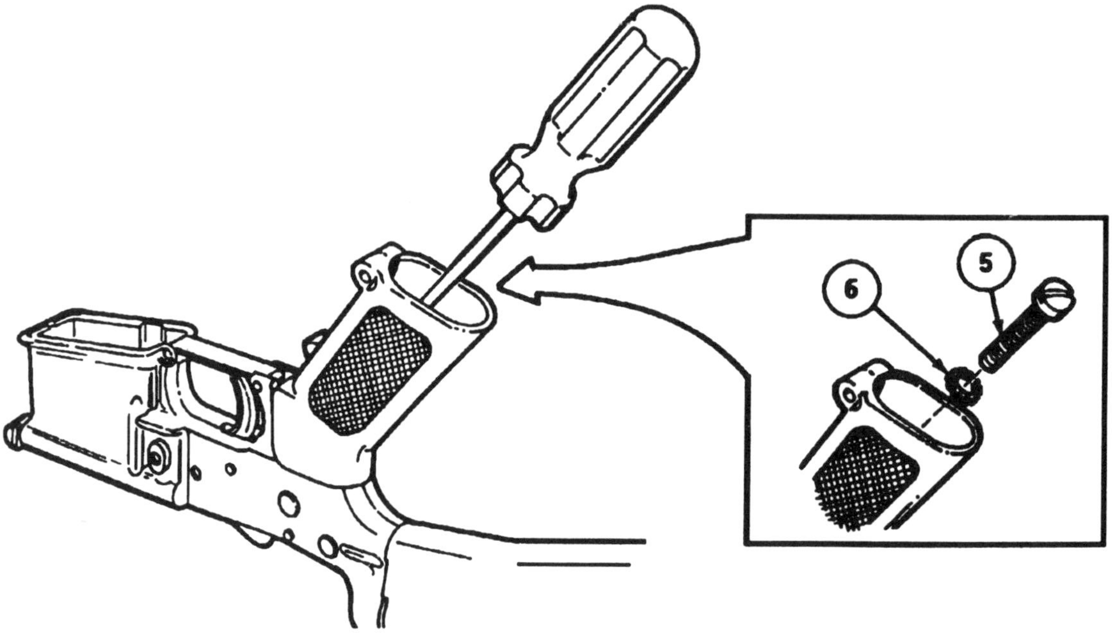

LOCATION	ITEM	ACTION	REMARKS
	b. Rifle grip (7) and helical spring (8).	Carefully remove rifle grip. Hold helical spring in place.	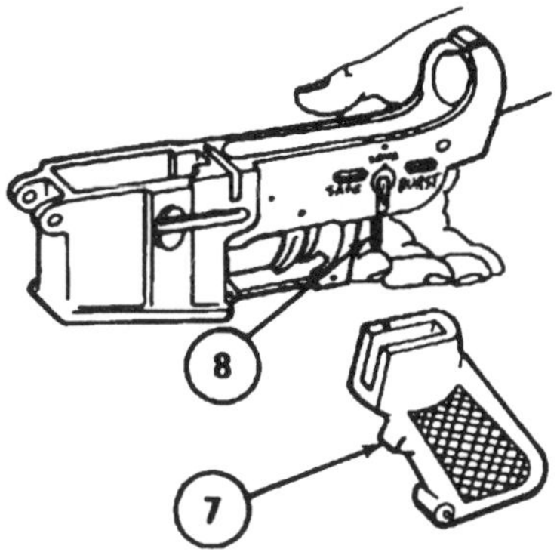
	c. Lock plate (9)	Install lock plate with the detent spring passing through the hole in the right side, and the arm on the outside of the receiver and pointing to the SAFE position.	

	d. Rifle grip (7)	Carefully compress the detent spring install the rifle grip (7).	

LOCATION	ITEM	ACTION	REMARKS
	e. Lock washer (11) and screw (10)	Using screwdriver, install lock washer and screw.	

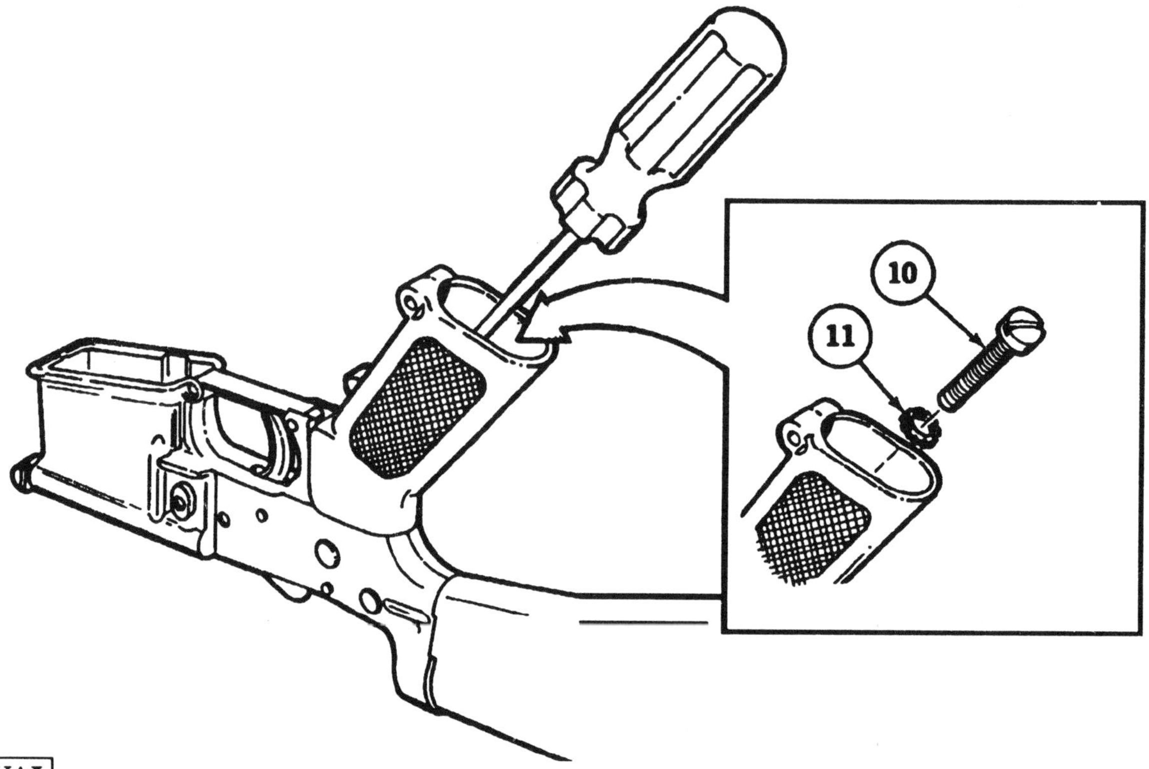

REMOVAL

Reverse of installation.

INSPECTION

Lower Receiver and Buttstock Assembly	Lock plate (9)	If arm is broken off, Replace lock plate.	

4-5. TOP SLING ADAPTER.

This task covers:

a. Installation
b. Removal
c Inspection

LOCATION	ITEM	ACTION	REMARKS

INITIAL SETUP

Materials/Parts

Top Sling Adapter Kit 8448471

INSTALLATION

LOCATION	ITEM	ACTION	REMARKS
Rifle M16A2	a. Rifle sling	Remove.	
	b. Top sling strap	Install and tie	See TM 9-1005-249-10.

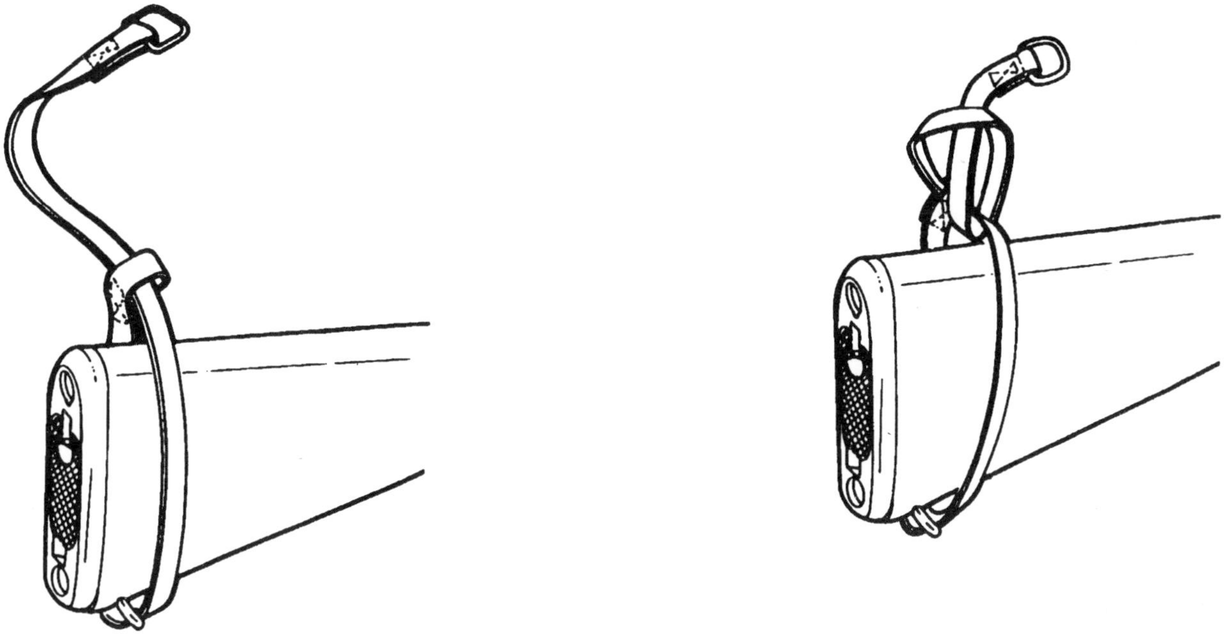

LOCATION	ITEM	ACTION	REMARKS
	c. Clamp	Install.	Remove upper hand-guard. Use pliers to force clamp.

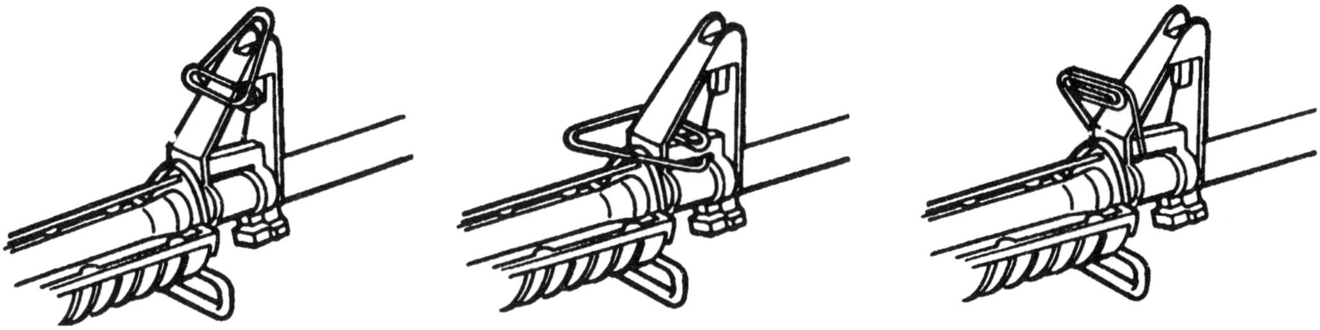

LOCATION	ITEM	ACTION	REMARKS
	d. Sling	Attach to adapter strap and front clamp. Adjust sling.	Reinstall upper hand-guard.

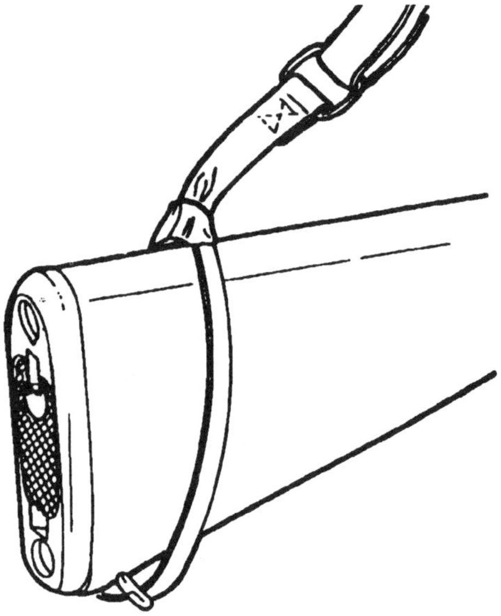

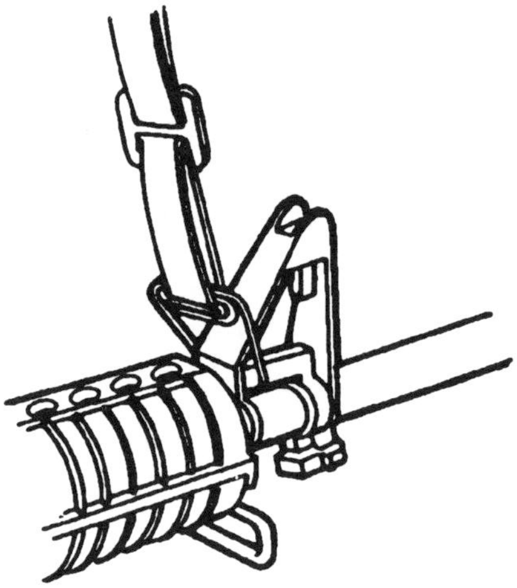

REMOVAL

Reverse of Installation.

INSPECTION

Rifle M16A2	Top sling adapter	Replace if badly worn or damaged.	

4-6. BLANK FIRING ATTACHMENT M15A2.

This task covers:

a. Installation
b. Removal
c. Cleaning
d. Inspection
e. Repainting
f. Replacement

LOCATION	ITEM	ACTION	REMARKS

INITIAL SETUP

Materials/Parts

Cleaner, lubricant and preservative (CLP) (item 6, app D)
Fluorescent coating compound (item 11, app D)

General Safety Instructions

Do not keep live ammunition near the work area. Only blank cartridge M200 is to be used when the blank firing attachment is attached to the rifle.

INSTALLATION

LOCATION	ITEM	ACTION	REMARKS
Blank Firing Attachment M15A2	a. Slide (12)	Unscrew and pull slide all the way out.	

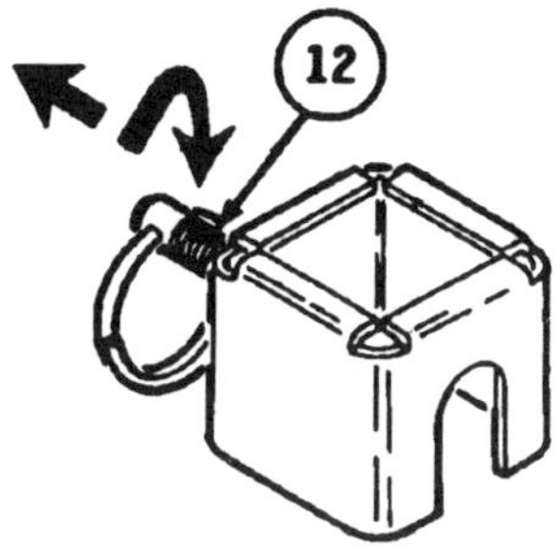

LOCATION	ITEM	ACTION	REMARKS
	b. Blank firing attachment (13) and compensator (14).	Hook blank firing attachment behind the first groove of the compensator.	

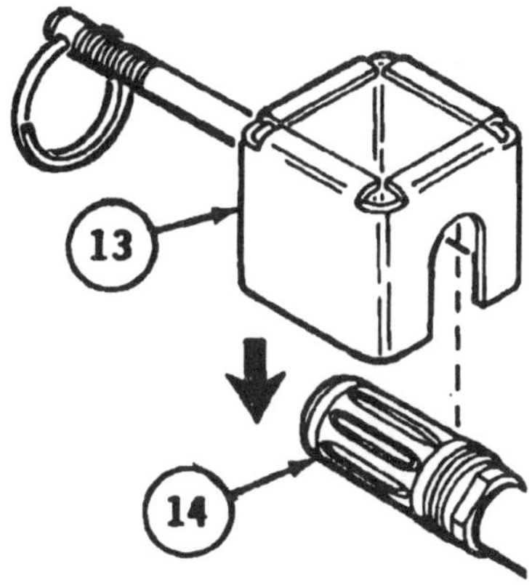

CAUTION

Do not use tools to tighten the blank firing attachment, HANDS ONLY.

LOCATION	ITEM	ACTION	REMARKS
	c. Slide (12).	Push slide into compensator and hand tighten.	

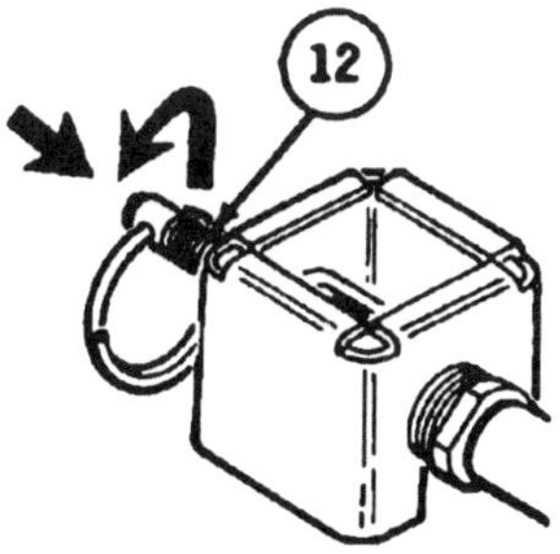

NOTE

Check and retighten after firing approximately 50 rounds.

LOCATION	ITEM	ACTION	REMARKS
REMOVAL			
Reverse of installation.			
CLEANING			
Blank Firing Attachment M15A2		Clean with CLP (item 6, app D), wipe dry, and coat with CLP.	
INSPECTION			
Blank Firing Attachment M15A2		Inspect for cracks or distortion. Be sure the parts in the slide are clear and clean.	If blank firing attachment is cracked or distorted, it is unserviceable.

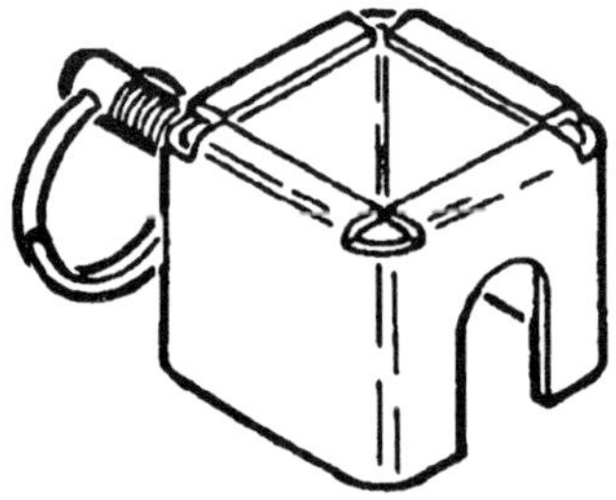

LOCATION	ITEM	ACTION	REMARKS
REPAINTING			
Blank Firing Attachment M15A2		Repaint blank firing attachment using fluorescent coating compound (item 11, app D)	Painting is the only repair authorized.
REPLACEMENT			
Blank Firing Attachment M15A2		Replace if unserviceable.	

Section II. INTERMEDIATE LEVEL AUXILIARY EQUIPMENT REPAIR

4-7. GENERAL

a. The Bayonet-Knife M7 is used in conjunction with the M16A2 rifle.

b. Refer to TM 9-1010-221-24&P for direct support and general support maintenance for the Grenade Launcher M203.

4-8. BAYONET KNIFE M7.

This task covers:

a. Disassembly
b. Inspection/Repair
c. Reassembly

INITIAL SETUP

Tools

Small Arms Repairman Tool Kit
NSN 5180-00-357-7770/SL-3-00607A
Field Maintenance Basic Less Power
Small Arms Shop Set SC 4933-95-CL-A11 (19204)

General Safety Instructions

Keep tip of blade pointed away from body at all times.
To avoid injury to your eyes, use care when removing and installing spring-loaded parts.

LOCATION	ITEM	ACTION	REMARKS
DISASSEMBLY			
Bayonet-Knife M7	a. Grip screws (1)	Remove using flat tip screwdriver.	
	b. Lock washers (2), grip (3) and grip (4).	Remove.	

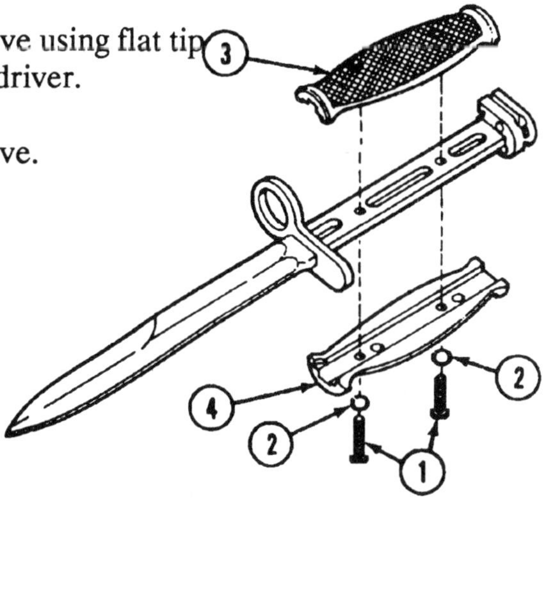

LOCATION	ITEM	ACTION	REMARKS

NOTE

Prior to disassembly, it is recommended that the right-hand release and plate be marked (using machinist's scriber) to assist in identification when assembling the left- and right-hand releases.

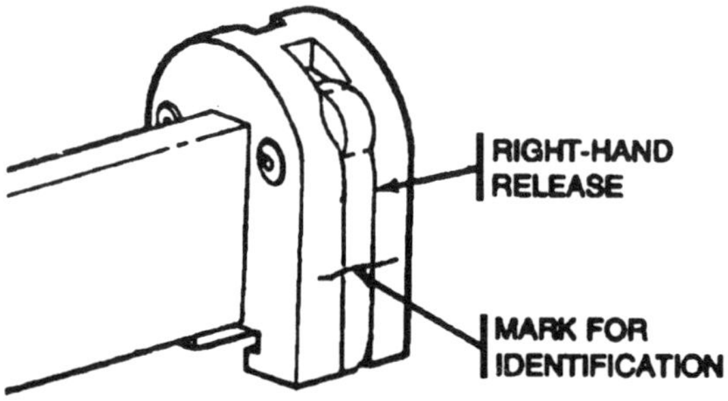

LOCATION	ITEM	ACTION	REMARKS
	c. Spring pin (15)	Remove using drive pin punch and hand hammer.	
	d. Release (16) and spring (17)	Remove.	
	e. Spring pin (18)	Remove using drive punch and hand hammer.	
	f. Release (19)	Remove.	Spring tension will be present if releases (16) was not removed.
	g. Blade assembly (20)		

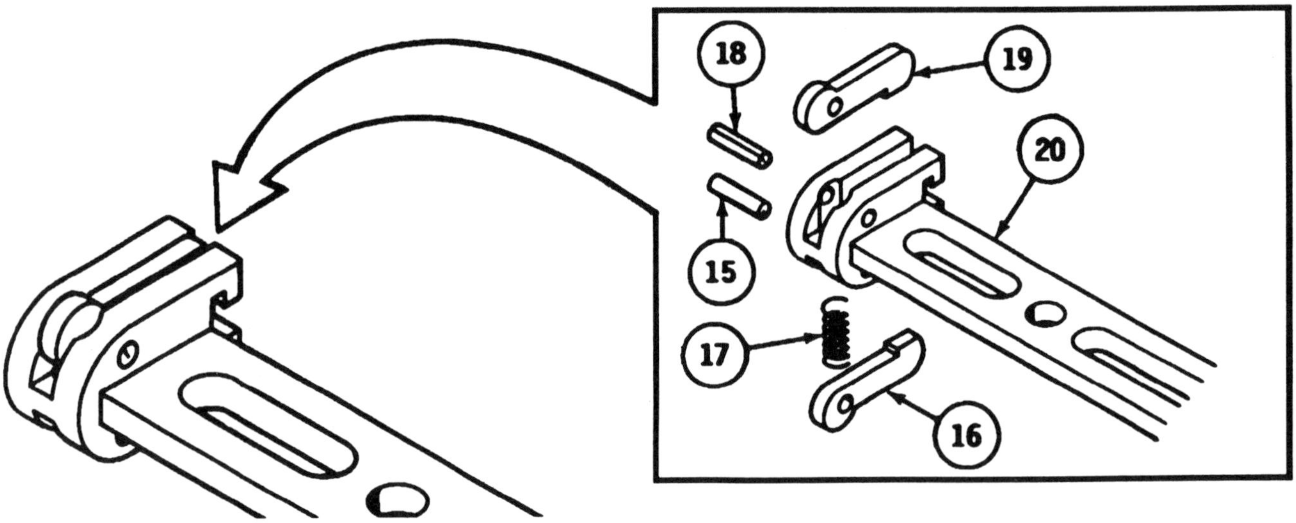

LOCATION	ITEM	ACTION	REMARKS

INSPECTION/REPAIR

Bayonet-Knife M7

a. Screws — Inspect threads and replace if stripped or damaged.

b. Grips — Inspect for cracks in both grips and stripped threads in the left grip. Replace if defective.

c. Spring pins — Replace if worn or damaged.

d. Spring — Inspect for kinked, set or broken springs. Replace if defective.

e. Release — Inspect release camming area for wear if positive retention is questionable. Replace the release. Inspect release for bends. Repair by straightening or replacing, as required.

f. Blade assembly

Inspect blade assembly for nicks, breaks, or dents. Repair by grinding and/or stoning. The length of the blade (measures from the front face of the guard) must not be less then 6 1/8 inches after repointing. Nicks on the cutting edge not exceeding 3/16 inch in-depth may be removed by grinding.

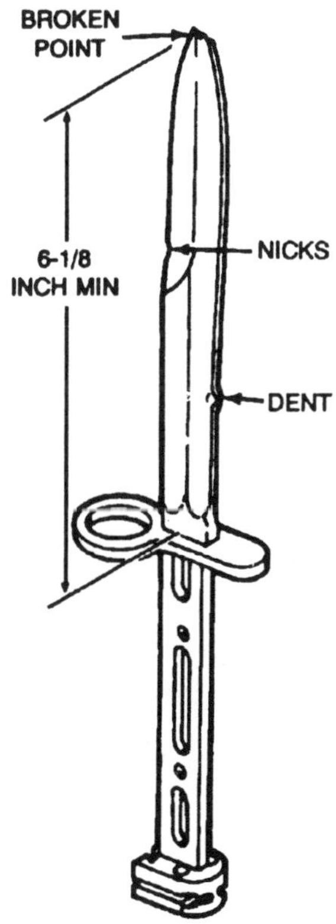

LOCATION	ITEM	ACTION	REMARKS
		Ground areas shall be blended into adjacent surfaces. Using a sharpening stone, smooth rough edges caused by grinding and hone blade to sharpness. Inspect plates for looseness. Stake or peen to tighten. If unable to tighten, spot or arc weld. Make certain when repairing that sufficient clearance exists after repairs to permit positive retention of bayonet to the rifle.	
		Inspect for loose guard. Repair by swaging the link using a large diameter drive pin punch and steel hammer.	

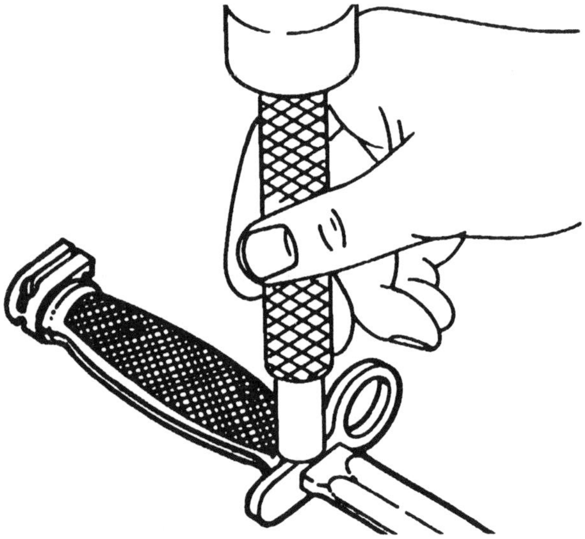

LOCATION	ITEM	ACTION	REMARKS
REASSEMBLY			
Bayonet-Knife M7	a. Release (19) and blade assembly (20)	Install.	
	b. Spring pin (18)	Install using drive pin punch and hand hammer.	
	c. Spring (17) and release (16)	Install.	
	d. Spring pin (15)	Install using drive pin punch and hand hammer.	

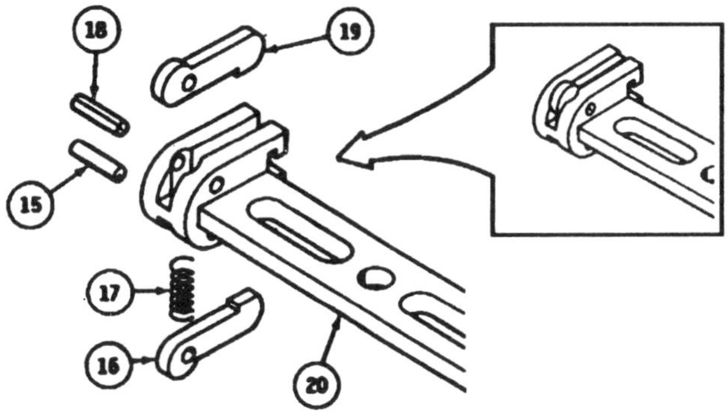

LOCATION	ITEM	ACTION	REMARKS
	e. Grip (21), grip (22) and lock washers (23)	Install.	
	f. Screw (24)	Install using flat tip screwdriver.	

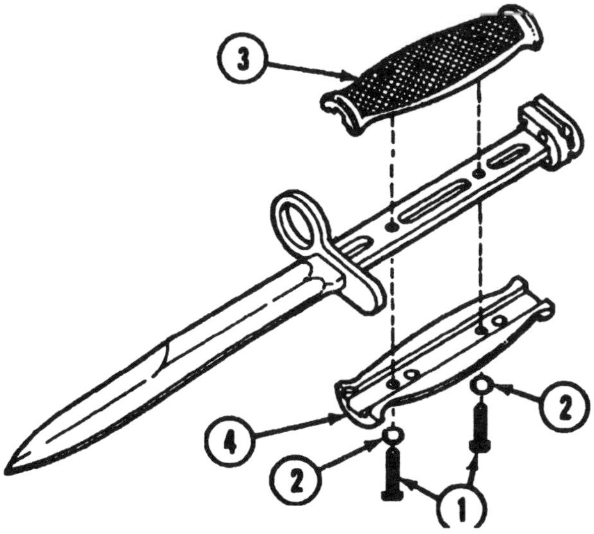

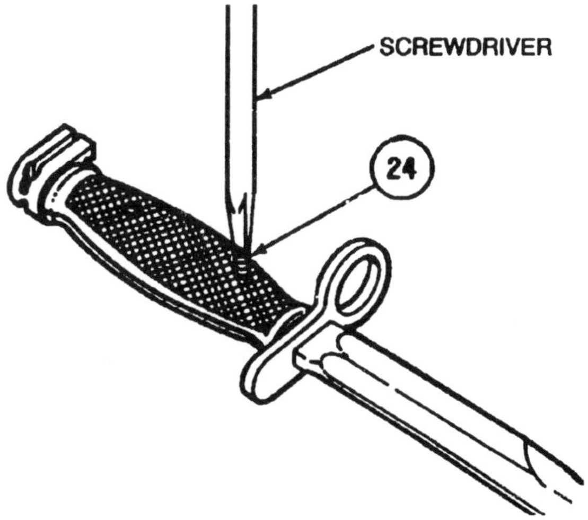

APPENDIX A
REFERENCES

A-1. TECHNICAL BULLETINS.

TB 9-1000-247-	Standards for Oversea Shipment or Domestic Issue Small Arms, Aircraft Armament, Towed Howitzers, Mortars, Recoilless Rifles, Rocket Launchers and Associated Fire Control Equipment.
TB 43-0196	Inspection and Certification of Gages, Small Arms

A-2. TECHNICAL MANUALS.

TM 05538C-10/1A	U.S Marine Corps Operator's Manual W/Components List M16A2 Rifle
TM 9-1005-301-30	Direct Support Maintenance Manual: Repair of Wooden, Fiber Glass/Plastic or Plastic Components of Small Arms Weapons
TM 9-1010-221-24&P	Organizational, Direct Support and General Support Maintenance Manual (including Repair Parts and Special Tools List) for Launcher, Grenade: 40-mm M203 W/E (NSN 1010-00-179-6447)
TM 740-90-1	Administrative Storage of Equipment
TM 750-244-7	Procedures for Destruction of Equipment to Prevent Enemy Use
TM 4700-15/1	Equipment Record Procedures
TM 9-1005-249-10	Operator's Manual M16/M16A1 Rifle

A-3. TECHNICAL INSTRUCTIONS.

TI 05538A-15/2A	Early Warning Indications of Malfunctions
TI 05538A-35/12A	Checking Muzzle and Breech Erosion in Barrel
TI 8005-24/20	Prefire Inspection, Small Arms Weapons, Ordnance Material

APPENDIX A
REFERENCES

A-4. FIELD MANUALS.

FM 21-11	First Aid for Soldiers
FM 23-9	M16A1 Rifle and Rifle Marksmanship

A-5. RELATED PUBLICATIONS.

FMFM 1-3A....................	Field Firing Techniques
FMFM 6-5	Marine Rifle Squad
MIL-STD-1169.................	Packaging, Packing and Marking for Shipment of Inert Ammunition Components
SI-1300-15/1....................	Ammo Data Cards, Marine Corps Ammo
SI-1300-15/2B	Procedure for Requesting Disposition for Class V (W) Materiel
SL-3-06229A	Components List for Tool and Gage Set for M16A1 Rifle

A-6. REFERENCES FOR ARMY USE ONLY.

TM 3-220	Chemical, Biological, and Radiological (CBR) Decontamination
TM 9-1005-237-23&P	Organizational and Direct Support Maintenance Manual (Including Repair Parts and Special Tools List) for Bayonet-Knife M6 and M7 with Bayonet-Knife Scabbard M10.
FM 21-40	NBC (Nuclear, Biological andChemical) Defense
FM 3-87........................	Nuclear, Biological and Chemical (NBC) Reconnaissance and Decontamination Operations (How to Fight)
CTA 50-970....................	Expendable Items (Except Medical Class V, Repair Parts and Heraldic Items)

APPENDIX
REFERENCES

DA PAM 738-750	The Army Maintenance Management System (TAMMS)
SB 38-100	Packing Materials Supplies and Equipment

APPENDIX B
MAINTENANCE ALLOCATION CHART
Section I. INTRODUCTION

B-1. GENERAL.

a. This section provides a general explanation of all maintenance and repair functions authorized at various maintenance categories.

b. The Maintenance Allocation Chart (MAC) in section II designates overall authority and responsibility for the performance of maintenance functions on the identified end item or component. The application of the maintenance functions to the end item or component will be consistent with the capacities and capabilities of the designated maintenance categories.

c. Section III lists the tools and test equipment (both special tools and common tool sets) required for each maintenance function as referenced from section II.

d. Section IV contains supplemental instructions and explanatory notes for a particular maintenance function.

B-2. MAINTENANCE FUNCTIONS. Maintenance functions will be limited to and defined as follows: (except for ammunition MAC).

a. *Inspect*. To determine the serviceability of an item by comparing its physical, mechanical, and/or electrical characteristics with established standards through examination (e.g., by sight, sound, or feel).

b. *Test*. To verify serviceability by measuring the mechanical, pneumatic, hydraulic, or electrical characteristics of an item and comparing those characteristics with prescribed standards.

c. *Service*. Operations required periodically to keep an item in proper operating condition, i.e., to clean (includes decontaminate, when required), to preserve, to drain, to paint, or to replenish fuel, lubricants, chemical fluids, or gases.

d. *Adjust*. To maintain or regulate, within prescribed limits, by bringing into proper or exact position, or by setting the operating characteristics to specified parameters.

e. *Align*. To adjust specified variable elements of an item to bring about optimum or desired performance.

f. *Calibrate*. To determine and cause corrections to be made or to be adjusted on instruments or test, measuring, and diagnostic equipments used in precision measurement. Consists of comparisons of two instruments, one of which is a certified standard of known accuracy, to detect and adjust any discrepancy in the accuracy of the instrument being compared.

g. *Remove/Install.* To remove and install the same item when required to perform service or other maintenance functions. Install may be the act of emplacing, seating, or fixing into positive a spare, repair part, or module (component or assembly) in a manner to allow the proper functioning of an equipment or system.

h. *Replace.* To remove an unserviceable item and install a serviceable counterpart in its place. "Replace" is authorized by the MAC and is shown as the 3d position code of the SMR code.

i. *Repair.* The application of maintenance services[1], including fault location/troubleshooting [2], removal/installation, and disassembly/assembly [3] procedures, and maintenance actions [4] to identify troubles and restore serviceability to an item by correcting specific damage, fault, malfunction, or failure in a part, subassembly, module (component or assembly), end item, or system.

j. *Overhaul.* That maintenance effort (service/action) prescribed to restore an item to a completely serviceable/operational condition as required by maintenance standards in appropriate technical publications (i.e, DMWR). Overhaul is normally the highest degree of maintenance performed by the Army. Overhaul does not normally return an item to like new condition.

k. *Rebuild.* Consists of those services/actions necessary for the restoration of unserviceable equipment to a like new condition in accordance with original manufacturing standards. Rebuild is the highest degree of materiel maintenance applied to Army equipment. The rebuild operation includes the act of returning to zero those age measurements (hours/miles, etc.) considered in classifying Army equipment/components.

[1]Services - inspect, test, service, adjust, align, calibrate, and/or replace.

[2]Fault locate/troubleshoot - The process of investigating and detecting the cause of equipment malfunctioning; the act of isolating a fault within a system or unit under test (UUT).

[3]Disassemble/assemble - encompasses the step-by-step taking apart (or breakdown) of a spare-/functional group coded item to the level of its least componency identified as maintenance significant (i.e., assigned an SMR code) for the category of maintenance under consideration.

[4]Actions - welding, grinding, riveting, straightening, facing, remachining and/or resurfacing.

B-3. EXPLANATION OF COLUMNS IN THE MAC, SECTION II.

a. *Column 1, Group Number.* Column 1 lists functional group code numbers, the purpose of which is to identify maintenance significant components, assemblies, subassemblies, and modules with the next higher assembly. End item group number shall be "00".

b. *Column 2, Component/Assembly.* Column 2 contains the names of components, assemblies, subassemblies, and modules for which maintenance is authorized.

c. *Column 3, Maintenance Function.* Column 3 lists the functions to be performed on the item listed in Column 2. (for detailed explanation of these functions, see paragraph B-2).

d. *Column 4, Maintenance Category.* Column 4 specifies, by the listing of a work time figure in the appropriate subcolumn(s), the category of maintenance authorized to perform the function listed in Column 3. This figure represents the active time required to perform that maintenance function at the indicated category of maintenance. If the number or complexity of the tasks within the listed maintenance function vary at different maintenance categories, appropriate work time figures will be shown for each category. The work time figure represents the average time required to restore an item (assembly, subassembly, component, module,end item, or system) to a serviceable condition under typical field operating conditions. This time includes preparation time (including any necessary disassembly/assembly time), troubleshooting/fault location time, and quality assurance/quality control time in addition to the time required to perform the specific tasks identified for the maintenance functions authorized in the maintenance allocation chart. The symbol designations for the various maintenance categories are as follows:

C.... Operator or Crew

O.... Organizational Maintenance

I..... Intermediate Maintenance

L..... Specialized Repair Activity (SRA)

e. *Column 5, Tools and Equipment.* Column 5 specifies, by code, those common tool sets (not individual tools) and special tools, TMDE, and support equipment required to perform the designated function.

f. *Column 6, Remarks.* This column shall, when applicable, contain a letter code, in alphabetic order, which shall be keyed to the remarks contained in Section IV.

B-4. EXPLANATION OF COLUMNS IN TOOL AND TEST EQUIPMENT REQUIREMENTS, SECTION III.

a. *Column 1, Reference Code.* The tool and test equipment reference code correlates with a code used in the MAC, Section II, Column 5.

b. *Column 2, Maintenance Category.* The lowest category of maintenance authorized to use the tool or test equipment.

c. *Column 3, Nomenclature.* Name or identification of the tool or test equipment.

d. *Column 4, National Stock Number.* The National stock number of the tool or test equipment.

e. *Column 5, Tool Number.* The manufacturer's part number.

B-5. EXPLANATION OF COLUMNS IN REMARKS, SECTION IV.

a. *Column 1, Reference Code.* The code recorded in column 6, Section II.

b. *Column 2, Remarks.* This column lists information pertinent to the maintenance function being performed as indicated in the MAC, Section II.

Section II. MAINTENANCE ALLOCATION CHART

(1) GROUP NUMBER	(2) COMPONENT\ ASSEMBLY	(3) MAINTENANCE FUNCTION	(4) MAINTENANCE CATEGORY C	O	I	(5) TOOLS & EQUIP	(6) REMARKS
00	M16A2 RIFLE, 5.56MM	Inspect	0.1	0.2	0.3		
		Test		0.1	03	4	
		Service	0.2	0.3			
		Replace		0.1			
		Repair		0.1	1.5		A
01	BOLT CARRIER	Inspect	0.1	0.1	0.1		
		Test			0.1	4	
		Service	0.1	0.1			
		Install	0.1	0.1	0.1		
		Replace	0.1				
		Repair		0.1	0.2	2,3	
0101	BOLT ASSEMBLY	Inspect	0.1	0.1	0.1		
		Test			0.1	4	
		Service	0.1	0.1			
		Install	0.1	0.1	0.1		
		Replace		0.1			
		Repair		0.2	0.2	2,3	
0102	KEY AND BOLT CARRIER ASSEMBLY	Inspect	0.1	0.1	0.1		
		Service	0.1	0.1			
		Install	0.1	0.1	0.1		
		Replace			0.1		
		Repair			0.2	2,3	A
02	HANDLE ASSEMBLY	Inspect	0.1	0.1	0.1		
		Service	0.1				
		Install	0.1	0.1			
		Replace		0.1			
		Repair		0.1		2	
03	UPPER RECEIVER AND BARREL ASSEMBLY	Inspect	0.1	0.2	0.1		
		Test			0.2		
		Service	0.2	0.2			
		Install	0.1	0.1	0.1		

(1) GROUP NUMBER	(2) COMPONENT\ ASSEMBLY	(3) MAINTENANCE FUNCTION	(4) MAINTENANCE CATEGORY C	O	I	(5) TOOLS & EQUIP.	(6) REMARKS
		Replace			0.2		
		Repair		0.1	0.5	2,3,4	
0301	BARREL ASSEMBLY	Inspect	0.1	0.2			
		Replace			0.5		
		Repair		0.2	0.5	2	B,C
0302	UPPER RECEIVER ASSEMBLY	Inspect	0.1		0.1		
		Install			0.2		
		Replace			0.5		
		Repair		0.3	0.3	2,3	
030201	FORWARD ASSIST ASSEMBLY	Inspect	0.1	0.1	0.1		
		Install			0.2		
		Replace			0.2		
		Repair			0.2	2,3	
030202	REAR SIGHT ASSEMBLY	Inspect			0.1		
		Install			0.2		
		Replace			0.5		
		Repair			0.3		
04	LOWER RECEIVER AND BUTTSTOCK ASSEMBLY	Inspect	0.1	0.2	0.2		
		Test			0.1	4	
		Service	0.2	0.2			
		Install	0.1	0.1	0.1		
		Repair		0.3	0.3	2,3,4	D,E, F G,H
0401	BUTTSTOCK ASSEMBLY	Inspect	0.1	0.1	0.1		
		Install		0.1	0.1		
		Replace		0.1			
		Repair		0.3	0.3	2	H
0402	HAMMER ASSEMBLY	Inspect	0.1	0.1	0.1		
		Install			0.1		
		Replace		0.1			
		Repair			0.1	2,3	

(1) GROUP NUMBER	(2) COMPONENT\ ASSEMBLY	(3) MAINTENANCE FUNCTION	(4) MAINTENANCE CATEGORY C	O	I	(5) TOOLS & EQUIP.	(6) REMARKS
0403	TRIGGER ASSEMBLY	Inspect	0.1	0.1	0.1		
		Install			0.1		
		Replace			0.1		
		Repair			0.1	2,3	
0404	LOWER RECEIVER	Inspect			0.1		
		Test			0.1	4	
		Install			0.1		
		Repair			0.3	2,3,4	
05	BAYONET-KNIFE M7	Inspect	0.1				
		Service	0.2				
		Replace		0.1			
		Repair		0.2	0.4	2,3	

Section III. TOOL AND TEST EQUIPMENT REQUIREMENTS FOR M16A2 RIFLE

(1) TOOL OR TEST EQUIP CODE	(2) MAINT-ENANCE CATE-GORY	(3) NOMEN-CLATURE	(4) NATIONAL NATO STOCK NO.	(5) TOOL NO.
1	O	Tool Kit, Small Arms Repairman	5180-00-357-7770	SL-3-00607A SC 5180-95-CL-A07
2	F	Shop Set, Small Arms: Field Maintenance, Basic Less Pow.	4933-00-754-0664	SC 4933-95-CL-A11
3	F	Tool & Gage Set, DS/GS Maintenance for 5.56-mm Rifle M16 Series & M231 Firing Port Weapon	4933-00-056-7106 8426685	SL-3-06229A
(MC ONLY) 4	F	Magnet, Permanent	5340-01-054-0124	1809

Section IV. REMARKS

REFERENCE CODE	REMARKS
A	Tool, Key
B	Tool, Sight Remover
C *(MC ONLY)*	Depressor, Front Sight Detent
D	Tool, Pivot Pin Removing
E	Tool, Pivot Pin Installation
F *(MC ONLY)*	Gage, Receiver
G	Pin, Modified Old Trigger "Slave"
H	TM 9-1005-301-30

APPENDIX C
ORGANIZATIONAL AND INTERMEDIATE MAINTENANCE REPAIR PARTS AND SPECIAL TOOLS LIST

Section I. INTRODUCTION

C-1. SCOPE. This appendix lists and authorizes spares and repair parts; special tools; special test, measurement, and diagnostic equipment (TMDE); and other special support equipment required for performance of organizational and intermediate maintenance of the 5.56-mm Rifle M16A2. It authorizes the requisitioning, issue, and disposition of spares, repair parts and special tools as indicated by the Source, Maintenance and Recoverability (SMR) codes.

C-2. GENERAL. This Repair Parts and Special Tools List (RPSTL) is divided into the following sections:

a. Section II. Repair Parts List. A list of spares and repair parts authorized by this RPSTL for use in the performance of maintenance. The list also includes parts which must be removed for replacement of the authorized parts. Parts lists are composed of functional groups in ascending alphanumeric sequence, with the parts in each group listed in ascending figure and item number sequence. Bulk materials are listed in NSN sequence.

b. Section III. Special Tools List. A list of special tools, special TMDE, and other special support equipment authorized by this RPSTL for the performance of maintenance.

c. Section IV. National Stock Number and Part Number Index. A list, in National item identification number (NIIN) sequence, of all National stock numbers (NSN) appearing in the listings, followed by a list in alphanumeric sequence of all part numbers appearing in the listings. National stock numbers and part numbers are cross-referenced to each illustration figure and item number appearance.

C-3. EXPLANATION OF COLUMNS.

a. ILLUSTRATION (Column (1)). This column is divided as follows:

(1) (a) FIG NO. Figure number. Indicates the figure number illustrating an exploded view of a functional group.

(b) ITEM NO. Indicates the number used to identify items called out in the illustration.

b. SMR CODE (Column (2)). The Source, Maintenance, and Recoverability (SMR) code is a 5-position code which provides requisitioning, maintenance level authority, and maintenance level disposal authority information and is further described in the following:

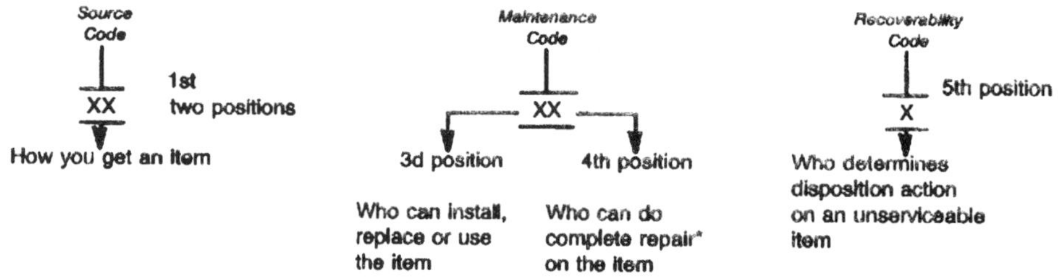

* Complete Repair: Maintenance capacity, capability, and authority to perform all the corrective maintenance tasks of the "Repair" function in a use/user environment in order to restore serviceability to a failed item.

(1) Source Code. The source code tells you how you get an item needed for maintenance, repair, or overhaul of an end item/equipment. Source codes are always the first two positions of the SMR code. Explanations of source codes follow:

Code	Explanation
PA PB PC PD PE PF PG	Stocked items; use the applicable NSN to request/requisition items with these source codes. They are authorized to the category indicated by the code entered in the 3d position of the SMR code. The complete kit must be requisitioned and applied.
KD KF KB	Items with these codes are not to be requested/requisitioned individually. They are part of a kit which is authorized to the maintenance category indicated in the 3d position of the SMR code. The complete kit must be requisitioned and applied.
MO-(Made at Org/ AVUM Category) MF-(Made at INTMD/ AVIM MD-(Made at Depot)	Items with these codes are not to be requested/requisitioned individually. They must be made from bulk material which is identified by NSN in the Description column and listed in the Bulk Material group in the repair parts list in this appendix. If the item is authorized to you by the 3d position code of the SMR code, but the source code indicates it is made at a higher category, order the item from the higher category of maintenance.
AO-(Assembled by Org/AVUM Category)	Items with these codes are not to be requested/requisitioned individually. The parts that make up the assembled item must

Code	Explanation
AF-(Assembled by INTMDA/AVIM Category) AD-(Assembled b Depot)	be requisitioned or fabricated and assembled at the category of maintenance indicated by the source code. If the 3rd position code of the SMR code authorizes you to replace the item, but the source code indicates the item is assembled at a higher category, order the item from the higher category of maintenance.
XA	Do not requisition an "XA" coded item. Order its next higher assembly. (Also, refer to the NOTE below.)
XB	If an "XB" item cannot be obtained from salvage, order it using the FSCM and part number given.
XD	Item is not stocked. Order an "XD" coded item through normal supply channels using the FSCM and part number given, if no NSN is available.

NOTE

Cannibalization or controlled exchange, when authorized, may be used as a source of supply for items with the above source codes, except for those source coded "XA" .

(2) Maintenance code. Maintenance codes tell you the category(s) of maintenance authorized to USE and REPAIR support items. The maintenance codes are entered in the third and fourth positions of the SMR Codes as follows:

(a) The maintenance code entered in the third position tells you the lowest maintenance category authorized to remove, replace, and use an item. The maintenance code entered in the third position will indicate authorization to one of the following categories of maintenance.

Code	Application/Explanation
C	Crew or operator maintenance done within organizational or aviation unit maintenance.
O	Organizational or aviation unit category can remove, replace, and use the item.
F	Intermediate or aviation intermediate category can remove, replace, and use the item.
L	Specialized repair activity can remove replace, and use the item.

Code	Explanation
D	Depot category can remove, replace, and use the item.

(b) The maintenance code entered in the fourth position tells you whether or not the item is to be repaired and identifies the lowest maintenance category with the capability to do complete repair (i.e., perform all authorized repair functions). (NOTE: Some limited repair may be done on the item at a lower category of maintenance, if authorized by the Maintenance Allocation Chart (MAC) and SMR codes.) This position will contain one of the following maintenance codes.

O	Organizational or aviation unit is the lowest category that can do complete repair of the item.
F	Intermediate or aviation intermediate is the lowest category that can do complete repair of the item.
L	Specialized repair activity is the lowest category that can do complete repair of the item.
D	Depot is the lowest category that can do complete repair of the item.
Z	Nonreparable. No repair is authorized.
B	No repair is authorized. (No parts or special tools are authorized for the maintenance of a "B" coded item). However, the item may be reconditioned by adjusting, lubricating, etc., at the user level.

(3) Recoverability code. Recoverability codes are assigned to items to indicate the disposition action on unserviceable items. The Recoverability code is entered in the fifth position of the SMR Code as follows:

Recoverability Codes	Definition
Z	Nonreparable item. When unserviceable, condemn and dispose of the item at the category of maintenance shown in 3d position of SMR Code.
O	Reparable item. When uneconomical reparable, condemn and dispose of the item at organizational or aviation unit category

Recoverability Codes	Definition
F	Reparable item. When uneconomical reparable, condemn and dispose of the item at the intermediate or aviation intermediate category.
D	Reparable item. When beyond lower category repair capability, return to depot. Condemnation and disposal of item not authorized below depot category.
L	Reparable item. Condemnation and disposal not authorized below specialized repair activity.
A	Item requires special handling or condemnation procedures because of specific reasons (i.e., precious metal content, high solar value, critical material, or hazardous material). Refer to appropriate manuals/directives for specific instructions.

c. *NATIONAL STOCKNUMBER (Column (3))*. Lists the National stock number (NSN) assigned to the item. Use the NSN for requests/requisitions.

d. *FSCM (Column (4))*. The Federal Supply Code for Manufacturer (FSCM) is a 5-digit numeric code which is used to identify the manufacturer, distributor, or Government agency, etc., that supplies the item.

e. *PART NUMBER (Column (5))*. Indicates the primary number used by the manufacturer (individual, company, firm, corporation, or Government activity), which controls the design and characteristics of the item by means of its engineering drawings, specifications standards, and inspection requirements to identify an item or range of items.

NOTE

When you use an NSN to requisition an item, the item you receive may have a different part number from the part ordered, but go ahead and use or furnish it as the replacement part.

f. *DESCRIPTION (Column (6))*. This column provides the following information:

(1) The Federal Item Name and , when required, a minimum description to identify the item parts that make up an assembled item are listed immediately following the assembled item line entry and are indicated by an asterisk in front of the name.

(2) NSN's for bulk materials are referenced in the description column in the line item entry for the item to be manufactured/fabricated.

(3) When the part to be used differs between serial numbers of the same model, the effective serial numbers are shown as the last line of the description.

(4) The USABLE ON CODE, when applicable (see paragraph C- 4, SPECIAL INFORMATION).

(5) In the Special Tool List Section, the basis of issue (BOI) appears as the last line(s) in the entry for each special tool, special TMDE, and other special equipment. When density of equipments supported exceeds density spread indicated in the basis of issue, the total authorization is increased proportionately.

g. *U/M (Column (7).* The Unit of Measure (UM) indicates the measure (e.g., foot, gallon, pound) or count (e.g., each, dozen, gross) of a listed item. A two-character alpha code (e.g., FT, GL, :B. EA, DZ, GR) appears in this column to indicate the measure or count. If the U/M code appearing in this column differs from the Unit of Issue (U/I) code listed in the Army Master Data File (AMDF), request the lowest U/I that will satisfy your needs.

h. *QTY INCIN UNIT (Column (8)).* The Quantity Incorporated in Unit (QTY INCIN UNIT) indicates the quantity of the item used in the breakout shown on the illustration figure, which is prepared for a functional group, subfunctional group, or an assembly. A "V" appearing in this column in lieu of a quantity indicates that no specific quantify is applicable (e.g., shims, spacers).

C-4. SPECIAL INFORMATION

a. The USABLE ON CODE" title appears in the lower right corner of column (6), Description. Usable on codes are shown in the right-hand margin of the description column. Uncoded items are applicable to all models. Identification of the usable on codes used in this publication are:

Code	Used ON
M52	M16A2
538	Bayonet-Knife M7
000	Tool and Gage Set P/N 8426685

b. Detailed assembly instructions for items source coded to be assembled from component spare/repair parts are found in chapter 3. Items that make up the assembly are listed immediately following the assembled item entry or appropriate group header.

C-5. HOW TO LOCATE REPAIR PARTS.

a. When National Stock Number or Part Number is not Known:

(1) First. Using the table of contents, determine the functional group or subfunctional group to which the item belongs. This is necessary since figures are prepared for functional groups and subfunctional groups, and listings are divided into the same groups.

(2) Second. Find the figure covering the functional group or subfunctional group to which the item belongs.

(3) Third. Identify the item on the figure and note the item number of the item.

(4) Fourth. Refer to the Repair Parts List for the figure to find the line item entry for the item number noted on the figure.

b. When National Stock Number or Part Number is Known:

(1) First. Using the index of National Stock Numbers and Part Numbers, find the pertinent National Stock Number or part number. The NSN index is in National Item Identification Number (NIIN)* sequence. The part numbers in the Part Number index are listed in ascending alphanumeric sequence. Both indexes cross- reference you to the illustration figure and item number of the item you are looking for.

NSN

* The NIIN consists of the last 9 digits of the NSN (i.e., 5305-01-674-1467).

NIIN

(2) Second. After finding the figure and item number, verify that the item is the one you're looking for, then locate the item number in the repair parts list for the figure.

C-6. FEDERAL SUPPLY CODE FOR MANUFACTURERS.

CODE	MANUFACTURER
13629	COLT INDUSTRIES OPERATING CORP. FIREARMS DIVISION 150 HUYSHOPE AVE HARTFORD, CT 06102
6059	DEVCON CORP 61 ENDICOTT ST DANVERS, MA 01923
19200	ROCK ISLAND ARSENAL ROCK ISLAND, IL 61299
19204	ROCK ISLAND ARSENAL ROCK ISLAND, IL 61299

CODE	MANUFACTURER
27412	SANIBAR CORP 9999 MUIRLAND BLVD IRVINE, CA 92714
58536	FEDERAL COMMERCIAL ITEM DESCRIPTION EXECUTED BY GENERAL SERVICE ADMINISTRATION WASHINGTON, DC 20406
64484	SERGEANT-WELCH SCIENTIFIC CO 7300 N. LINDER AVE P.O. BOX 1026 SKOKIE, IL 60077
80205	NATIONAL AEROSPACE STANDARDS COMMITTEE AEROSPACE INDUSTRIES ASSOCIATION OF AMERICA INC. 1725 DE SALES, N.W.W. WASHINGTON, DC
1349	MILITARY SPECIFICATIONS PROMULGATED BY MILITARY DEPARTMENT/AGENCIES UNDER AUTHORITY OF DEFENSE STANDARDIZATION MANUAL 4120 3-M
88044	AERONAUTICAL STANDARDS GROUP DEPARTMENT OF NAVY & AIR FORCE
89855	AMERICAN BRANDS INC. AMERICAN TOBACCO DIVISION 245 PARK AVE NEW YORK, NY 10167
6906	MILITARY STANDARDS PROMULGATED BY MILITARY DEPARTMENTS UNDER AUTHORITY OF DEFENSE STANDARDIZATION MANUAL 4120 3-M

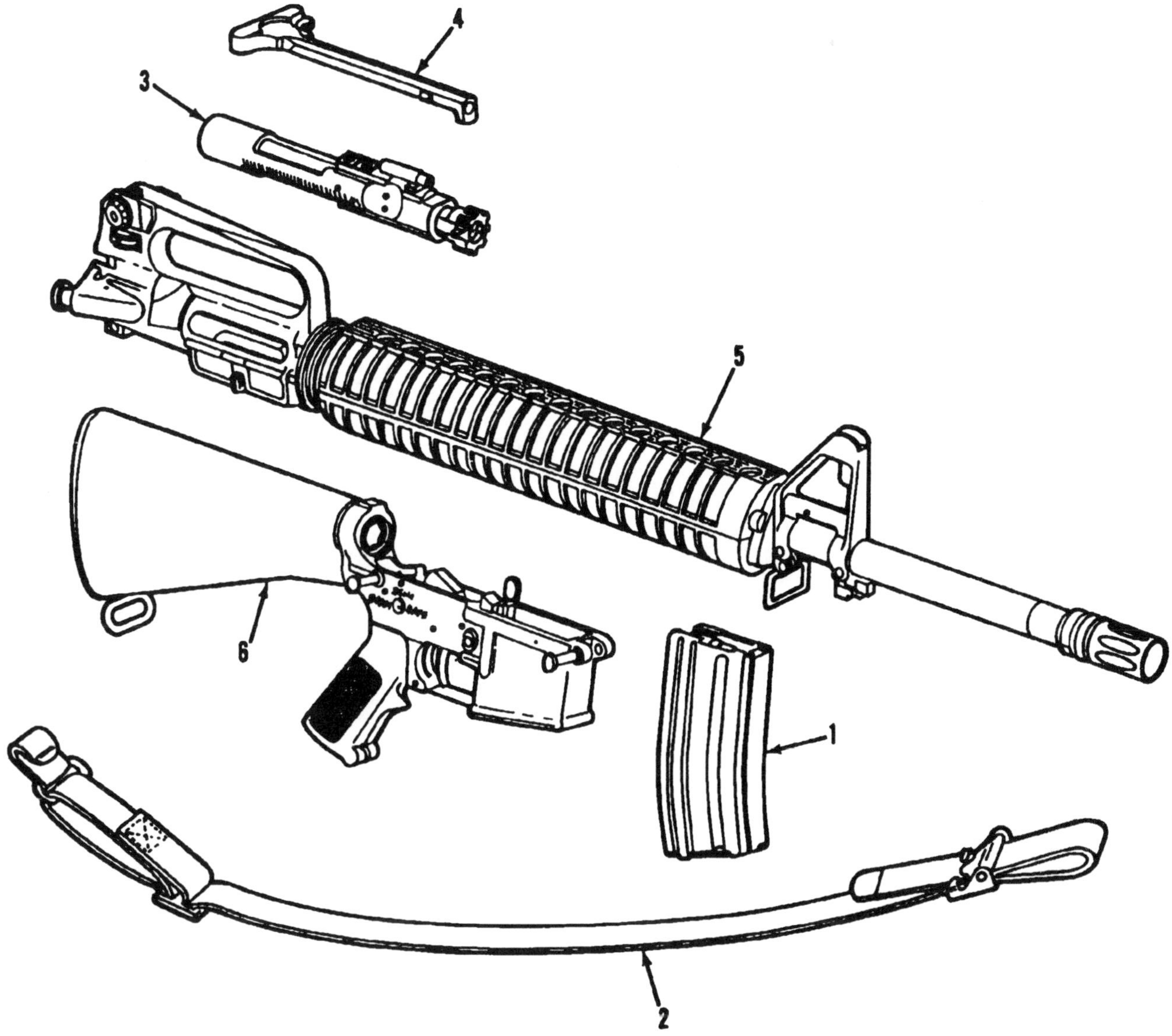

Figure C-1. 5.56-mm rifle, M16A2 9349000

Section II. REPAIR PARTS LIST

(1) ILLUSTRATION (a) FIG. NO.	(b) ITEM NO.	(2) SMR CODE	(3) NATIONAL STOCK NUMBER	(4) FSCM	(5) PART NUMBER	(6) DESCRIPTION	(7) USABLE ON CODE	(8) U/M	(9) QTY INC IN UNIT
						GROUP 00 5.56-MM RIFLE, M16A2 9349000			
C -1	1	PAOZZ	1005-00-927-5004	19200	8448670	MAGAZINE, CARTRIDGE	M52	EA	1
C-1	2	PACZZ	1005-01-083-8113	19200	11833432	SLING, SMALL ARMS (MC ONLY)	M52	EA	1
C-1	2A	PACZZ	1005-01-216-4510	19204	12624561	SLING, SMALL ARMS (ARMY ONLY)	M52	EA	1
C-1	3	AFFFF		19200	8448501	BOLT CARRIER ASSEMBLY	M52	EA	1
C-1	4	PAOZZ	1005-00-017-9546	19204	9349050	HANDLE ASSEMBLY	M52	EA	1
C-1	5	AFFFF		1920	9349050	UPPER RECEIVER & BARREL ASSEMBLY	M52	EA	1
C-1	6	XAFFA		19200	9349100	LOWER RECEIVER & BUTTSTOCK ASSE	M52	EA	1

NOTE

(ARMY ONLY)

ITEM NO.	SMR CODE	PART NUMBER
1	PACZZ	8448670

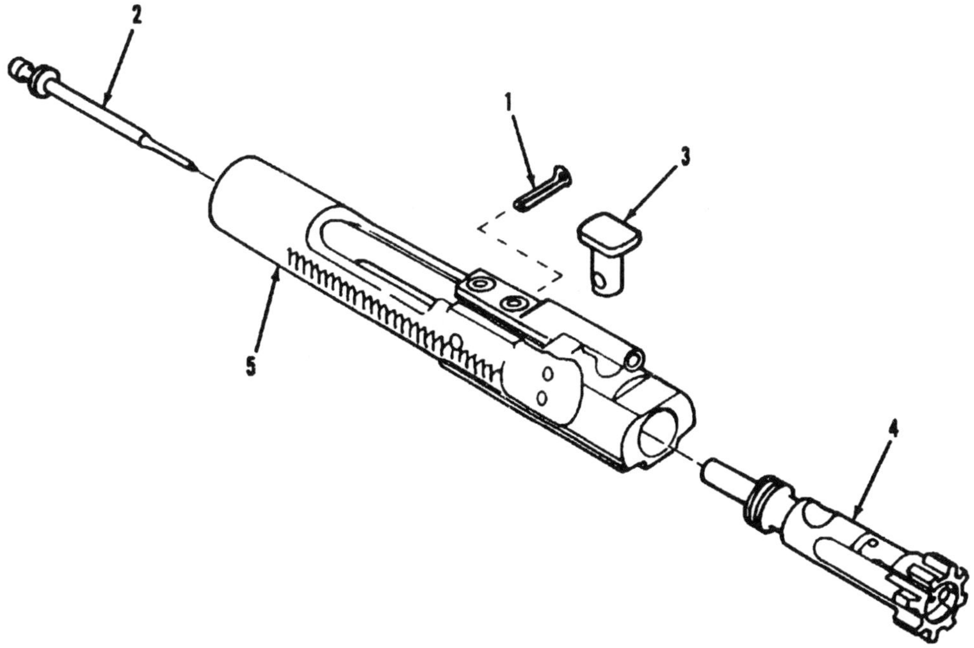

Figure C-2 Bolt Carrier Assembly 8448501

(1) ILLUSTRATION (a) FIG. NO.	(b) ITEM NO.	(2) SMR CODE	(3) NATIONAL STOCK NUMBER	(4) FSCM	(5) PART NUMBER	(6) DESCRIPTION	(7) USABLE ON CODE	(8) U/M	(9) QTY INC IN UNIT
						GROUP 01 BOLT CARRIER ASSEMBLY			
						8448501			
C-2	1	PAOZZ	1005-00-999-1509	19204	8448504	PIN, FIRING PIN RETAINING	M52	EA	1
C-2	2	PAOZZ	1005-00-017-9547	19204	8448503	PIN, FIRING	M52	EA	1
C-2	3	PAOZZ	1005-00-992-7294	19204	8448502	PIN, BOLT CAM	M52	EA	1
C-2	4	PAOFF	1005-00-992-7285	19200	8448509	BOLT ASSEMBLY	M52	EA	1
C-2	5	AFFFF		19200	8448505	KEY AND BOLT CARRIER ASSEMBLY	M52	EA	1

NOTE

(ARMY ONLY)

ITEM NO.	SMR CODE	PART NUMBER
2	PAFZZ	8448503
4	PAFZZ	8448509

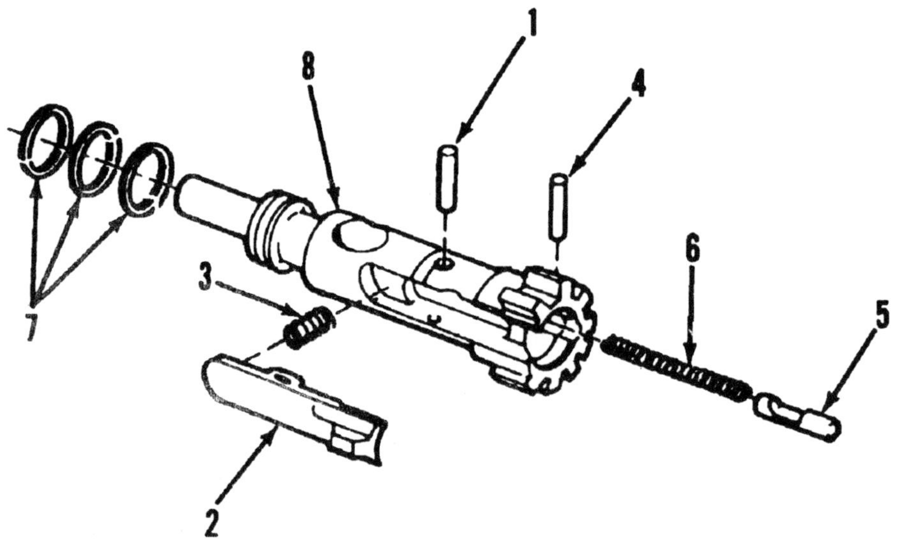

Figure C-3. Bolt assembly 8448509

(1) ILLUSTRATION (a) FIG. NO.	(b) ITEM NO.	(2) SMR CODE	(3) NATIONAL STOCK NUMBER	(4) FSCM	(5) PART NUMBER	(6) DESCRIPTION	(7) USABLE ON CODE	(8) U/M	(9) QTY INC IN UNIT
						GROUP 0101 BOLT ASSEMBLY			
						8448509			
C-3	1	PAOZZ	1005-00-992-7290	19204	8448513	PIN, EXTRACTOR	M52	EA	1
C-3	2	PAOZZ	1005-00-992-7288	19204	8448512	EXTRACTOR, CARTRIDGE	M52	EA	1
C-3	3	PAOZZ	1005-00-760-3768	19200	8448755	SPRING ASSEMBLY	M52	EA	1
C-3	4	PAOZZ	5315-00-597-5086	96906	MS16562-98	PIN, SPRING	M52	EA	1
C-3	5	PAOZZ	1005-00-992-7291	19204	8448515	EJECTOR, CARTRIDGE	M52	EA	1
C-3	6	PAOZZ	5360-00-992-7292	19204	8448516	SPRING, HELICAL	M52	EA	1
C-3	7	PAFZZ	1005-00-992-7287	19204	8448511	RING, BOLT	M52	EA	3
C-3	8	XAFZZ		19200	8448510	BOLT	M52	EA	1

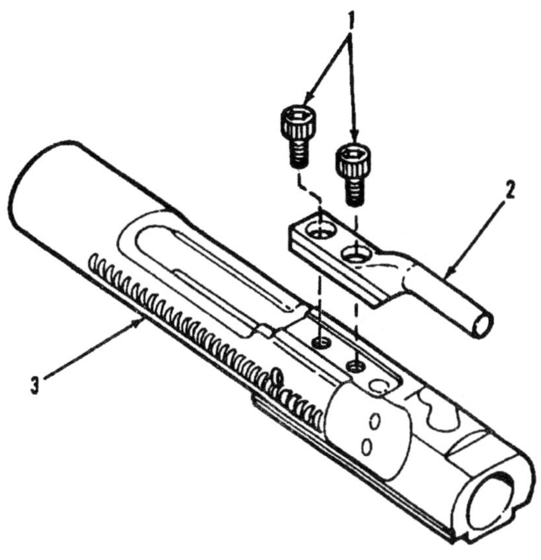

Figure C-4. Key and bolt carrier assembly 8448505

(1) ILLUSTRATION (a) FIG. NO.	(b) ITEM NO.	(2) SMR CODE	(3) NATIONAL STOCK NUMBER	(4) FSCM	(5) PART NUMBER	(6) DESCRIPTION	(7) USABLE ON CODE	(8) U/M	(9) QTY INC IN UNIT
						GROUP 0102 KEY & BOLT CARRIER ASSEMBLY			
						8448505			
C-4	1	PAFZZ	1005-00-992-7284	19204	8448508	SCREW, CARRIER AND KEY	M52	EA	2
C-4	2	PAFZZ	1005-00-992-7283	19200	8448506	KEY, BOLT CARRIER	M52	EA	1
C-4	3	PAFZZ	1005-00-738-6213	19200	8448507	CARRIER, BOL	M52	EA	1

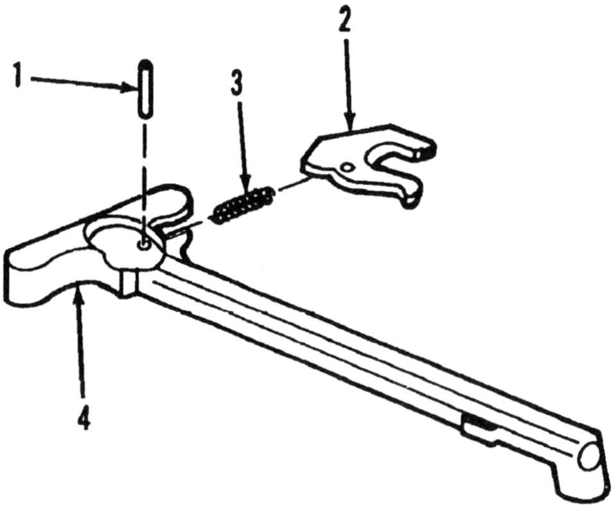

Figure C-5. Handle assembly 8448517

(1) ILLUSTRATION (a) FIG. NO.	(b) ITEM NO.	(2) SMR CODE	(3) NATIONAL STOCK NUMBER	(4) FSCM	(5) PART NUMBER	(6) DESCRIPTION	(7) USABLE ON CODE	(8) U/M	(9) QTY INC IN UNIT
						GROUP 02 HANDLE ASSEMBLY			
						8448517			
C-5	1	PAOZZ	5315-00-017-9552	13629	95113	PIN, SPRING	M52	EA	1
C-5	2	PAOZZ	1005-00-999-0405	19200	8448520	LATCH, CHARGING, HANDLE	M52	EA	1
C-5	3	PAOZZ	5360-00-999-0404	19204	8448507	SPRING, HELICAL	M52	EA	1
C-5	4	XAOZZ		19200	8448518	HANDLE	M52	EA	1

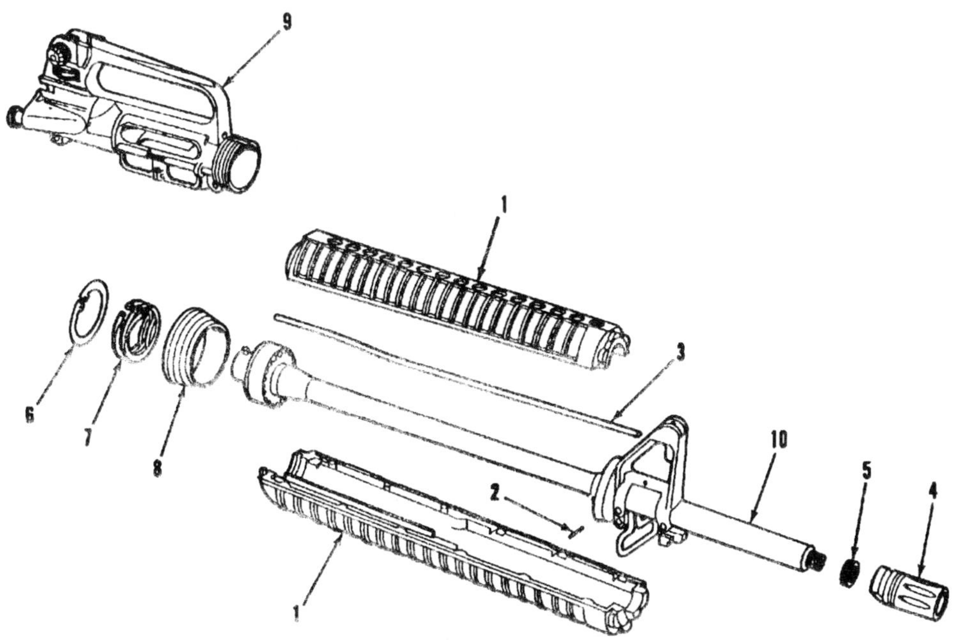

Figure C-6. Upper receiver and barrel assembly 9349050

(1) ILLUSTRATION (a) FIG. NO.	(b) ITEM NO.	(2) SMR CODE	(3) NATIONAL STOCK NUMBER	(4) FSCM	(5) PART NUMBER	(6) DESCRIPTION	(7) USABLE ON CODE	(8) U/M	(9) QTY INC IN UNIT
						GROUP 03 UPPER RECEIVER AND BARREL ASSEMBLY 9349050			
C-6	1	PAOZZ	1005-01-134-3629	19200	9349059	HANDGUARD ASSEMBLY	M52	EA	2
C-6	2	PAFZZ	5315-00-058-6044	96906	MS16562-106	PIN, SPRING	M52	EA	1
C-6	3	PAFZZ	1005-00-978-1038	19200	8448567	TUBE, GAS.	M52	EA	1
C-6	4	PAFZZ	1005-01-134-3633	19200	9349051	COMPENSATOR	M52	EA	1
C-6	5	PAFZZ	5365-01-144-1496	19200	9349052	SHIM.	M52	EA	1
C-6	6	PAFZZ	5365-00-252-6853	96906	MS16626-1137	RING, RETAINING	M52	EA	1
C-6	7	PAFZZ	1005-00-978-1036	19204	8448555	SPRING,SLIP RING, HANDGAURD UPPER RECEIVER	M52	EA	1
C-6	8	PAFZZ	1005-00-087-8998	19204	8448712	RING, SLIP, HANDGUARD	M52	EA	1
C-6	9	AFFFF		19200	9349062	UPPER RECEIVER ASSEMBLY	M52	EA	1
C-6	10	PAFFF	1005-01-143-7694	19200	9349124	BARREL ASSEMBLY	M52	EA	1

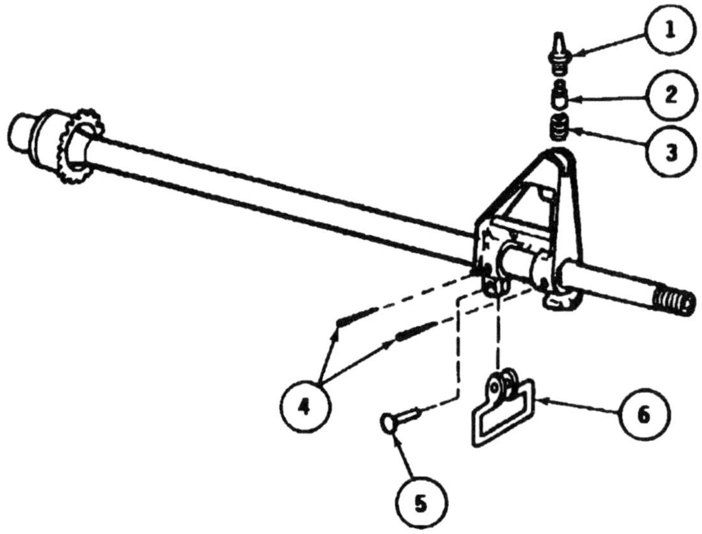

Figure C-7. Barrel assembly 9349124

(1) ILLUSTRATION (a) FIG. NO.	(b) ITEM NO.	(2) SMR CODE	(3) NATIONAL STOCK NUMBER	(4) FSCM	(5) PART NUMBER	(6) DESCRIPTION	(7) USABLE ON CODE	(8) U/M	(9) QTY INC IN UNIT
						GROUP 0301 BARREL ASSEMBLY			
						9349124			
C-7	1	PAOZZ	1005-01-134-3625	19200	9349056	POST, FRONT SIGHT	M52	EA	1
C-7	2	PAOZZ	1005-00-979-3930	19204	8448573	DETENT, FRONT SIGHT	M52	EA	1
C-7	3	PAOZZ	5360-00-979-3931	19204	8448574	SPRING, HELICAL	M52	EA	1
C-7	4	PAFZZ	1005-00-979-3926	19204	8448575	PIN, FRONT SIGHT	M52	EA	2
C-7	5	PAOZZ	5320-01-063-7635	19204	8448697	RIVET, TUBULAR	M52	EA	1
C-7	6	PAOZZ	1005-00-017-9543	19204	8448571	SWIVEL, SLING SMALL	M52	EA	1

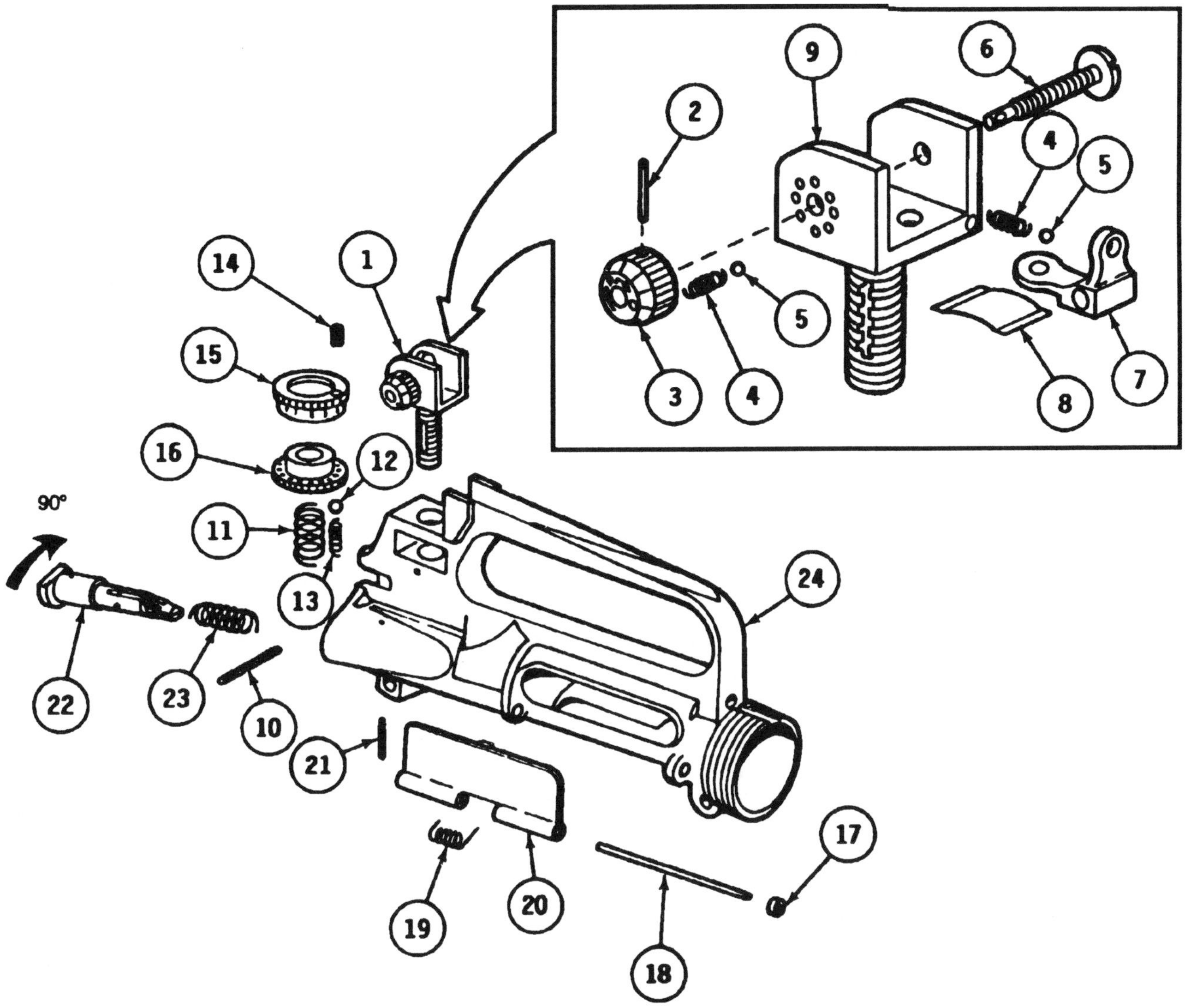

Figure C-8. Upper receiver assembly 9349062 and rear sight assembly 9349072

(1) ILLUSTRATION (a) FIG. NO.	(b) ITEM NO.	(2) SMR CODE	(3) NATIONAL STOCK NUMBER	(4) FSCM	(5) PART NUMBER	(6) DESCRIPTION	(7) USABLE ON CODE	(8) U/M	(9) QTY INC IN UNIT
						GROUP 0302 UPPER RECEIVER ASSEMBLY 9349062 AND GROUP 030202 REAR SIGHT ASSEMBLY 9349072			
C-8	1	AFFFF		19200	9349072	REAR SIGHT ASSEMBLY	M52	EA	1
C-8	2	PAFZZ	5315-00-058-6678	96906	MS16562-103	* PIN, SPRING	M52	EA	1
C-8	3	PAFZZ	1005-01-134-3627	19200	9349077	* KNOB, WINDAGE	M52	EA	1
C-8	4	PAFZZ	5360-01-148-1751	19200	9349069	* SPRING, HELICAL	M52	EA	2
C-8	5	PAFZZ	3110-01-148-7438	96906	MS1906-20003	* BALL, BEARING	M52	EA	2
C-8	6	PAFZZ	5305-01-144-1490	19200	9349076	* SCREW, WINDAGE	M52	EA	1
C-8	7	PAFZZ	1005-01-135-3697	19200	9349075	* APERTURE, SIGHT	M52	EA	1
C-8	8	PAFZZ	5360-00-978-1027	19200	8448536	* SPRING, FLAT	M52	EA	1
C-8	9	PAFZZ	1005-01-134-3631	19200	9349074	* BASE, REAR SIGHT	M52	EA	2
C-8	10	PAFZZ	5315-01-027-4759	80205	NAS561-3-10	PIN, SPRING	M52	EA	1
C-8	11	PAFZZ	5360-01-134-3710	19200	9349070	SPRING, HELICAL	M52	EA	1
C-8	12	PAFZZ	3110-01-148-7438	96906	MS19061-20003	BALL, BEARING	M52	EA	1
C-8	13	PAFZZ	5360-01-148-1751	19200	9349069	SPRING, HELICAL	M52	EA	1
C-8	14	PAFZZ	1005-01-134-3622	19200	9349065	SCREW, INDEX	M52	EA	1
C-8	15	PAFZZ	1005-01-134-3621	19200	9349066	INDEX, ELEVATION	M52	EA	1
C-8	16	PAFZZ	1005-01-135-4972	19200	9349067	KNOB, ELEVATION	M52	EA	1
C-8	17	PAOZZ	5365-00-064-2652	96906	MS16632-1012	RING, RETAINING	M52	EA	1
C-8	18	PAOZZ	1005-00-978-1023	19204	8448533	PIN, EJECTION PORT COVER	M52	EA	1
C-8	19	PAOZZ	5360-00-978-1025	19204	8448532	SPRING, HELICAL	M52	EA	1
C-8	20	PAOZZ	1005-00-978-1022	19204	8448525	COVER, EJECTION PORT	M52	EA	1
C-8	21	PAFZZ	5315-00-058-6678	96906	MS16562-103	PIN, SPRING	M52	EA	1
C-8	22	AFFFF		19200	9349086	FORWARD ASSIST ASSEMBLY	M52	EA	1
C-8	23	PAFZZ	5360-00-017-9541	19200	8448540	SPRING, HELICAL, COMPRESSION	M52	EA	1
C-8	24	PAFZZ	1005-01-134-3701	19200	9349063	RECEIVER, CARTRIDGE	M52	EA	1

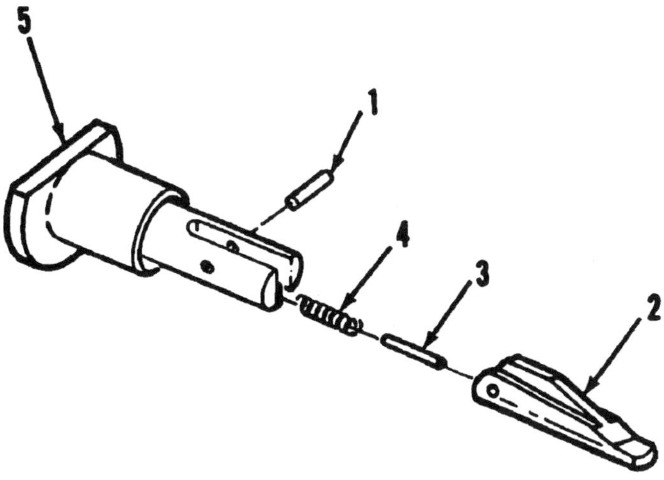

Figure C-9. Forward assist assembly 9349086

(1) ILLUSTRATION (a) FIG. NO.	(b) ITEM NO.	(2) SMR CODE	(3) NATIONAL STOCK NUMBER	(4) FSCM	(5) PART NUMBER	(6) DESCRIPTION	(7) USABLE ON CODE	(8) U/M	(9) QTY INC IN UNIT
						GROUP 030201 FORWARD ASSIST ASSEMBLY 9349086			
C-9	1	PAFZZ	5315-00-017-9552	13629	95113	PIN,SPRING	M52	EA	1
C-9	2	PAFZZ	1005-00-017-9539	19204	8448543	PAWL, FORWARD ASSIST	M52	EA	1
C-9	3	PAFZZ	1005-00-017-9540	19204	8448544	DENT, PAWL	M52	EA	1
C-9	4	PAFZZ	5360-00-523-8084	19200	8448542	SPRING, HELICAL, COMPRESSION	M52	EA	1
C-9	5	PAFZZ	1005-01-144-1468	19200	9349085	PLUNGER ASSEMBLY	M52	EA	1

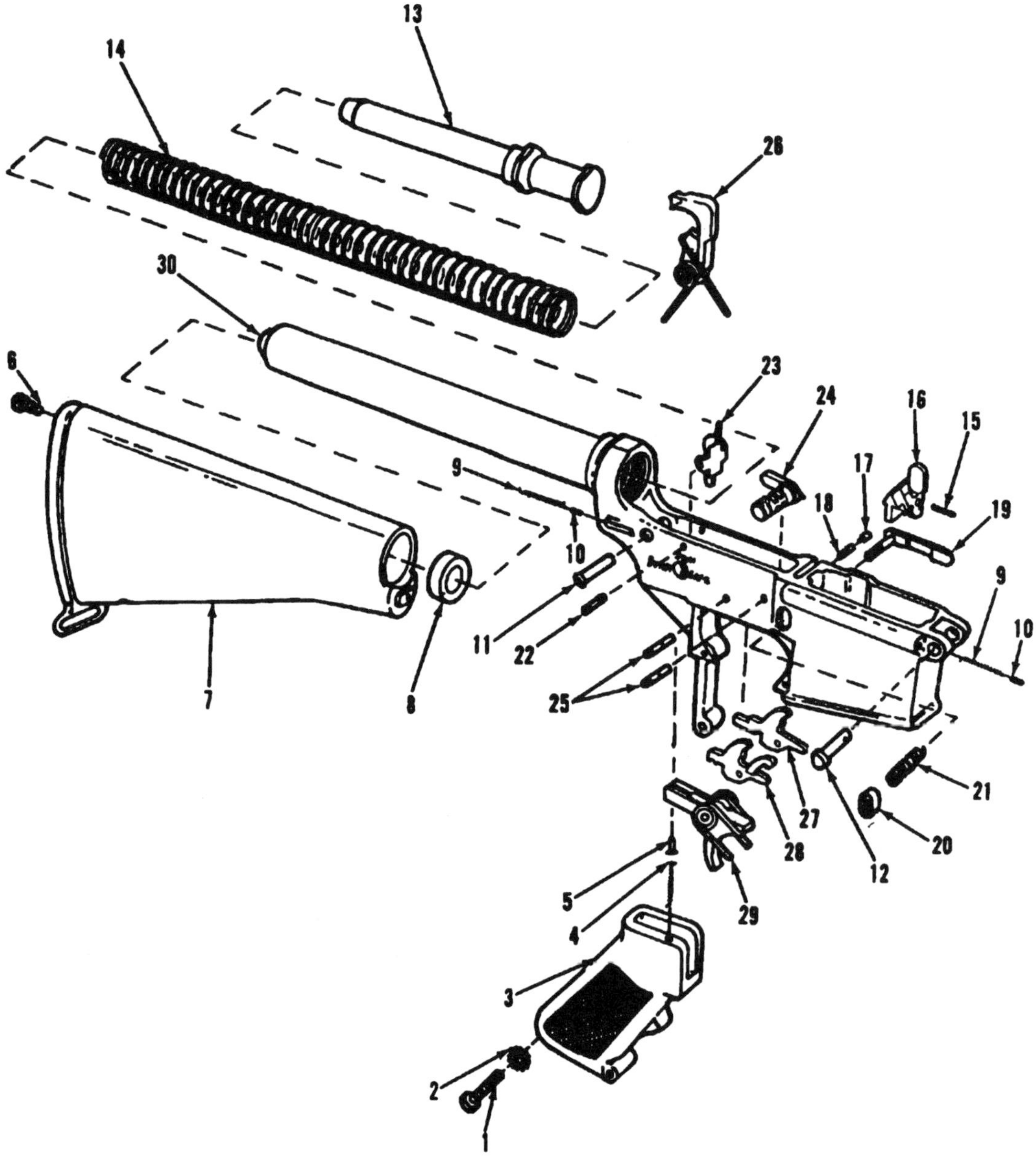

Figure C-10. Lower receiver and buttstock assembly 9349100

(1) ILLUSTRATION (a) FIG. NO.	(b) ITEM NO.	(2) SMR CODE	(3) NATIONAL STOCK NUMBER	(4) FSCM	(5) PART NUMBER	(6) DESCRIPTION	(7) USABLE ON CODE	(8) U/M	(9) QTY INC IN UNIT
						GROUP 04 LOWER RECEIVER AND BUTTSTOCK ASSEMBLY 9349072			
C-10	1	PAOZZ	5305-01-147-0777	88044	AN501D416-16	SCREW, MACHINE	M52	EA	1
C-10	2	PAOZZ	5315-00-527-3634	96906	MS35335-61	WASHER, LOCK	M52	EA	1
C-10	3	PAOZZ	1005-01-148-4805	19200	9349127	GRIP, RIFLE PLASTIC, BLACK	M52	EA	1
C-10	4	PAOZZ	5360-01-992-7292	19204	8448516	SPRING, HELICAL, COMPRESSION	M52	EA	1
C-10	5	PAOZZ	1005-00-992-6667	19204	8448631	DETENT, SAFETY	M52	EA	1
C-10	6	PAOZZ	5305-01-147-8585	19200	9349128	SCREW, SELF-LOCKING	M52	EA	1
C-10	7	PAOZZ	1005-01-135-4973	19200	9349119	BUTTSTOCK ASSEMBLY	M52	EA	1
C-10	8	PAOZZ	5365-01-146-7692	19200	9349129	SPACER, STEPPED	M52	EA	1
C-10	9	PAOZZ	5360-00-992-6655	19204	8448586	SPRING, HELICAL, COMPRESSION	M52	EA	2
C-10	10	PAOZZ	1005-00-992-6654	19204	8448585	DETENT, TAKEDOWN PIN	M52	EA	2
C-10	11	PAOZZ	1005-00-992-6653	19204	8448584	PIN, TAKEDOWN	M52	EA	1
C-10	12	PAOZZ	1005-00-017-9537	19204	8448621	PIN, PIVOT	M52	EA	1
C-10	13	PAOZZ	1005-00-937-3078	19200	8848615	BUFFER ASSEMBLY	M52	EA	1
C-10	14	PAOZZ	5360-00-992-6665	19204	8848629	SPRING, HELICAL, COMPRESSION	M52	EA	1
C-10	15	PAFZZ	5315-00-812-3312	96906	MS16562-119	PIN, SPRING	M52	EA	1
.C-10	16	PAFZZ	1005-00-017-9548	19200	8448628	CATCH, BOLT	M52	EA	1
C-10	17	PAFZZ	1005-00-056-2247	19204	8448634	PLUMBER, BOLT CATCH	M52	EA	1
C-10	18	PAFZZ	5360-00-056-2246	19204	8448633	SPRING, HELICAL, COMPRESSION	M52	EA	1
C-10	19	PAFZZ	1005-00-056-2201	19204	8448638	CATCH, MAGAZINE	M52	EA	1
C-10	20	PAFZZ	1005-00-992-7302	19204	8448636	BUTTON, MAGAZINE CATCH	M52	EA	1
C-10	21	PAFZZ	5360-00-992-7301	19204	8448637	SPRING, HELICAL, COMPRESSION	M52	EA	1
C-10	22	PAFZZ	1005-00-992-6650	19204	8448599	PIN, AUTOMATIC SEAR	M52	EA	1
C-10	23	PAFZZ	1005-00-992-6649	19200	8448595	SEAR	M52	EA	1
C-10	24	PAFZZ	1005-00-992-6666	19204	8448630	LEVER, SELECTOR	M52	EA	1
C-10	25	PAFZZ	1005-00-992-7309	19204	8448609	PIN, HAMMER AND TRIGGER	M52	EA	2
C-10	26	AFFFF		19200	9349106	HAMMER ASSEMBLY	M52	EA	1
C-10	27	PAFZZ	1005-01-145-7910	19200	9349114	LEVER, LOCK-RELEASE	M52	EA	1
C-10	28	PAFZZ	1005-01-144-1499	19200	9349113	LEVER, LOCK-RELEASE	M52	EA	1
C-10	29	AFFFF		19200	9349115	TRIGGER ASSEMBLY	M52	EA	1
C-10	30	XAFFA		19200	9349101	LOWER RECEIVER & RECEIVER EXTENSION ASSEMBLY	M52	EA	1

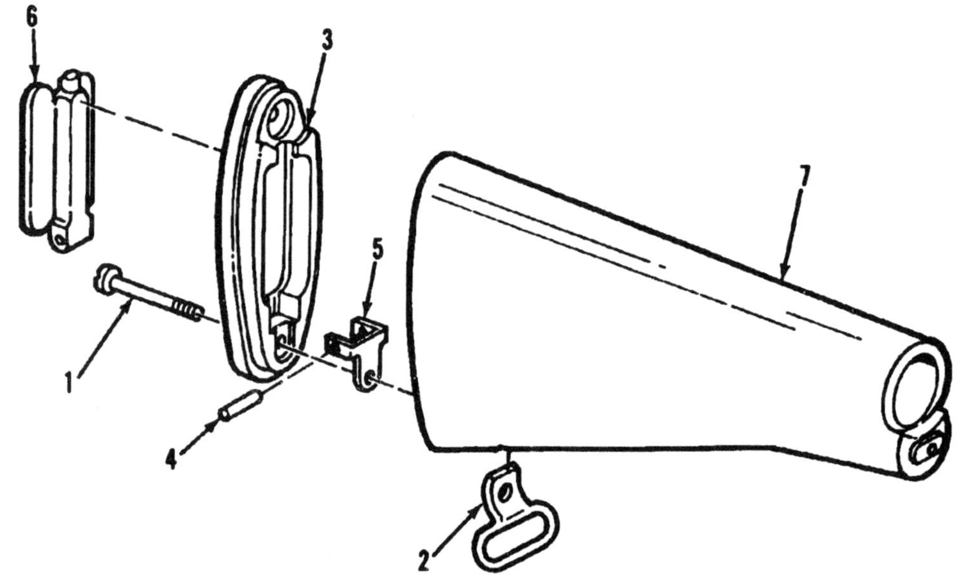

Figure C-11. Buttstock assembly 9349119

(1) ILLUSTRATION (a) FIG. NO.	(b) ITEM NO.	(2) SMR CODE	(3) NATIONAL STOCK NUMBER	(4) FSCM	(5) PART NUMBER	(6) DESCRIPTION	(7) USABLE ON CODE	(8) U/M	(9) QTY INC IN UNIT
						GROUP 0401 BUTTSTOCK ASSEMBLY			
						9349119			
C-11	1	PAOZZ	5305-01-144-1494	19200	9349120	SCREW, SELF-LOCKING	M52	EA	1
C-11	2	PAOZZ	1005-00-403-0964	19204	8448652	SWIVEL, SLING, SMALL	M52	EA	1
C-11	3	PAOZZ	1005-01-146-7685	19200	9349130	PLATE, BUTT, SHOULDER GUN STOCK	M52	EA	1
C-11	4	PAOZZ	5315-00-463-3894	19204	8448655	PIN, STRAIGHT, HEADLESS	M52	EA	1
C-11	5	PAOZZ	5340-00-463-3892	19200	8448653	HINGE, ACCESS DOOR BUTT PLATE	M52	EA	1
C-11	6	PAOZZ	1005-00-403-0962	19200	8448658	DOOR ASSEMBLY, STOWAGE	M52	EA	1
C-11	7	XAOFF		19200	9349121	BUTTSTOCK	M52	EA	1

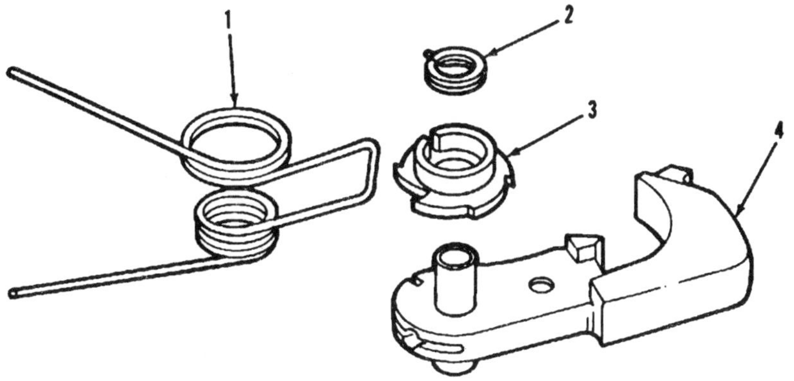

Figure C-12. Hammer assembly 9349106

(1) ILLUSTRATION (a) FIG. NO.	(b) ITEM NO.	(2) SMR CODE	(3) NATIONAL STOCK NUMBER	(4) FSCM	(5) PART NUMBER	(6) DESCRIPTION	(7) USABLE ON CODE	(8) U/M	(9) QTY INC IN UNIT
						GROUP 0402 HAMMER ASSEMBLY 9349106			
C-12	1	PAFZZ	5360-01-144-1492	19200	9349107	SPRING, HELICAL	M52	EA	1
C-12	2	PAFZZ	5360-01-136-5471	19200	9349109	SPRING, HELICAL	M52	EA	1
C-12	3	PAFZZ	1015-01-148-0172	19200	9349108	CAM, BURST	M52	EA	1
C-12	4	PAFZZ	1005-01-134-3630	19200	9349110	HAMMER & HAMMER PIN RETAIN ASSY	M52	EA	1

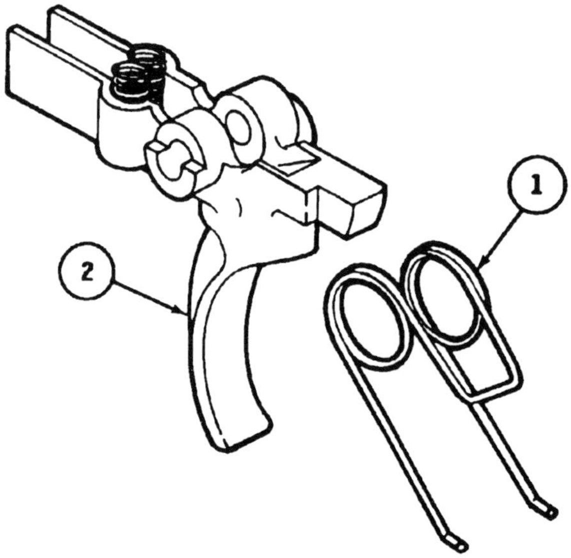

Figure C-13. Trigger Assembly 9349115

(1) ILLUSTRATION (a) FIG. NO.	(b) ITEM NO.	(2) SMR CODE	(3) NATIONAL STOCK NUMBER	(4) FSCM	(5) PART NUMBER	(6) DESCRIPTION	(7) USABLE ON CODE	(8) U/M	(9) QTY INC IN UNIT
						GROUP 0403 TRIGGER ASSEMBLY 9349115			
C-13	1	PAFZZ	5360-00-992-7308	19204	8448593	SPRING, HELICAL TORSION	M52	EA	1
C-13	2	PAFFF	1005-01-219-2402	19200	9392518	TRIGGER SUB-ASSEMBLY	M52	EA	1

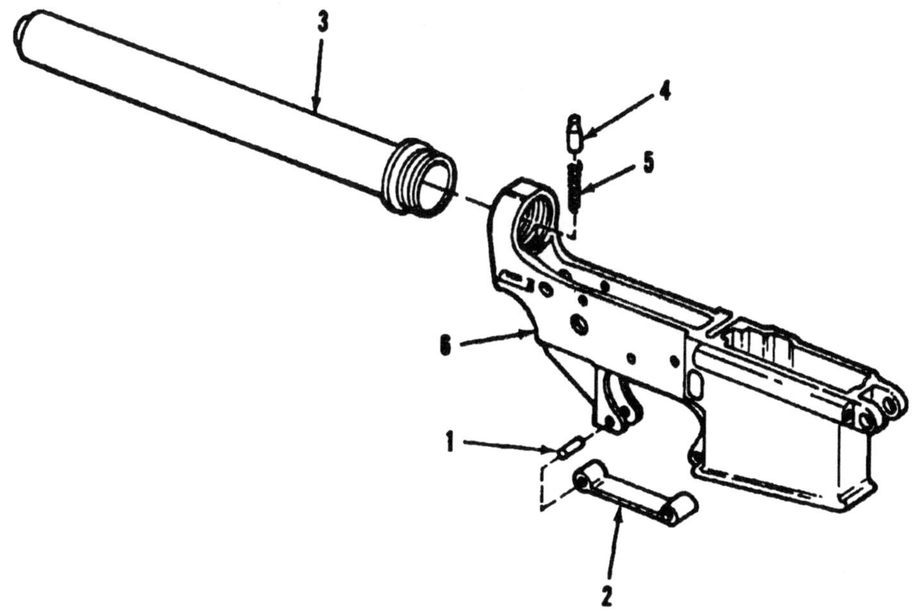

Figure C-14. Lower receiver and receiver extension assembly 9349101

(1) ILLUSTRATION (a) FIG. NO.	(b) ITEM NO.	(2) SMR CODE	(3) NATIONAL STOCK NUMBER	(4) FSCM	(5) PART NUMBER	(6) DESCRIPTION	(7) USABLE ON CODE	(8) U/M	(9) QTY INC IN UNIT
						GROUP 0404 LOWER RECEIVER AND RECEIVER EXTENSION ASSEMBLY 9349101			
C-14	1	PAFZZ	5315-00-058-6081	96906	MS16562-129	PIN, SPRING	M52	EA	1
C-14	2	PAFZZ	1005-00-992-7299	19204	8448587	GUARD, TRIGGER	M52	EA	1
C-14	3	PAFZZ	1005-00-992-7297	19200	8448581	EXTENSION, LOWER RECEIVER	M52	EA	1
C-14	4	PAFZZ	1005-00-992-6651	19204	8448582	RETAINER, BUFFER	M52	EA	1
C-14	5	PAFZZ	5360-00-992-6652	19200	8448583	SPRING, HELICAL COMPRESSION	M52	EA	1
C-14	6	XAFDA		19200	9349102	RECEIVER, LOWER	M52	EA	1

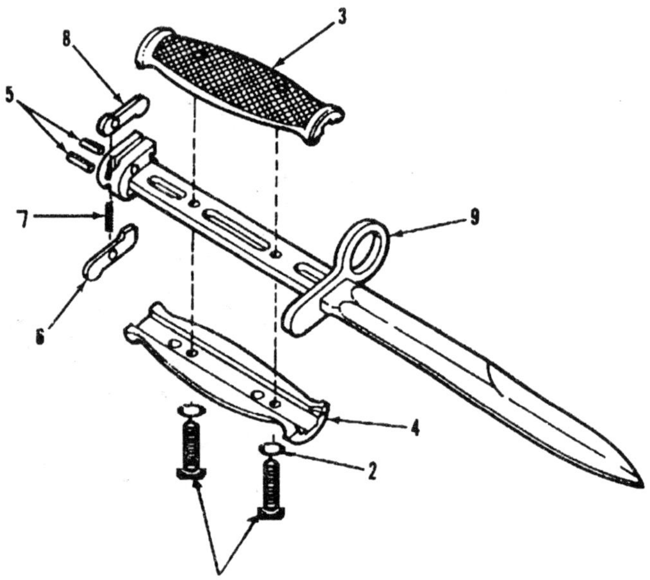

Figure C-15. Bayonet-knife M7 11010077

(1) ILLUSTRATION (a) FIG. NO.	(b) ITEM NO.	(2) SMR CODE	(3) NATIONAL STOCK NUMBER	(4) FSCM	(5) PART NUMBER	(6) DESCRIPTION	USABLE ON CODE	(7)	(8) U/M	(9) QTY INC IN UNIT
						GROUP 05 BAYONET-KNIFE M7				
						11010077				
C-15	1	PAOZZ	5305-00-051-3609	19204	11010078	SCREW, MACHINE GRIP	538		EA	2
C-15	2	PAOZZ	5310-00-579-0079	96906	MS35333-37	WASHER, LOCK LOCK INT-TEETH, S,CD-PLTD,NO.6				
						SCREW SIZE	538		EA	2
C-15	3	PAFZZ	1005-00-051-3607	19204	11010068	GRIP, BAYONET-KNIFE LH,				
						PLASTIC, KNURLED BLK 4.400 LOA, 1.250 W	538		EA	1
C-15	4	PAFZZ	1005-00-051-3608	19204	11010069	GRIP, BAYONET-KNIFE RH, PLASTIC				
						KNURLED, BLK, 1.250 W, 4.400 LOA	538		EA	1
C-15	5	PAFZZ	5315-00-058-6077	96906	MS16562-125	PIN, SPRING S, PHOS-CTD,				
						1/8 X 3/8	538		EA	1
C-15	6	PAFZZ	1005-00-051-3899	19204	11010010	LEVER, LOCK-RELEASE BAYONET RH	538		EA	1
C-15	7	PAFZZ	5360-00-716-0949	19205	7160949	SPRING, HELICAL, COMPRESSION				
						S. 0.023 STK DIA, 0.170 FREE OD,				
						0.763 FREE LG, 14 TOTAL COILS	538		EA	1
C-15	8	PAFZZ	1005-00-051-3901	19204	11010011	LEVER, LOCK-RELEASE BAYONET LH	538		EA	1
C-15	9	XAFDA		19204	11010067	BLADE ASSEMBLY	538		EA	1

Section III. SPECIAL TOOLS LIST

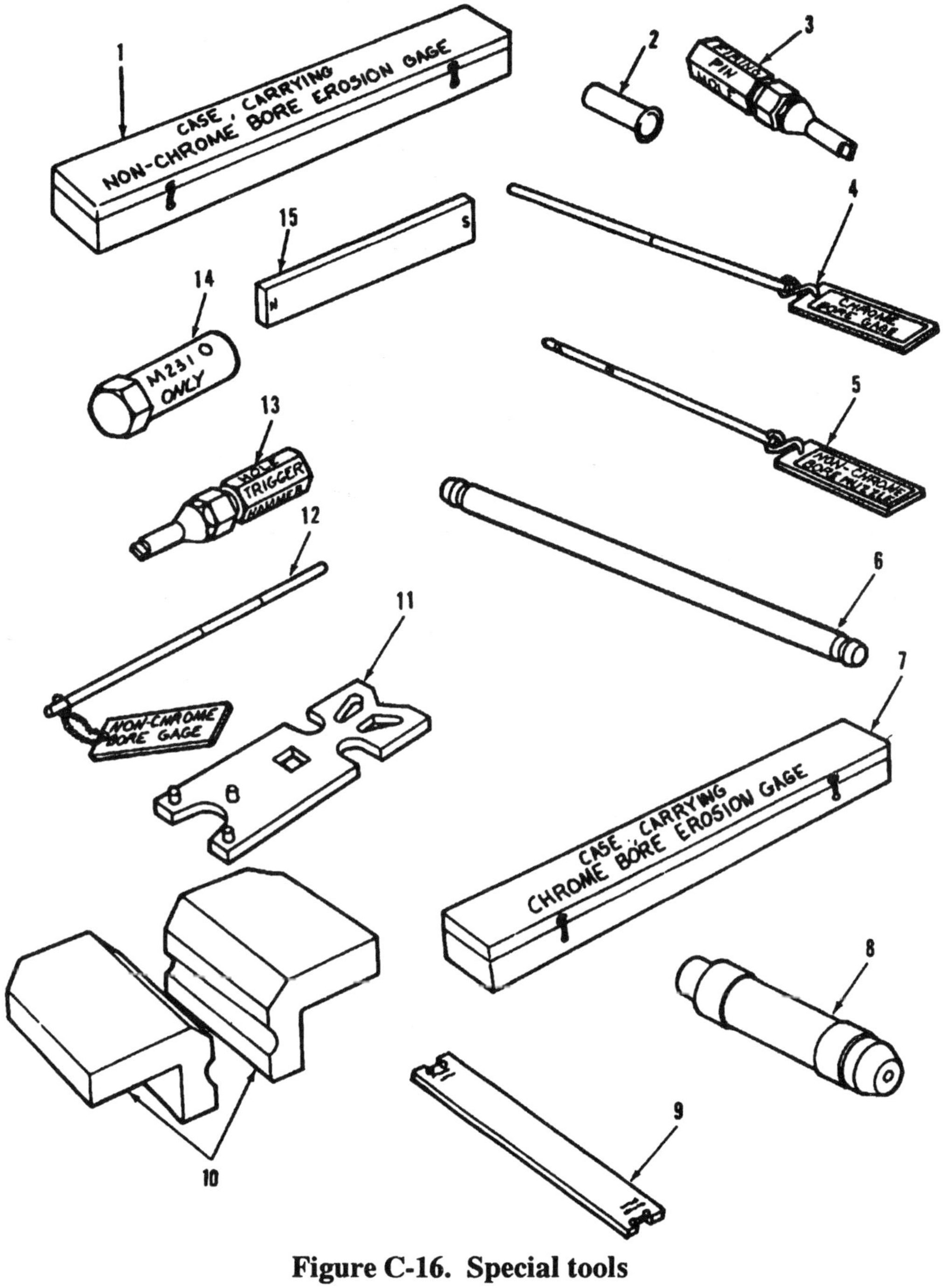

Figure C-16. Special tools

(1) ILLUSTRATION (a) FIG. NO.	(b) ITEM NO.	(2) SMR CODE	(3) NATIONAL STOCK NUMBER	(4) FSCM	(5) PART NUMBER	(6) DESCRIPTION	(7) USABLE ON CODE	(8) U/M	(9) QTY INC IN UNIT
						GROUP 9500 SPECIAL TOOLS			
C-16		ADFFA		19204	8426685	TOOL & GAGE SET DS/GS SUPPORT MAINTENANCE FOR 5.56MM RIFLE, M16 RIFLE SERIES & M231 FIRING PORT WEAPON BOI: 2 PER SUPPORTING DSU/GSU		SE	
C-16	1	PAFZZ	4933-00-944-7084	19205	7799809	* CASE, CARRYING, GAGE		EA	
C-16	2	PAFZZ	4933-00-800-7508	19204	8448201	* REFLECTOR TOOL, CHAMBER		EA	
C-16	3	PAFZZ	5220-01-075-5004	19200	12620101	* GAGE, PLUG, PLAIN CYLINDER		EA	
C-16	4	PAFZZ	5220-01-014-8183	19204	8448498	* GAGE, BARREL, EROSION		EA	
C-16	5	PAFZZ	5220-00-155-4935	19204	8448677	* GAGE, MUZZLE EROSION		EA	
C-16	6	PAFZZ	4933-00-221-9391	19204	8448202	* GAGE STRAIGHTNESS		EA	
C-16	8	PAFZZ	4933-00-070-7814	19204	7799734	* GAGE, HEADSPACE		EA	
C-16	9	PAFZZ	4933-00-070-7815	19204	7799735	* GAGE, FIRING PIN PROTRUSION		EA	
C-16	10	PAFZZ	4933-00-070-9151	19204	11010032	* FIXTURE, BARREL REMOVAL		EA	
C-16	12	PAFZZ	4933-00-912-3409	19205	7799792	* GAGE, BARREL EROSION PART OF KIT P/N			
C-16	11	PAFZZ	4933-00-070-9152	19204	11010033	* WRENCH, COMBINATION		EA	
C-16	13	PAFZZ	5220-01-043-9473	19204	12006472	* GAGE PLUG, TAPER CYLINDER		EA	
C-16	14	PAFZZ	1005-01-081-4835	19200	11828589	* WRENCH, EXTENSION, (M231 ONLY)		EA	
C-16	15	PAFZZ	5340-01-054-0124	64484	1809	MAGNET, PERMANENT BOI: 2 PER SUPPORTING DSU/GSU		EA	

Section IV NATIONAL STOCK NUMBER AND PART NUMBER INDEX

STOCK NO.	FIGURE NO.	ITEM NO.
5315-00-017-9537	C-10	12
1005-00-017-9539	C-9	2
1005-00-017-9540	C-9	3
5360-00-017-9541	C-8	23
1005-00-017-9543	C-7	6
1005-00-017-9546	C-1	4
5315-00-017-9547	C-2	2
1005-00-017-9548	C-10	16
5315-00-017-9552	C-5	1
5315-00-017-9552	C-9	1
1005-00-051-3607	C-15	3
1005-00-051-3608	C-15	4
5305-00-051-3609	C-15	1
1005-00-051-3899	C-15	6
1005-00-051-3901	C-15	8
1005-00-056-2201	C-10	19
5360-00-056-2246	C-10	18
1005-00-056-2247	C-10	17
5315-00-058-6044	C-6	2
5315-00-058-6077	C-15	5
5315-00-058-6081	C-14	1
5315-00-058-6678	C-8	2
5315-00-058-6678	C-8	21
5365-00-064-2652	C-8	17
4933-00-070-7814	C-16	8
4933-00-070-7815	C-16	9
4933-00-070-9151	C-16	10
4933-00-070-9152	C-16	11
1005-00-087-8998	C-6	8
5220-00-155-4925	C-16	5
4933-00-221-9391	C-16	6
5365-00-252-6853	C-6	6
1005-00-403-0962	C-11	6
1005-00-403-0964	C-11	2
5340-00-463-3892	C-11	5
5315-00-463-3894	C-11	4
5360-00-523-8084	C-9	4
5310-00-527-3634	C-10	2
5310-00-579-0079	C-15	2
5315-00-597-5086	C-3	4
5360-00-716-0949	C-15	7
5360-00-992-6665	C-10	14
1005-00-992-6666	C-10	24
1005-00-992-6667	C-10	5
1005-00-992-7283	C-4	2
1005-00-992-7284	C-4	1
1005-00-992-7285	C-2	4
1005-00-992-7287	C-3	7
1005-00-992-7288	C-3	2
1005-00-992-7290	C-3	1
1005-00-992-7291	C-3	5
5360-00-992-7292	C-10	4
5360-00-992-7292	C- 3	6
1005-00-992-7294	C-2	3
1005-00-992-7297	C-14	3
1005-00-992-7299	C-14	2
5360-00-992-7301	C-10	21
1005-00-992-7302	C-10	20
5360-00-992-7308	C-13	1
1005-00-992-7309	C-10	25
5360-00-999-0404	C-5	3
1005-00-999-0405	C-5	2
1005-00-999-1509	C-2	1
5220-01-014-8183	C-16	4
5315-01-027-4759	C-8	10
4933-01-035-5607	C-16	7
5220-01-043-9473	C-16	13
5340-01-054-0124	C-16	15
5320-01-063-7635	C-7	5
5220-01-075-5004	C-16	3
1005-01-081-4835	C-16	14
1005-01-083-8113	C-1	2
1005-01-134-3621	C-8	15
5305-01-134-3622	C-8	14
1005-01-134-3625	C-7	1
1005-01-134-3627	C-8	3
1005-01-134-3629	C-6	1
1005-01-134-3630	C-12	4
1005-01-134-3631	C-8	9
1005-01-134-3633	C-6	4
1005-01-134-3701	C-8	24
1005-01-134-3702	C-13	3

STOCK NO.	FIGURE NO.	ITEM NO.
1005-00-738-6213	C-4	3
1005-00-760-3768	C-3	3
4933-00-800-7508	C-16	2
5315-00-812-3312	C-10	15
4933-00-912-3409	C-16	12
1005-00-921-5004	C-1	1
1005-00-937-3078	C-10	13
4933-00-944-7084	C-16	1
1005-00-978-1022	C-8	20
1005-00-978-1023	C-8	18
5360-00-978-1025	C-8	19
5360-00-978-1027	C-8	8
1005-00-978-1036	C-6	7
1005-00-978-1038	C-6	3
1005-00-979-3926	C-7	4
1005-00-979-3930	C-7	2
5360-00-979-3931	C-7	3
1005-00-992-6649	C-10	23
1005-00-992-6650	C-10	22
1005-00-992-6651	C-14	4
5360-00-992-6652	C-14	5
1005-00-992-6653	C-10	11
1005-00-992-6654	C-10	10
5360-00-992-6655	C-10	9

STOCK NO.	FIGURE NO.	ITEM NO.
5360-01-134-3710	C-8	11
5360-01-135-0353	C-13	2
1005-01-135-3697	C-8	7
1005-01-135-4972	C-8	16
1005-01-135-4973	C-10	7
5360-01-136-5471	C-12	2
1005-01-144-1468	C-9	5
5305-01-144-1490	C-8	6
5360-01-144-1492	C-12	1
5305-01-144-1494	C-11	1
5365-01-144-1496	C-6	5
1005-01-144-1499	C-10	28
1005-01-145-7910	C-10	27
1005-01-146-7684	C-6	10
1005-01-146-7685	C-11	3
5365-01-146-7692	C-10	8
5305-01-147-0777	C-10	1
5305-01-147-8585	C-10	6
1015-01-148-0172	C-12	3
5360-01-148-1751	C-8	4
5360-01-148-1751	C-8	13
1005-01-148-4805	C-10	3
3110-01-148-7438	C-8	5
3110-01-148-7438	C-8	12

FSCM	PART NO.	FIGURE NO.	ITEM NO.
88044	AN501DA416-16	C-10	1
96906	MS16562-103	C-8	2
96906	MS16562-103	C-8	21
96906	MS16562-106	C-6	2
96906	MS16562-119	C-10	15
96906	MS16562-125	C-15	5
96906	MS16562-129	C-14	1
96906	MS16562-98	C-3	4
96906	MS16626-1137	C-6	6
96906	MS16632-1012	C-8	17
19204	11010068	C-15	3
19204	11010069	C-15	4
19204	11010078	C-15	1
19200	11828589	C-16	14
19200	11833432	C-1	2
19204	12006359	C-16	7
19204	12006472	C-16	13
19200	12620101	C-16	3
64484	1809	C-16	15
19205	7160949	C-15	7
19204	7799734	C-16	8
19204	7799735	C-16	9
19205	7799792	C-16	12
19205	7799809	C-16	1
19204	8426685	C-16	
19204	8448201	C-16	2
19204	8448202	C-16	6
19204	8448496	C-16	4
19200	8448501	C-1	3
19204	8448502	C-2	3
19204	8448503	C-2	2
19204	8448504	C-2	1
19200	8448505	C-2	5
19200	8448506	C-4	2
19200	8448507	C-4	3
19204	8448508	C-4	1
19200	8448509	C-2	4
19200	8448510	C-3	8
19204	8448511	C-3	7
19204	8448512	C-3	2
19204	8448513	C-3	1
19204	8448515	C-3	5
19204	8448516	C-10	4
96906	MS19061-20003	C-8	5
96906	MS19061-20003	C-8	12
96906	MS35333-37	C-15	2
96906	MS35335-61	C-10	2
80205	NAS561-3-10	C-8	10
19204	11010010	C-15	6
19204	11010011	C-15	8
19204	11010032	C-16	10
19204	11010033	C-16	11
19204	11010067	C-15	9
19200	8448615	C-10	13
19204	8448621	C-10	12
19200	8448628	C-10	16
19204	8448629	C-10	14
19204	8448630	C-10	24
19204	8448631	C-10	5
19204	8448633	C-10	18
19204	8448634	C-10	17
19204	8448636	C-10	20
19204	8448637	C-10	21
19204	8448638	C-10	19
19204	8448652	C-11	22
19200	8448653	C-11	5
19204	8448655	C-11	4
19200	8448658	C-11	6
19200	8448670	C-1	1
19204	8448677	C-16	5
19204	8448697	C-7	5
19204	8448712	C-6	8
19200	8448755	C-3	3
19200	9349050	C 1	5
19200	9349051	C-6	4
19200	9349052	C-6	5
19200	9349056	C-7	1
19200	9349059	C-6	1
19200	9349062	C-6	9
19200	9349063	C-8	24
19200	9349065	C-8	14
19200	9349066	C-8	15
19200	9349067	C-8	16
19200	9349069	C-8	4
19200	9349069	C-8	13
19200	9349070	C-8	11

FSCM	PART NO.	FIGURE NO.	ITEM NO.
19204	8448516	C-3	6
19204	8448517	C-1	4
19200	8448518	C-5	4
19200	8448519	C-5	2
19204	8448520	C-5	3
19204	8448525	C-8	20
19204	8448532	C-8	19
19204	8448533	C-8	18
19200	8448536	C-8	8
19200	8448540	C-8	23
19200	8448542	C-9	4
19204	8448543	C-9	2
19204	8448544	C-9	3
19204	8448555	C-6	7
19200	8448567	C-6	3
19204	8448571	C-7	6
19204	8448573	C-7	2
19204	8448574	C-7	3
19204	8448575	C-7	4
19200	8448581	C-14	3
19204	8448582	C-14	4
19200	8448583	C-14	5
19204	8448584	C-10	11
19204	8448585	C-10	10
19204	8448586	C-10	9
19204	8448587	C-14	2
19204	8448593	C-13	1
19200	8448595	C-10	23
19204	8448599	C-10	22
19204	8448609	C-10	25

FSCM	PART NO.	FIGURE NO.	ITEM NO.
19200	9349072	C-8	1
19200	9349074	C-8	9
19200	9349075	C-8	7
19200	9349076	C-8	6
19200	9349077	C-8	3
19200	9349085	C-9	5
19200	9349086	C-8	22
19200	9349100	C-1	6
19200	9349101	C-10	30
19200	9349102	C-14	6
19200	9349106	C-10	26
19200	9349107	C-12	1
19200	9349108	C-12	3
19200	9349109	C-12	2
19200	9349110	C-12	4
19200	9349113	C-10	28
19200	9349114	C-10	27
19200	9349115	C-10	29
19200	9349116	C-13	2
19200	9349117	C-13	3
19200	9349119	C-10	7
19200	9349120	C-11	1
19200	9349121	C-11	7
19200	9349124	C-6	10
19200	9349127	C-10	3
19200	9349128	C-10	6
19200	0349129	C-10	8
19200	9349130	C-11	3
13629	95113	C-5	1
13629	95113	C-9	1

APPENDIX D
EXPENDABLE/DURABLE SUPPLIES AND MATERIALS LIST

Section I. INTRODUCTION

D-1. SCOPE. This appendix lists expendable supplies and materials you will need to operate and maintain the 5.56-mm Rifle M16A2.

(ARMY ONLY) These items are authorized for your use by CTA 5-970, Expendable Items (Except Medical, Class V, Repair Parts, and Heraldic Items).

D-2. EXPLANATION OF COLUMNS.

a. *Column 1 - Item Number.* This is the numerical identification of the items on the list.

b. *Column 2 - Level.* This column identifies the lowest level of maintenance that requires the listed item.

C - Operator/Crew Maintenance

O - Organizational Maintenance

F - Intermediate Maintenance

c. *Column 3 - National Stock Number.* This is the National stock number assigned to the item; use it to request or requisition the item.

d. *Column 4 - Description.* Indicates the Federal item name and, if required, a description to identify the item. The last line for each item indicates the Federal Supply Code for Manufacturer (FSCM) in parentheses followed by the part number.

e. *Column 5 - Unit of Measure (U/M).* Indicates the measure used in performing the actual maintenance function. This measure is expressed by a two-character alphabetical abbreviation (e.g., ea, in.,pr). If the unit of measure differs from the unit of issue, requisition the lowest unit of issue that will satisfy your requirements.

Section II. EXPENDABLE/DURABLE SUPPLIES AND MATERIALS LIST

(1) ITEM NO.	(2) LEVEL	(3) NATIONAL STOCK NUMBER	(4) DESCRIPTION	(5) U/M
1	F	8040-00-944-7292	ADHESIVE KIT (81348) MMM-A-1754	KT
2	O	8020-00-244-0153	BRUSH, ARTISTS: metal ferrule flat, chisel edge, 7/16 w, 1 1/8 I, exposed bristle (81348) H-B-241	EA
3	F	1005-00-716-2702	BRUSH, CLEANING, SMALL: (19205) 7162702	EA
4	O	7920-00-205-2401	BRUSH, CLEANING, TOOLS & PARTS: (81349) MILS43871	EA
5	O	6850-00-965-2332	CARBON REMOVING COMPOUND (81348) P-C-111	GL
6			CLEANER, LUBRICANT & PRESERVATIVE: (27412)	
	O	9150-01-079-6124	CLP-4 4 oz bottlle	EA
	O	9150-01-054-6453	CLP-5 pt bottle	EA
	O	9150-01-053-6688	CLP-7 gal bottle	EA
7	C	9150-01-102-1473	CLEANER, LUBRICANT & PRESERVATIVE (81349) MIL-L-63460 1/2 oz bottle	EA

(1) ITEM NUMBER	(2) LEVEL	(3) NATIONAL STOCK NUMBER	(4) DESCRIPTION	(5) U/M
8	C	9920-00292-9946	CLEANER, TOBACCO PIPE: cotton turf, wire core (89855) DILLSPIPE CLEANER 36 PER PKG	EA
9	C	6850-00-224-6656	(ARMY ONLY) CLEANING COMPOUND, RIFLE BORE: small arms bore cleaning solution (RBC) 2-oz (59.15-ml) bottle (81349) MIL-C-372	OZ
10	O	5350-00-221-0872	CLOTH, ABRASIVE: (58536) A-A-1206	SH
11	O	8010-00-181-7859	COATING COMPOUND, FLUORESCENT: paint for blank firing attach. (81349) MIL-P-21563 1 pt can	EA
12	F		DICHLOROMETHANE, TECHNICAL: (81349) MIL-D-6998	
		6810-00-244-0290	5 gal pail	CN
		6810-00-616-9188	600 lb drum	DR
13	O	6850-00-281-1985	DRY CLEANING SOLVENT (81348) A-A-711 1 gal can	GL
14	O	8010-00-297-0560	ENAMEL: olive drab No. 3407 (81348) TT-E-527 1 gal can	GL

(1) ITEM NUMBER	(2) LEVEL	(3) NATIONAL STOCK NUMBER	(4) DESCRIPTION	(5) U/M
15	O	8415-00-823-7456	GLOVES, CHEMICAL AND OIL PROTECT-IVE: (81348) ZZ-G-381	PR
16	F	9150-00-754-2595	GREASE, MOLYBDE-NUM DISULFIDE: (81349) MIL-21164	LB
17	*	8010-00-527-2884	LACQUER: black lusterless (81349) MIL-L-19538	GL
18	O	9150-00-168-2000	LUBRICANT, SOLID FILM: (81349) MIL-L-46147 16 oz spray can	OZ
19	C	9150-00-292-9680	LUBRICATING OIL, WEAPONS: (LAW) for cold weather operation (81349) MIL-L-14107 1 qt (0.95-1) can (ARMY ONLY)	QT
20	C C	 9150-00-935-6597 9150-00-889-3522	LUBRICATING OIL, WEAPONS: (LSA), semifluid 2-oz(59.15ml) bottle 4-oz(118.30-ml) bottle (81349) MIL-L-46000	OZ OZ

(1) ITEM NUMBER	(2) LEVEL	(3) NATIONAL STOCK NUMBER	(4) DESCRIPTION	(5) U/M
21	F	6850-00-826-0981	PENETRANT KIT: (81349) MIL-I-25135	KT
22	C	7920-00-205-1711	RAG, WIPING (58536) A-A531 50 lb bdl	LB
23	F	8030-00-670-8553	SEALING COMPOUND DEVCON F (16059)	KT
24	C	1005-00-912-4248	SWAB, SMALL ARMS: (19204) 11686408	EA
25	C	6920-01-152-2891	TARGET, ZEROING: (19200) 9357935	EA

* No longer authorized at organizational or intermediate maintenance level.

** Whenever the term "Cleaner Lubricant and Preservative" (CLP) or the words "lubricant", "lube", "LSA", or "LAW" are cited in this TM, they are to be interpreted to mean that CLP, LSA or LAW can be utilized as applicable. Follow constraints noted in paragraph 1-9.

APPENDIX E
LIST OF LOCALLY MANUFACTURED TOOLS

E-1. INTRODUCTION.

a. This appendix contains instructions for making the tools at the organizational or intermediate maintenance levels.

b. An index references the tool to the figure that describes how to build it.

c. All bulk materials needed to build the tools are listed in the figure.

INDEX

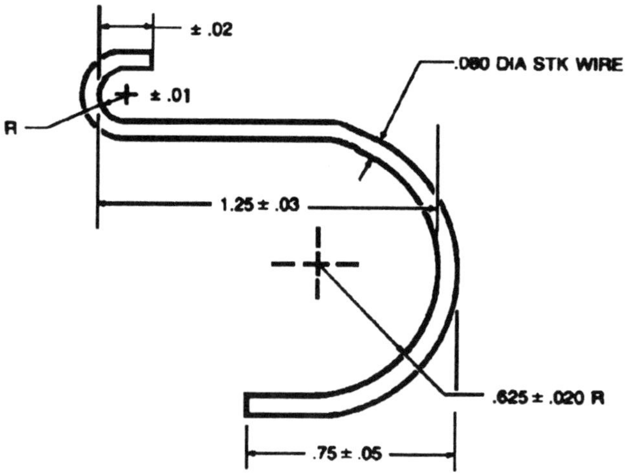

FABRICATE FROM .08 IN. MUSIC WIRE OR EQUIVALENT.
FINISH: NO. 5.3.1.2 OR 5.3.2.2 OF MIL-STD-17

NOTE: ALL DIMENSIONS ARE IN INCHES.

Figure E-1. Front sight detent depressor. *(MC ONLY)*

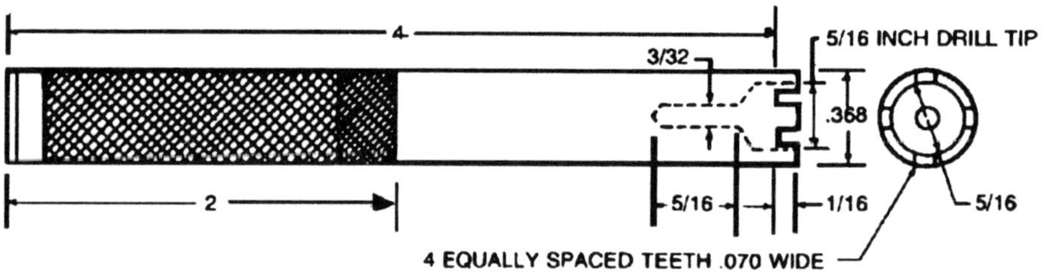

FABRICATE FROM 0.375 INCH
ROUND METAL BAR, QQ-T-580,
FSCM 81348, GRADE C, CLASS W2-09,
NSN 9510-00-640-4407 OR EQUIVALENT.

NOTE: ALL DIMENSIONS ARE IN INCHES

Figure E-2. Square front sight post removing and installation tool.

FABRICATE FROM 1/16 IN. SOCKET HEAD SCREW KEY
NSN 120-00-198-5398 OR EQUIVALENT

NOTE: ALL DIMENSIONS ARE IN INCHES.

Figure E-3. Pivot pin removing tool.

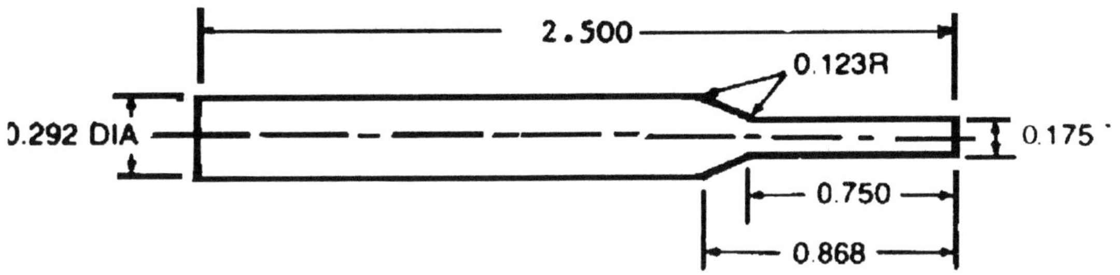

FABRICATE FROM 0.375 INCH
ROUND METAL BAR, QQ-T-580,
FSCM 81348, GRADE C, CLASS W2-09
NSN 9510-00-640-4407 OR EQUIVALENT.

NOTE: ALL DIMENSIONS ARE IN INCHES.

Figure E-4. Key tool.

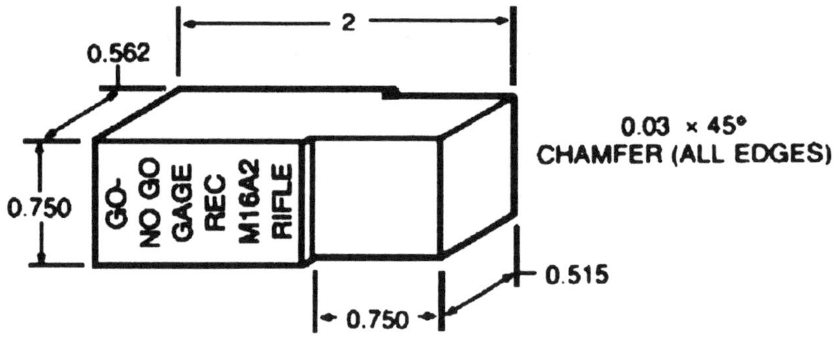

FABRICATE FROM 0.750 SQUARE
METAL BAR, QQ-T-580, GRADE C,
CLASS W2-09 OR CLASS 62-10
NSN 9510-00-541-958 OR EQUIVALENT.

NOTE: **1. ALL DIMENSIONS SHALL BE TOLERANCE +/- 0.0005 EXCEPT GAGING WIDTH (0.515) WHICH SHALL BE TOLERANCE -0.002**

2. ALL DIMENSION ARE IN INCHES

Figure E-5. Lower receiver go-no go gage M16A2 rifle. (MC ONLY)

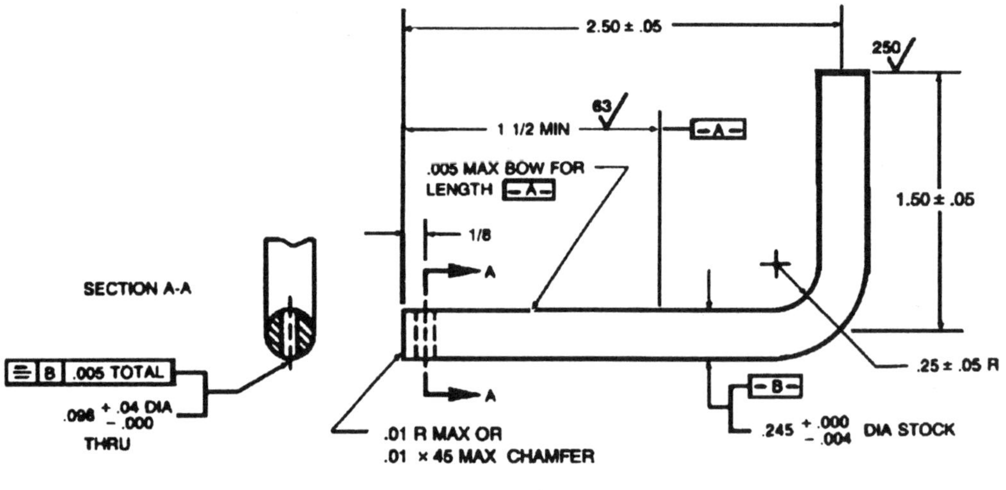

FABRICATE FROM .245 IN. STEEL A1S1 1095 OR EQUIVALENT.
HARDEN AND TEMPER TO RC-57-61 FOR LENGTH - A-.
FINISH 5.3.1.2 OR 5.3.2.2 OF MIL-STD-171.

NOTE: **ALL DIMENSIONS ARE IN INCHES.**

Figure E-6. Pivot pin installation tool.

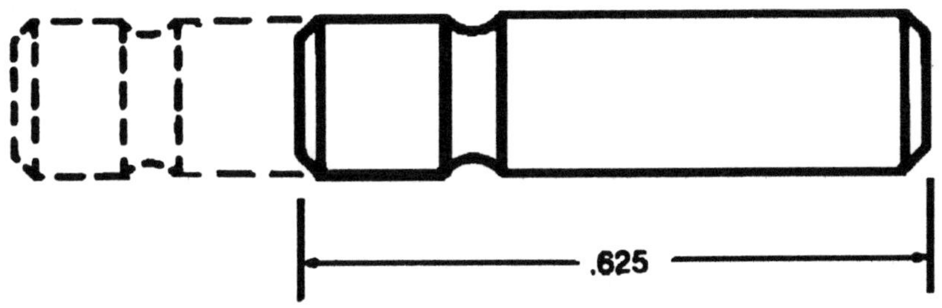

FABRICATE FROM P/N 8448609.

NOTE: ALL DIMENSIONS ARE IN INCHES.

Figure E-7. Modified old trigger "slave" pin.

APPENDIX F
TORQUE LIMITS

F-1. INTRODUCTION. This appendix lists the torque limits for the compensator, barrel nut, carrier key screws, and lower receiver extension.

ITEM	TORQUE TO
COMPENSATOR	15 FT LBS TO 20 FT LBS
BARREL NUT	31 FT LBS MIN. DO NOT EXCEED 80 FT LBS TO ALIGN SLOT
CARRIER KEY SCREWS	35 IN. LBS TO 40 IN. LBS
LOWER RECEIVER EXTENSION	35 FT LBS TO 39 FT LBS

ALPHABETICAL INDEX

Subject *Page*

A

Subject *Page*

Subject *Page*

Subject *Page*

Subject *Page*

Subject *Page*

Subject *Page*

Subject *Page*

Subject *Page*

Subject *Page*

M

N

Subject *Page*

O

P

R

Subject *Page*

Subject *Page*

S

Subject *Page*

T

Subject *Page*

U

★U.S. GOVERNMENT PRINTING OFFICE: 1988-541-931/60225

Notes

Notes

11/30/97

Other Books Available From Desert Publications

001	Firearms Silencers Volume 1	$9.95
003	The Silencer Cookbook	$9.95
004	Select Fire Uzi Modification Manual	$9.95
005	Expedient Hand Grenades	$16.95
007	007 Travel Kit, The	$8.00
008	Law Enforcement Guide to Firearms Silencer	$8.95
009	Springfield Rifle, The	$11.95
010	Full Auto Vol 3 MAC-10 Mod Manual	$9.95
012	Fighting Garand, The	$11.95
013	M1 Carbine Owners Manual	$9.95
014	Ruger Carbine Cookbook	$11.95
015	M-14 Rifle, The	$9.95
016	AR-15, M16 and M16A1 5.56mm Rifles	$11.95
017	Shotguns	$11.95
019	AR15 A2/M16A2 Assault Rifle	$8.95
022	Full Auto Vol 7 Bingham AK-22	$9.95
027	Full Auto Vol 4 Thompson SMG	$9.95
030	STANAG Mil-Talk	$12.95
031	Thompson Submachine Guns	$13.95
033	H&R Reising Submachine Gun Manual	$12.95
035	How to Build Silencers	$6.95
036	Full Auto Vol 2 Uzi Mod Manual	$9.95
049	Firearm Silencers Vol 3	$13.95
050	Firearm Silencers Vol 2	$19.95
054	Company Officers HB of Ger. Army	$11.95
056	German Infantry Weapons Vol 1	$14.95
058	Survival Armory	$27.95
060	Survival Gunsmithing	$9.95
061	FullAuto Vol 1 Ar-15 Mod Manual	$8.95
064	HK Assault Rifle Systems	$27.95
065	SKS Type of Carbines, The	$16.95
066	Private Weaponeer, The	$9.95
067	Rough Riders, The	$24.95
068	Lasers & Night Vision Devices	$29.95
069	Ruger P-85 Family of Handguns	$14.95
071	Dirty Fighting	$11.95
072	Live to Spend It	$29.95
073	Military Ground Rappelling Techniques	$11.95
074	Smith & Wesson Autos	$27.95
080	German MG-34 Machinegun Manual	$9.95
081	Crossbows/ From 35 Years With the Weapon	$11.95
082	Op. Man. 7.62mm M24 Sniper Weapon	$7.95
083	USMC AR-15/M-16 A2 Manual	$16.95
084	Urban Combat	$21.95
085	Caching Techniques of U.S. Army Special Forces	$9.95
086	US Marine Corps Essential Subjects	$16.95
087	The L'il M-1, The .30 Cal. M-1 Carbine	$14.95
088	Concealed Carry Made Easy	$14.95
089	Apocalypse Tomorrow	$17.95
090	M14 and M14A1Rifles and Rifle Marksmanship	$16.95
091	Crossbow As a Modern Weapon	$11.95
092	MP40 Machinegun	$11.95
093	Map Reading and Land Navigation	$19.95
094	U. S. Marine Corps Scout/Sniper Training Manual	$16.95
095	Clear Your Record & Own a Gun	$14.95
096	Sig Handguns	$16.95
097	Poor Man's Nuclear Bomb	$19.95
098	Poor Man's Sniper Rifle	$14.95
100	Submachine Gun Designers Handbook	$16.95
101	Lock Picking Simplified	$8.50
102	Combination Lock Principles	$8.95
103	How to Fit Keys by Impressioning	$7.95
104	Keys To Understanding Tubular Locks	$9.95
105	Techniques of Safe & Vault Munipulation	$9.95
106	Lockout -Techniques of Forced Entr	$11.95
107	Bugs Electronic Surveillance	$11.95
110	Improvised Weapons of Amer. Undergrnd	$10.00
111	Training Handbook of the American Underground	$10.00
114	FullAuto Vol 8 M14A1 & Mini 14	$9.95
116	Handbook Bomb Threat/Search Procedures	$8.00
117	Improvised Lock Picks	$10.00
119	Fitting Keys By Reading Locks	$7.00
120	How to Open Handcuffs Without Keys	$9.95
121	Electronic Locks Volume 1	$8.00
122	With British Snipers, To the Reich	$24.95
125	Browning Hi-Power Pistols	$9.95
126	P-08 Parabellum Luger Auto Pistol	$9.95
127	Walther P-38 Pistol Manual	$9.95
128	Colt .45 Auto Pistol	$9.95
129	Beretta - 9MM M9	$11.95
130	FullAuto Vol 5 M1 Carbine to M2	$9.95
132	Ranger Handbook	$16.95
133	FN-FAL Auto Rifles	$13.95
135	AK-47 Assault Rifle	$11.95
136	UZI Submachine Gun	$9.95
139	USMC Battle Skills Training Manual	$24.95
140	Sten Submachine Gun, The	$9.95
141	Terrorist Explosives Handbook	$6.95
142	U. S. Army Counterterrorism Training Manual	$14.95
143	Sniper Training	$24.95
144	The Butane Lighter Handgrenade	$9.95
146	The Official Makarov Pistol Manual	$12.95
147	Official Makarov 9mm Pistol Manual	$12.95
148	Unarmed Against the Knife	$9.95
149	Black book of Booby Traps	$14.95
151	Militia Battle Manual	$18.95
152	Glock's Handguns	$17.95
153	Heckler and Koch's Handguns	$17.95
154	The Poor Man's R. P. G.	$14.95
155	The Poor Man's Ray Gun	$9.95
156	The Anachist Handbook Vol. 2	$11.95
157	How to Make Disposable Silencers Vol. 2	$16.95
158	Modern Day Ninjutsu	$14.95
159	The Squeaky Wheel	$12.95
160	The Sicilian Blade	$13.95
162	The Anarchist Handbook Vol. 1	$11.95
163	How to Make Disposable Silencers Vol. 1	$16.95
164	The Anarchist Handbook Vol. 3	$11.95
165	How to Build Practical Firearm Silencers	$14.95
200	Fighting Back on the Job	$11.95
202	Secret Codes & Ciphers	$9.95
204	Improvised Munitions Black Book Vol 1	$14.95
205	Improvised Munitions Black Book Vol 2	$14.95
206	CIA Field Exp Preparation of Black Powder	$8.95
207	CIA Field Exp. Meth/Explo. Preparat	$8.95
209	CIA Improvised Sabotage Devices	$12.00
210	CIA Field Exp. Incendiary Manual	$12.00
211	Science of Revolutionary Warfare	$9.95
212	Agents HB of Black Bag Ops.	$9.95
214	Electronic Harassment	$11.95
217	Improvised Rocket Motors	$6.95
218	Impro. Munitions/Ammonium Nitrate	$9.95
219	Improvised Batteries/Det. Devices	$8.95
220	Improvised Explosives for Detonators	$7.95
221	Evaluation of Imp Shaped Charges	$8.95
222	American Tools of Intrigue	$12.00
225	Impro. Munitions Black Book Vol 3	$23.95
226	Poor Man's James Bond Vol 2	$24.95
227	Explosives and Propellants	$11.95
229	Select Fire 10/22	$11.95
230	Poor Man's James Bond Vol 1	$24.95
231	Assorted Nasties	$19.95
232	Full Auto Modification Manual	$18.95
234	L.A.W. Rocket System	$8.00
240	Clandestine Ops Man/Central America	$11.95
241	Mercenary Operations Manual	$9.95
250	Improvised Shaped Charges	$8.95
251	Two Component High Exp. Mixtures	$9.95
260	Survival Evasion & Escape	$13.95
262	Infantry Scouting, Patrol. & Sniping	$13.95
263	Engineer Explosives of WWI	$7.95
300	Brown's Alcohol Motor Fuel Cookbook	$13.95
301	How to Build a Junkyard Still	$11.95
303	Alcohol Distillers Handbook	$17.95
306	Brown's Book of Carburetors	$11.95
310	MAC-10 Cookbook	$9.95
350	Cheating At Cards	$12.00
367	Brown's Lawsuit Cookbook	$18.95
400	Hand to Hand Combat	$11.95
401	USMC Hand to Hand Combat	$7.95
402	US Marine Bayonet Training	$8.95
404	Camouflage	$12.95
409	Guide to Germ Warfare	$13.95
410	Emergency War Surgery	$24.95
411	Homeopathic First Aid	$9.95
412	Defensive Shotgun	$12.95
414	Hand to Hand Combat by D'Eliscue	$7.95
415	999 Survived	$6.00
416	Sun, Sand & Survival	$6.00
420	USMC Sniping	$16.95
424	Prisons Bloody Iron	$13.95
425	Napoleon's Maxims of War	$9.95
429	Invisible Weapons/Modern Ninja	$11.95
432	Cold Weather Survival	$11.95
435	Homestead Carpentry	$10.00
436	Construction Secret Hiding Places	$11.95
437	US Army Survival	$29.95
438	Survival Shooting for Women	$11.95
440	Survival Medicine	$11.95
442	Can You Survive	$12.95
443	Canteen Cup Cookery	$9.95
444	Leadership Hanbook of Small Unit Ops	$11.95
445	Vigilante Handbook	$11.95
447	Shootout II	$14.95
448	Catalog of Military Suppliers	$14.95
454	Survival Childbirth	$8.95
455	Police Karate	$10.95
456	Survival Guns	$21.95
457	Water Survival Training	$5.95
470	Emergency Medical Care/Disaster	$11.95
500	Guerilla Warfare	$14.95
504	Ranger Training & Operations	$14.95
507	Spec. Forces Demolitions Trng HB	$16.95
510	Battlefield Analysis/Inf. Weapons	$9.95
511	US Army Bayonet Training	$7.95
512	Desert Storm Weap. Recog. Guide	$9.95
542	Professional Homemade Cher Bomb	$10.95
544	Combat Loads for Sniper Rifles	$12.00
551	Take My Gun..If You Dare	$10.95
552	Aunt Bessie's Wood Stove Cookbook	$7.50
610	Trapping & Destruc. of Exec. Cars	$10.00
C-002	How To Open A Swiss Bank Account	$6.95
C-011	Defending Your Retreat	$9.95
C-020	Methods of Long Term Storage	$8.95
C-023	Federal Firearms Laws	$4.50
C-029	M1 Carbine Arsenal History	$6.95
C-038	Hw To Build A Beer Can Morter	$4.95
C-040	Criminal Use of False ID	$11.95
C-050	Surviving Doomsday	$11.95
C-052	CIA Explosives for Sabotage	$9.00
C-175	Beat the Box	$7.95
C-386	Self-Defense Requires No Apology	$11.95
C-679	M16A1 Rifle Manual Cartoon Version	$6.95
FP-9	Micro Uzi Select Fire Mod Manual	$9.95

PRICES SUBJECT TO CHANGE WITHOUT NOTICE

DESERT Publications
215 S. Washington Ave.
El Dorado, AR 71730-1751 USA

870-862-2077

$5.95 shipping & handling